THE RETREAT OF TUBERCULOSIS 1850–1950

The Retreat of
TUBERCULOSIS
1850~1950

F.B. SMITH

CROOM HELM
London • New York • Sydney

© 1988 F.B. Smith
Croom Helm Ltd, Provident House, Burrell Row,
Beckenham, Kent, BR3 1AT
Croom Helm Australia, 44-50 Waterloo Road,
North Ryde, 2113, New South Wales

Published in the USA by
Croom Helm
in association with Methuen, Inc.
29 West 35th Street
New York, NY 10001

British Library Cataloguing in Publication Data

Smith, F.B. (Francis Barrymore)
    The retreat of tuberculosis 1850–1950.
    1. Tuberculosis — Great Britain — History
    — 19th century 2. Tuberculosis — Great
    Britain — History — 20th century
    I. Title
    616.9′95′00941   RC316.G7
    ISBN 0-7099-3383-5

Library of Congress Cataloging in Publication Data

ISBN 0-7099-3383-5

Printed and bound in Great Britain by Mackays of Chatham Ltd, Kent

CONTENTS

For my sons, Andrew and Ivan

PREFACE

I am indebted yet again to my marvellous colleagues in the Research School of Social Sciences, Janice Aldridge, Anthea Bundock, Pam Crichton, Bev Gallina, Oliver MacDonagh, Allan Martin, Helen Macnab, Marie Penhaligon and Marion Stell for their unfailing support and sympathetically deployed expertise. Ken Inglis read the whole manuscript with great generosity and acuity.

My old Cambridge friends, Judith and John O'Neill, with characteristic kindness, helped me just when I needed it.

I have also to thank the Warden and Fellows of All Souls College Oxford who elected me to a visiting fellowship which enabled me at a crucial stage to press on with this book.

1 INCIDENCE

Tuberculosis was inscrutable as Providence. In its pulmonary form it prodigally disabled and killed men and women at all ages and especially at the peak of their early maturity between 15 and 35. In its various manifestations in other parts of the body it was a major destroyer of young life. Tuberculosis wrecked hopes, broke courtships, crushed breadwinners as they neared their maximum earning capacity and bereaved young families. As a fundamental destructive social force it was rivalled among illnesses only by the venereal diseases and insanity; but until about 1890 sufferers' kin, philanthropists and legislators were resigned to it as a morally neutral, ubiquitous affliction beyond official intervention. Hence investigative reports upon tuberculosis are rare until the twentieth century, as compared with evidence about venereal complaints, cholera or smallpox, although tuberculosis devoured more people than these two latter diseases put together. Historians have been deterred by the thinness of public sources and misled by the silence of contemporaries, and have concentrated hitherto on these other more accessible killers with their more immediate legislative outcomes.

Inscrutable though it was, tuberculosis in the century after 1850 is also an index. Throughout this period, in Great Britain at least, tuberculosis in all its forms killed and disabled at a steadily decreasing rate. We do not know why this was so. The improvements embraced by 'sanitary reform', the provision of clean water, effective waste disposal, safer food handling and drier housing appear to have little direct bearing on the incidence of tuberculosis. We remain unclear about the interactions between the bacillus and its likely genetic shifts, and poverty, anxiety, comfort and nutrition and their further complex outcomes in probable changes in human - and bovine - heredity and immunological gains and losses. Yet the beneficent fact stands: the easing of deprivation amongst the British peoples during the 120 years to 1960 was coincident with a fall in the general death-rate from around 22.3 per 1000 to around 10.6 per 1000. Within this trend, the death-rates attributed to infectious diseases fell steadily from above 11 per 1000 to about

2.5 per 1000; tuberculosis accounted for nearly half this diminution.[1]

Tuberculosis is now a conquered disease in the British Isles and the rest of the industrialised world. But it still ravages the peoples of the poor nations despite expensive efforts to control it: up to five millions were estimated to die annually from it during the early 1980s.[2] This toll exceeds the whole number of people reported to have died from tuberculosis in the United Kingdom over the century covered by this book. Set against this continuum of near inconceivable misery our story is a miniature - a miniature moreover, with a happy ending.

Tuberculosis of the lungs - consumption - phthisis - decline - wasting disease - delicacy of the lungs - graveyard cough - lung weakness - could be acute and galloping or chronic, or intermittent. Its general symptoms varied, especially in the early stages, and some cases were asymptomatic. Lassitude, irregular appetite, flatulence and loss of weight, irritability, raised and unstable pulse rates, night sweats, facial pallor contrasted with flushed cheeks and wan eyes, emaciation, female amenhorrhoea and male impotence, running nose and frequent colds, harsh coughing and frequent spitting of foul mucoid sputum, coughing up blood - haemoptysis - hoarseness or loss of control of the pitch of the voice, sometimes a hissing or wheezing in the chest, could appear singly or more usually in unpredictable combinations and irregular sequences. The one common indication was fever, especially in the late afternoon and at night, but this was difficult to detect and interpret, particularly in the early stages of a developing infection. When consumption was finally diagnosed, that is, usually after the bacillus had become ensconced and begun to destroy tissue, it might suddenly advance and kill within weeks, or arrest, or reappear after months or years, or spontaneously go away, independent, seemingly, of the victim's therapeutic regimen. These strange sequences encouraged patients and doctors to persist in hope and claim marvellous short-term 'cures' by specific treatments even while they were baffled as to their working.

The process of infection, activation and reinfection were - and are - imperfectly understood. Consumption did not behave like other fevers. Its incubation period was apparently long and indiscernible, its normal progress was chronic rather than acute and it exhibited no palpable climacteric. Beyond the difficulties of diagnosis, doctors could not palliate, heal or prevent it. Contemporaries rightly feared it as a ubiquitous, insidious, cruelly destructive malady. Violetta and Mimi notwithstanding, it was not a gentle, ethereal way to die.

Manifestations in other parts of the body of what we now know to be infection by *Mycobacterium tuberculosis* were until the 1880s usually regarded by lay and medical observers as separate but related conditions, with distinct etiologies in so far as these were postulated. More than any other affliction, excepting madness, it appeared to be a generalised condition of disease, rather than a specific entity amenable to secure diagnosis and reliable prognosis. Most of these afflictions were chronic, painful, debilitating, some were disfiguring, and all could kill, especially if secondary or intercurrent infections set in. None could be certainly cured. Scrofula - king's evil - usually comprised inflammation and degeneration of the lymph nodes at the sides of the neck with ulceration of the surface skin. Nineteenth-century people recognised it in the tumid appearance of the upper lip and nostrils, puffiness of the fleshy parts of the face, and the hard feel of the glands of the neck and jowls which could be enlarged or suppurating. Tabes mesenterica - wasting - involved similar inflammation and degeneration of the abdominal lymph nodes, particularly in infants and children. Lupus vulgaris, infection of the skin, usually developed as brownish nodules in the inner layers of the skin with ulceration at the surface, especially of the soft facial tissues: the tuberculosis bacillus is a near relative to the leprosy bacillus. When the bacillus lodged in a joint or bone, usually in childhood, it might become the focus of chronic painful inflammation accompanied by decay, ulceration and suppuration of the tissues. Tubercular meningitis - brain fever - sometimes developed directly and sometimes ensued as a complication of other forms of the disease. It was almost invariably acute and fatal. Tubercular caries of the vertebrae could produce those contorted spidery figures we know from illustrations to Dickens, or when the infected area of thoracic spine caseated, the sufferer might develop a hunchback, often set upon spindly legs. In the affluent world such beings are now infrequent but they are still commonplace among the crowds of Bombay or Jakarta.

During the two centuries before 1840 tuberculosis in all its forms very likely had been a major endemic killer in Great Britain. Between 1485 and 1507 it was the main cause of death among the monks of Christ Church, Canterbury, and destroyed almost as many men as the other endemic illnesses combined.[3] George Gregory, physician to the London Small-Pox Hospital, calculated in 1840 from Rickman's survey of the London bills of mortality from 1657 that about 20 per cent of all deaths had been regularly ascribed to consumption. His estimates confirm those developed by William Woolcombe in 1808.[4] 'Consumption', as applied to phthisical decline, entered into general usage about 1660. Doctors had begun to use 'phthisis' about a century earlier. In 1680 John Bunyan referred to consumption as the captain of the men of death and throughout his century it preoccupied brilliant medical observers in Christopher Bennet, Thomas Willis and Thomas Sydenham, as during the eighteenth century it fascinated Richard Morton, Benjamin Marten and William Stark. Tuberculosis possibly ascended to its leading place as a killer when endemic plague and malaria receded after the mid-seventeenth century.[5] William Farr, the great medical statistician, calculated that the reported London consumption death rate reached 13 per 1000 between 1660 and 1679.[6] 'It's a great chance', wrote Gideon Harvey in *Morbus Anglicus* in 1672, '... to arrive at one's grave in this English climate without a smack of consumption, death's door direct to most hard students, divines, physicians, philosophers, deep lovers, zealots in religion'.[7] These likely transitions in causes of mortality and probable high tuberculosis rates are questions of profound importance to British history but as yet we know little about them.

The turning point in the reign of consumption, so far as Gregory's limited but numerically significant sample is concerned, had come between 1829 and 1833 when the proportion of attributed phthisis deaths to deaths from all causes fell from 22 per cent to 16 per cent, within an overall decrement in mortality rates.[8] We lack death rates for these years for other parts of the kingdom, but Gregory noted that the phthisis share of all deaths at 18-20 per cent returned for Devon and Cornwall in 1838-9, after official registration began, matched the figures for London. Again, his calculations generally coincide with those of William Farr, who set the turning point

during 1831-5 when the rate fell for the first time to 9 per 1000.[9]
These reported phthisis deaths doubtless included many from
non-tuberculous respiratory and organic illnesses, but very
likely these were far outbalanced by the under-reporting of such
deaths among infants. Deaths attributed to 'atrophy' and
'marasmus' probably included a large tuberculous component,
if we consider contemporary poor world evidence, not least
because tubercular infection often upsets nutrition. Overall in
1838-9 60,000 deaths in England and Wales were ascribed to
phthisis, divided nearly equally between males and females.[10]

In Scotland, too, the eighteenth-century bills of mortality are
said to record phthisis as the leading destroyer. The reported
Scottish phthisis rates throughout the nineteenth century were
higher than the English ones.[11]

Doctors in Ireland asserted in the 1820s that consumption was
'infinitely more rare' than in Great Britain. During the
registration period Irish rates remained lower than the British
ones throughout the century, although the gap closed after the
1870s as the British rates continued to fall and the Irish
mortality continued to rise until 1901.[12] (See Table I on page 6)

These rates represent roughly 53,000 deaths ascribed to
pulmonary tuberculosis in England and Wales in 1871, 49,000 in
1881, 41,400 in 1901, 35,600 in 1921, 23,000 in 1947 (representing
half the deaths from all diseases and the major cause of death at
ages 15 to 24) and 3000 in 1960. In Scotland consumption was
reported to account for over 8000 deaths in 1881, nearly 7000 in
1901, 4000 in 1921, 3400 in 1947 and 1000 in 1960. In Ireland
between 1871 and 1880 over 10,000 people perished annually
from pulmonary tuberculosis, representing one-tenth of all
deaths and over half the deaths between 15 and 45. In 1921
there were 5600 deaths, in 1947, 2831, and 416 in 1960.

Other forms of tuberculosis were reported to have killed
about 19,500 people in England and Wales in 1881, 18,000 in
1901, 8000 in 1921 and 2300 in 1957, while in Scotland other
forms were still destroying over 1800 lives a year in 1921 and
over 700 in 1947. Ireland recorded over 3200 deaths from other
forms in 1881, 2800 in 1901 and 1400 in 1921, 869 in 1947 and 52
in 1960.[13]

Among the other forms, scrofula, like pulmonary
tuberculosis, had probably entered upon its long-term retreat by
1840. (See Table II on page 7)

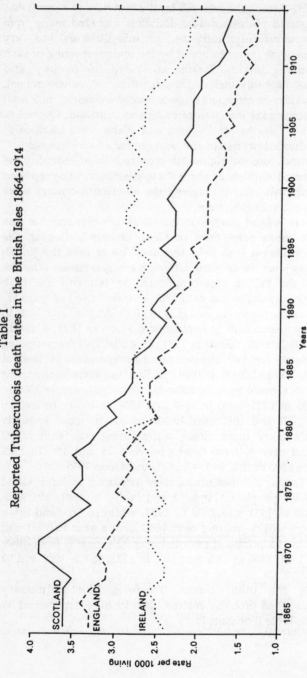

Table I
Reported Tuberculosis death rates in the British Isles 1864-1914

Source: 51st Report of Registrar General for Ireland, *BPP*, 1914-16, vol.ix, p.xxv.

Table II[14]
Respiratory Tuberculosis
Mean annual death rate per 100,000 living

Year	England and Wales Both Sexes	M	F	Scotland Both Sexes	M	F	Ireland Both Sexes	M	F
1851	277	269	285	-	-	-	-	-	-
1861	258	261	257	260	263	258	-	-	-
1871	232	239	226	261	259	261	189	187	191
1881	189	199	180	217	206	227	204	193	215
1891	156	173	140	178	176	179	213	202	223
1901	128	150	106	155	158	151	216	213	218
1911	104	121	87	115	120	110	173	171	175
1921	89	101	78	84	88	80	131	121	141
							All forms		
1931	74	87	62	62	68	55	137	-	-
1941	95	115	76	63	73	55	125	-	-
1951	98	115	81	37	45	29	73	79	67
1961	7	12	3	8	13	4	16	21	12
1971	1	-	-	3	4	2	5.6	-	-
1981	0	0	0	1	2	1	2.5	-	-

During the 1840s Benjamin Phillips and his colleagues claimed to have arranged the examination of 134,000 children aged 5 to 15 in charity schools, workhouses and factories 'in many districts'. Twenty-four per cent, were reported to show 'certain marks of scrofula'. Workhouse inmates displayed above average rates, charity school children below, but that was because badly affected individuals usually were excluded. Phillips also gathered returns from hospitals and dispensaries covering, he said, 255, 000 adults. (His survey was a remarkable enterprise and deserves more attention than I can give here). These returns showed a scrofula rate of 1.3 per cent, similar to the concurrent scrofula rejection rate for 95,000 army recruits. Phillips concluded that the incidence of scrofula was diminishing because the army rejection rate in Napoleonic times had been 5 per cent. If these figures are even near accurate, they represent a notable advance in the health and appearance - and possibly indeed a lift in the spirits - of young males among the common people at a period sometimes characterised as the hungriest of the century. Even convicts in Millbank penitentiary between 1840 and 1844 were returned as having 'external scrofula' at a rate slightly above one per cent. If scrofula is an index of deprivation we have extraordinary disparities reported between these poorest of English poor and their European contemporaries: the inmates of orphanages in Lisbon were said to exhibit scrofula at around 35 per cent, those of St Petersburg at 41 per cent, and Berlin at 53 per cent.[15]If expectations of health were low in Britain, they were apparently much worse in countries which had yet to increase their agricultural output and begin to industrialise.

Nonetheless, the reported crude mortality in England and Wales from 'scrofula and other tuberculosis (not phthisis) diseases' rose from 739 per 1 million in 1858-60 to a peak of 784 per 1 million in 1861-65 before declining unevenly to 777 per 1 million in 1876-80 and declining steadily to 524 per 1 million in 1901-05.[16] Scrofula, tabes mesenterica and tubercular meningitis were predominantly killers of infants and toddlers. The striking aspect of these figures is their close following of the birth-rate. Scrofula and tabes mesenterica were largely diseases of the poor; the decline in the national birthrate after 1876 and the decisive fall in the rate for England and Wales after 1901, from about 122 per 1000 in 1896 to 114 per 1000 in 1901, suggests that one fundamental contributor to the retreat of these forms of tuberculosis was the spread among the classes at risk of effective family limitation. Just as the professional middle classes had since at least 1851 improved the care, nutrition and life chances of each family member by controlling the size and birth spacing of their families, so the unskilled working classes began to improve their chances at the turn of the century. Exposure to the bacillus remained near universal until the 1940s, tuberculous mothers were still numerous, (76 per cent of a fair sample of English infants under one year with tuberculous mothers were positive reactors to tuberculin testing in the early 1970s),[17] yet child deaths from all forms of tuberculosis declined - and declined fastest during the years of the lower classes' fertility transition. Between 1906 and 1912 reported tuberculosis mortality among children under five in England and Wales fell by 30 per cent.[18] In 1898 over 7000 infants died in England and Wales from all forms of tuberculosis and in 1927, 718: this represented 89 per cent fewer deaths from abdominal tuberculosis, 62 per cent fewer for meningitis, 68 per cent fewer from pulmonary tuberculosis, and 77 per cent fewer from other forms.[19] By about 1950, before the effective advent of chemotherapy and BCG vaccination, only about 10 per cent of children under five were positive reactors to the Mantoux test.[20] It seems reasonable to suggest that the better nurture which each child could receive in a smaller completed working class family (excepting coal miners' families), the prerogative of children in the professional and urban gentry classes since the 1850s and 1860s, had an unplanned outcome in the heightened resistance to tuberculosis among the children of the lower classes. This prodigious reduction in suffering and death was achieved independently of, indeed despite, the interventions of influential medical leaders and Imperialist pro-natalists. It derived from private, domestic appraisals of improved prospects among working class wives and husbands. It constitutes the largest single advance in the life chances of the common people in British history. The doctors, politicians, priests and welfare professionals nonetheless pre-empted the opportunities created by the smaller working class family to impose rules about infant nurture and to build a supervisory system, and then to take the credit for reduced infant mortality rates. (See Table III on page 10)

Doctors and parents could soothe the feverishness of a tuberculous infant with opium-based cordials, but beyond that the choice lay between impotence and heroic interventions. In 1825 Dr Henry Clutterbuck, senior physician to the London General Dispensary, advised '*blood-letting*' as 'the remedy that chiefly merits confidence'. By 1841 Charles Clay of the Manchester Dispensary was ordering iodine-gentian poultices three times daily for scrofula cases, together with lead extract-lime water washings. The enthusiasm in the 1850s for flannel next to the body is reflected in Dr Copland's recommendation in 1861 that tuberculous infants be swathed in it and fed 'asses' milk boiled with suet, [with] cod liver ... oil on the surface of the milk.'[21] Blood-letting, among younger doctors, had become unfashionable. By the late 1880s poultices, for infants at least, had also become unscientific. One innovating, fresh-air

enthusiast declared that poultices made the skin 'rotten'. He
ordered sea-air and sea-bathing. By the turn of the century
exposure to sunlight and the elements became the regimen,
reinforced by cod-liver oil.[22] The results remained
indeterminate.

Table III[23]

Other Non-respiratory Tuberculosis

Mean annual death rate per 100,000 living

Year	England and Wales			Scotland			Ireland		
	Both Sexes	M	F	Both Sexes	M	F	Both Sexes	M	F
1861	-	-	-	109	-	-	-	-	-
1871	74	84	64	112	129	97	64	70	58
1881	75	84	67	94	104	84	63	67	58
1891	59	76	62	67	74	61	63	61	65
1901	54	60	50	69	75	63	63	65	61
1911	39	43	36	63	67	59	50	52	49
1921	25	27	22	38	41	35	37	37	37
1931	15	16	14	23	25	21	-	-	-
1941	5	6	5	21	-	-	-	-	-
1951	2	2	2	6	-	-	15	-	-
1961	0	0	0	1	1	1	1	-	-
1971	0	0	0	0	0	0	0	0	0
1981	0	0	0	1	2	1	0	0	0

Tuberculosis respected rank. Few escaped exposure, but richer
people had at every stage of the life cycle better chances than
poor people of escaping infection or of enjoying a remission or
cure.

The differentials began at birth. We know from studies of
tuberculosis in contemporary poor countries that it is
implicated in stillbirths, perinatal mortality and the
'convulsions' and digestive upsets that kill children under five.
Feeble tuberculous mothers are more likely to undergo
prolonged labours and to produce deadborn babies.[24] We lack
the detailed local studies which would secure our historical
understanding of these linkages but it seems reasonable to

propose that a sizeable proportion of the numerous deadborn infants, 1 in 9 for instance among the outdoor deliveries among a poor population reported by University College Hospital between 1829 and 1835, comprised the babies of tuberculous mothers. 'Delicate' mothers were usually unable to breast feed or cope with their infants.[25] The dangers of hand-raising, not least from unboiled cows' milk, must have been heightened by the digestive upsets and feverishness that tuberculosis can induce. Domestic medical guides are full of warnings about such hazards (although they rarely advised boiling) and the folklore got it right in one respect at least. The physician directing the care of newborn Prince Albert in 1842 ordered that when weaned, he should have milk from one cow only, although this plan was intended to secure consistency in the milk as much as to avoid the admixture of milk from obviously infected cows.[26] The bacillus must have contributed significantly to those 'convulsions' assigned as cause of death in almost 22 per cent of cases among children under five in St Bride's parish during 1821-5 and 1844-8. Another 12 per cent of St Bride's children's deaths were ascribed to 'water on the brain', that is, very probably tubercular meningitis.[27] We know that infant mortality rates between adjacent comfortable and impoverished neighbourhoods differed by over 300 per cent.[28] Tuberculosis must have fed these disparities by initiating or aggravating the 'convulsions', 'hydrocephalus', 'marasmus' diarrhoea and 'nervous' deaths that headed the lists in poor districts, where about 50 per cent of all deaths comprised children under five; and these attributions represented about 80 per cent of total infant mortality at mid-century. Insanitary, highly tuberculous areas of Carnarvon, Merthyr Tydvil and Wrexham, for example, reported 'nervous' infant death rates thirteen times higher than those for salubrious parts of England and Wales.[29] These ascriptions probably hide some deaths caused primarily by tuberculosis. Doctors avoided doubtful attributions to tuberculosis when certifying infant deaths, partly from honest bewilderment and partly because of a compassionate reluctance to invoke an 'hereditary' malady. 'Nervous' 'respiratory ' disease or 'convulsions' were convenient catch-alls. It is significant that deaths ascribed to 'bronchitis' and other generic respiratory complaints increased by 81 per cent after the mid 1870s as registration rules were tightened in England, Wales and Scotland. Forty-one per cent

of this increase comprised infants under one year.[30] Registrars
and doctors remained dependent upon the account of the cause
of death given by the notifying kin, who commonly avoided
mentioning tuberculosis.   Around 1900 the 'bronchitis'
mortality was said to be markedly higher among legitimate
children, while illegitimates were recorded as more likely to die
from tuberculosis, 'marasmus' or 'neglect'.   Even in 1931
'bronchitis' was alleged to cause relatively more deaths in Great
Britain than in any other nation.[31]

The few large-scale post mortem surveys we have reveal that
tuberculosis was widespread, largely undiagnosed and
inevitably under-reported.   Of 1420 post mortems on children
under twelve recorded as dying of 'all causes' at the London
Hospital for Sick Children in the 1880s over 30 per cent were
revealed as having been tuberculous. Nearly all of them were
under five. The Royal Hospital for Sick Children in Edinburgh
reported 39 per cent of post mortems between 1888 and 1909 to
reveal tuberculosis.   During 1914, 40 per cent of 150 poor
children who died in London general hospitals were found to
be tuberculous. Tuberculosis was recorded as still the largest
cause of death, at 25 per cent, of children under fifteen in
Newcastle-upon-Tyne between 1939 and 1947.[32]

Children between five and fourteen enjoyed a higher
resistance to infection than any other age group. The severely
infected had already been carried off and the ravages of
reactivated or new infections and probably renewed exposure to
severe open cases did not make inroads until about age fifteen.

The main manifestations of the disease among this age group
were scrofula and joint tuberculosis which crippled rather than
killed. But the important point is that tuberculosis rarely came
singly. As with infants, the conjunction of tuberculosis as a
debilitating illness with other illnesses could prove chronically
disabling and sometimes fatal. We can gain an indication of the
morbidity rates among children adjudged sufficiently well by
their parents, teachers and doctors to attend school from school
medical inspectors' reports. In 1913 inspectors reported 15.4 per
cent of elementary school children to show obvious signs of
tuberculosis. By the early 1920s that percentage had fallen to
below five: yet among nearly 20,000 children examined in the
Birkenhead area, the functional disorders were twice as
common in tubercular children as among their apparently non-
tubercular contemporaries.

per cent - A = obvious signs of tuberculosis   B = all cases[33]

	A	B
Bad teeth	27.7	13.3
tonsils	8.0	4.3
adenoids	4.7	2.0
nose-chronic catarrh	22.2	14.3
cervical glands	90.7	45.5
family history of phthisis	20.1	7.8
defective nutrition	50.7	26.8
deformities of chest	4.0	0.9

The inspectors probably examined pigeon-chested wheezy children less cursorily, but nonetheless the differentials are enormous and the general condition of the children, tuberculous and seemingly non-tuberculous alike, is wretched. The diagnoses were conducted without sputum tests or X-rays and the findings are probably understated. Fifty per cent of 563 children five to fifteen recorded as dying from all causes in Gloucestershire in 1931 were found on post mortem to have tubercular lesions.[34]

The Birkenhead findings on defective nutrition and family phthisis histories are revealing because they are probably the joint outcomes of a phenomenon that the investigators in the much larger Newcastle-upon-Tyne project discovered in the 1940s and 1950s - that tuberculin positive children showed distinctly more parental deprivation (they do not give the exact figures, but they may be extrapolated at about 70 per cent higher in the 1950s) than comparable groups in terms of class, housing, place in the family and maternal capacity, and that this deprivation related to the debility or deaths of parents themselves suffering from tuberculosis.[35] Poverty begot tuberculosis, but tuberculosis also begot poverty.

Provision for treatment of this awkward age group, without savings and uninsured, was minimal. In 1914 local authorities in England and Wales classed 8834 children as needing treatment or special schooling but receiving none. The phthisis cases were excluded from sanatoria and the cripples were usually excluded from the general hospitals for children.[36]

Defectives from 'inferior' dwellings could be selected for one of the dozen or so open air schools which spread in England after the first one was opened by the London County Council at

Plumstead in 1907. Their model was the German Charlottenberg 'open air recovery school' of 1904, devised to instruct and cure simultaneously . Pupils and teachers and teachers lived 'outdoors all day ... instead of in an artificially warmed and always more or less impure atmosphere ... no matter what the temperature may be'. Their 'tissue metabolism' was stimulated by the necessity to produce body heat. In cold weather the scholars had frequent 'runs around'.

Plumstead, like most of the schools which came after it, opened during the summer, taking 100 children daily, on recommendation by a school medical officer. They were over seven and under twelve. The staff comprised five teachers and a nurse.[37] It soon emerged that enfeebled children, whether rickets' sufferers, who formed the majority, or consumptive and joint cases, who comprised the next largest group, were backward children. Most had had little or no schooling. The work quickly became 'practical'. The pupils of the open-air school at Upper Holloway in 1912 learned history and geography by making models in sand and arithmetic by measuring trees and garden beds. Consonant with their surroundings and the aspirations of their teachers, they drilled, performed Morris dances, and learned to read from texts which celebrated 'country life' and 'flowers'.[38] The Preston, Lancashire, school in the late 1920s seems to have spent much time on the 'lore of snails and slugs'.[39] The pupils might never make soldiers but, as in Germany and France, their mentors hoped that they might replenish the countryside. Their bodies, exposed to all good influences, would become 'temples of bronze', according to Dr F.A. Sharpe, School Medical Officer for Preston. Thereby they would slough off the physical and moral defects inherited from their parents, escape the degenerative impacts of slum life, and make their contribution to the perfecting of the race.[40] To this end the children's three meals a day were 'specially nutritious', comprising porridge, tea, white bread, butter and dripping, boiled mutton or cod and boiled potato and cabbage, blancmange or pudding with sugar, and an 'occasional banana'. The children gained an average two and a half pounds each month during their lucky summer; and they lost weight when they went home. Teachers were surprised to find that their charges needed almost as many hours of sleep as they spent in class.[41]

Municipal authorities, prompted by the Childrens' Country
Holiday Fund and kindred bodies, established open-air annexes
to schools in Manchester, Leicester, Kettering, Sheffield and
Salford around 1912-13. 'Delicate' children excluded from
ordinary schools were enrolled for one year's attendance at a
parental payment around fourpence a day. But even before the
Great War made matters difficult, the open-air movement
began to falter. Parents of rickety and anaemic children
complained about the presence of tuberculous children.[42]
Medical officers of health were hostile because the schools were
outside their control and absorbed funds, over £1000 per three
month session, that the officers believed they could spend
better. They contended that open-air schools did not cure and
that they exhausted their pupils by the travel and exercise they
required. They also undermined the officers' work, as Dr
Taylor, Medical Officer of Health for Halifax, remarked in 1913,
by permitting the pupils to return each day to uninspected bad
homes replete with 'bad atmosphere', 'bad food', bad sleep in
unventilated rooms, and bad parents.[43]

The schools' proponents replied diffidently that the children
'showed signs of increased alertness', although they remained
slow learners. No one appears to have tested the programme
and no one seems to have asked the children or their parents
what they thought of it.[44]

By 1918 the London County Council led the way in redirecting
money to summer mass classes, 100 at a time, in the parks for
mixed 'delicate' and backward 'recommended' children drawn
from the 90 per cent of children nominated but unable to find a
place at the existing open-air schools. The staple was nature-
study and object lessons. Between times the children were
medically inspected, had spectacles prescribed, tonsils and
adenoids removed, heads scoured, new boots or clogs supplied,
while their homes were visited and cleansed under
supervision.[45]

The boots and free tonsilectomies were bribes. When the
visiting nurse found the home to be 'good', the child was
released from attendance in order to make room for a more
urgent case. But often the good child was encouraged to stay
because bad families proved uncooperative. Dr Sharpe
lamented in 1927 that 'the news of selection ... aroused a
parental storm ... against the singling out of their child'. The
languor of the children, interspersed by bouts of sickness and

sudden absences, readily enabled indifferent, suspicious parents to resist.[46]   As early as 1906 Sir John Gorst, the Imperialist Jeremiah of national deterioration, had declared that 'in bad cases, where the diseased glands are developing into ... tuberculosis, it would be ... much more economical ... for society to take the case in hand in time and remove the child'.[47]

This ambition was partially realised just before the War with the opening of at least seven residential sanatorium schools, a few of them replacing day schools. They numbered perhaps a dozen or so by 1930, all in the south of England, catering for about 500 children in each three monthly intake, and recognised for state subsidy under the Defectives' Act of 1899.[48]   The Boys' Garden City had been opened by Dr Barnardo's Homes in 1912 at Woodford Bridge in Essex. A projected 900 boys were to live in huts 'under country conditions' and thereby become 'physically ... as well as technically fit' to help arrest 'the rapid decline of agriculture in this country'.   The first hut was contributed by the King Edward VII Memorial Fund, the second by the Workers' Farthing Fund. A similar Girls' Village Home operated a few miles away.   London East End parents and kin were safely far away and unable to interfere.   They were permitted visits, as at most tuberculosis children's residential schools, for two hours once a month.[49]

During the 1920s most of these institutions changed into homes for cripples, as orthopaedic surgeons became interested in operating on 'surgical' tuberculosis cases.   The enforced immobility and frequent prolonged recovery periods after surgery meant that even nature study and object lessons were abandoned: but Henry Gauvain, a leading children's orthopaedic surgeon, offered the consoling reflection that the 'patients' - the pupils had become patients by 1915 - were 'often irritable and highly strung and languid' and therefore 'should not attend school or be subject to mental effort'.[50]   Eighty per cent of the estimated 100,000 or more cripples in England and Wales with decreased earning power in 1911 were said to owe their incapacity to tuberculosis.[51]   Quite apart from the relatively tiny proportion of this army which the children's sanatoria managed to house, there is no clear evidence to suggest that the regime and particularly the surgery, diminished the number.   Those released from sanatoria joined with the majority who had continued at home and together they swelled the tides of out-patients at the tuberculosis and general hospitals.

From about the onset of puberty until about age 30 tuberculosis mortality jumped, for both sexes. Thomas Reid had observed this phenomenon in the later eighteenth-century and it continued until the late 1930s, when death rates at over 65, particularly for males, overtook the rates for early adulthood.[52]

In England and Wales reported female phthisis death rates between ages ten and 35 generally exceeded those for males until 1866, when female rates began to decline faster, in urban England at least, until about 1900-4 when the female decline rate slowed and the males began to catch up. We do not know what happened in Wales in the nineteenth century, but between 1901 and 1925 female rates were said by Dr H. Old, in an unpublished report to the Ministry of Health, to be worse than male rates and between 1919 and 1925 'much worse'.[53] The peak mortality for females remained at around 25 to 35, while the male peak steadily shifted towards older ages. The United Kingdom appears to be distinctive, together with the United States, by comparison with France, Sweden, Denmark and Prussia, in having this pattern.[54] By contrast, the female death-rate from non-pulmonary tuberculosis for Wales from 1901 to 1910 is said to have been strikingly below the male rate and slightly lower than elsewhere in the United Kingdom.[55]

The predisposing causes of these differences remain elusive. The problem is complicated by the absence of local studies, particularly for Wales and Ireland, variable reporting, the scarcity of morbidity figures, and internal migration and emigration. The alleged low female mortality rate from non-pulmonary tuberculosis in Wales might be the result, for example, of Welsh girls consuming less milk than boys. The onset of menstruation in poorly nourished, anaemic females must have reduced their resistance, as Dr H. Handford suggested in 1887. He noticed that amenhorrhoea set in as the disease manifested itself.[56] The demands of pregnancy and childbirth on women whose lungs and heart were weakened by tuberculosis also must have raised their mortality rate, but the precise role of tuberculosis in this sequence is still unclear.[57] I shall return to this question later. The great William Thomson observed the sudden onset of disease among new domestic servants, although their general mortality, possibly because of better nutrition and shelter, was lower than that of their farm labouring and dressmaking sisters. Thomson argued in 1882 that they arrived from the country, naive to daily infection while 'cleaning bedrooms and ... inhaling dust of dried sputa'[58] Even so, in England and Wales the agricultural counties generally had the highest differential female rates, relative to industrial towns and London, where the male rates were higher.[59] Possibly the high rural rates were the outcomes of continual exposed drudgery, and much poorer nutrition among women than men. Into the 1930s many English country churches had clusters of yellowed white gloves and faded garlands hung around the cornices of the nave, memorials to young women newly deceased after their betrothal or marriage.[60]

Where women worked in factories alongside men the rates were close, and usually slightly worse for the men. In Lancashire textile towns, Dundee jute factory districts and Belfast linen mills areas between 1901 and 1907 the male phthisis rates were about 175 per 100,000 and the female, 170 per 100,000.[61] The improved nutrition underwritten by the spread of female urban employment and falling real prices between 1870 and 1900 might well have underpinned the faster improvement in female death rates in the younger employed age groups. Over this period the number of English women employed in tailoring, the drapery trade, hosiery manufacture, the stationery trades, and carpet manufacture, roughly doubled and the numbers in clerical jobs increased ninefold. Simultaneously, the number of female paupers aged over sixteen decreased at almost twice the male rate. Observers noticed that men expectorated more openly around the factory and frequented pubs more, where they spat, coughed over one another and drank from slimy glasses. They were much more likely than women to share a drinking vessel at work and at the pub. Pubs, as the high consumption rate among barmen and pub-keepers, attested, were hotbeds of infection.[62] These habits, within the context of the greater industrial employment rates among men, might help explain the regional patterns of sex differentiated mortality. Between 1898 and 1907 Birmingham, Wolverhampton, Leeds, Manchester, Salford and Bolton recorded male phthisis rates at least double those for females.

Ports including Cardiff, Plymouth, Glasgow, Bristol, Portsmouth and Sunderland showed male rates one and a half to twice those of females. Westmoreland, Cumberland, Bucks, Norfolk and Dorset had rates about equal or even slightly higher female rates. Coal mining areas, South Wales and Durham, had notably higher female rates, possibly expressing the nutritional and domestic deprivation women endured in such communities.[63] Of all the factors involved - housing, fatigue, anxiety, uncleanliness - poor nutrition with the impaired resistance that accompanied it seems to have been the crucial divider between exposure and active manifestation of disease.

The sexual differentiation in tuberculosis mortality also occurred within a class framework. Notwithstanding famous deaths among the comfortable classes, tuberculosis of all types was overwhelmingly a scourge of the labouring poor. The earliest estimates for England, derived from the 1851-60 returns, projected a 50 per cent difference in phthisis mortality between St Giles, Whitechapel and Westminster and Hampstead, Islington and Wandsworth.[64] Dr C.R. Drysdale, physician to the North London Consumption Hospital, claimed from his experience in the 1880s and early 1890s that tuberculosis mortality among the London poor was 350 per cent higher than among the rich. St Giles and St Saviour's recorded rates around 3300 per 1 million, while Hampstead reported 930 per 1 million. Hampstead's rate, corrected for age and sex, was still three times lower than that for Finsbury and Bermondsey in 1909. In Glasgow in 1921 the wards of St Giles, at 152 per 100,000 and St Leonards at 127 per 100,000 compared badly with the 'better class' Newington with 28 per 100,000 and Haymarket with 44 per 100,000. Overall, the differentials of about 3 to 1 for males in England and Wales between classes I and V remained constant between 1921 and 1950.[65] The reported differential between 'bad' and 'fair artisan areas' of Liverpool during three years probably immediately before 1914 was over 80 per cent. In Birmingham in the early 1930s the unskilled died from consumption at 275 per cent of the rate of the middle classes and of nearly 200 per cent the rate of skilled artisans.[66] Impoverished Dublin's rate of 3.71 per 1000 in the 1880s was 70 per cent higher than London's. Within that grim excess, the 'professional classes' rate was said to be 1.96 per 1000, that of the 'middle' and 'artisan' classes was 6.25 per 1000, while the 'general service class' suffered 8.64 per 1000. If 'bronchitis' and 'pneumonia' were added the differences would have been even greater. By 1914 these differentials had narrowed, but the 'general service class' still had a reported phthisis mortality rate worse than twice that of the 'Professional and Independent Class', and a death-rate from other forms of tuberculosis nearly 60 times worse.[67]

In 1931 Dr Letitia Fairfield reported yet another stark contrast in life chances according to class among English adolescents of both sexes. Fifteen to eighteen year olds from working-class families in paid employment were quickly ravaged with consumption: their middle-class contemporaries enrolled in secondary schools were almost free of it - there were only two definite cases reported among 90,000 secondary pupils in 1929.[68]

While we ponder these statistical categories it is salutary to remember the private, personal griefs bound with seemingly indiscriminate attacks of the disease related to hidden junctures between mind and body, resistance and infection. In all classes throughout the period widowers and widows of phthisis victims were more likely to die of phthisis than single or married persons at all adult ages.[69] No wonder the laity and doctors were baffled, and appalled by their ineffectuality. And no wonder many practitioners, registered and unregistered alike, were tempted to prodigies of bluster.

NOTES

[1]Thomas McKeown and C.R. Lowe, *An Introduction to Social Medicine*, 1968, pp.6-7.

[2]Saul Benison, 'Celebration and History: The Centenary of Robert Koch's Discovery of the Tubercle Bacillus', *Bulletin of the History of Medicine*, vol. 56, 1982, p.159.

[3]John Hatcher, 'Mortality in the Fifteenth Century: Some New Evidence', *Economic History Review*, vol. xxxix No.1, 1956, p.30.

[4]*Lancet*, 11 Apr. 1840, p.88; Woolcombe is quoted in Major Greenwood, *Epidemics And Crowd Diseases*, London 1935, pp.345-6

[5]Forbes, Thomas R., '"By what disease or casualty": the changing face of death in London', in Charles Webster (ed.), *Health, medicine and mortality in the sixteenth century*, Cambridge 1979, p.125.

[6]Greenwood, *Epidemics*, p.347.

[7]Quoted in H. Timbrell Bulstrode, 'Report on Sanatoria For Consumption'. *Supplement to 35th Annual Report of the Local Government Board 1905-06*, London 1907, p.3.

[8]*Lancet*, 11 Apr. 1840, p.88.

[9]Greenwood, *Epidemics*, p.347.

[10]Farr, *Lancet*, 22 Jan. 1842, p.575.

[11]David Hamilton, *The Healers*, Edinburgh 1981, p.95; *Lancet*, 3 Oct. 1868, p.468; Sir Robert Philip in *British Medical Journal*, 28 Apr. 1928, p.702.

[12]T.W. Grimshaw, 'The Prevalence of Tuberculosis in Ireland ...', in *Transactions of the Royal Academy of Medicine in Ireland*, vol. xvii, 1899, p.548. Edwards Crisp, 'On Tuberculous Affections in Man and in the Lower Animals ...', *Transactions of the St. Andrews Medical Graduates' Association,1867*, p.114.

[13]These totals have been garnered from several sources: 75th Annual Registrar-General's Report for England and Wales, *BPP* 1913, vol. xvii, table liv; Sir Robert Philip, 'Causes of the Decline in Tuberculosis Mortality', *BMJ*, 28 Apr. 1928, p.703; F.J.H. Coutts, *Transactions of the National Associationn for the Prevention of Tuberculosis*, 1932, p.48; *Report of the Department of Health for Scotland ... 1951*, p.79; *Report of the Ministry of Health for 1951*, p.82; *Registrar-General's Statistical Review of England and Wales*, 1957, part III, p.97; W.P.D. Logan and B. Benjamin, *Tuberculosis Statistics for England and Wales 1938-1955*, 1957; *United Nations Demographic Yearbooks*. The reader should bear in mind Dr Camac Wilkinson's remark of 1921: 'The truth is that any statistics upon the morbidity and mortality from tuberculosis are untrustworthy'. *Transactions of the International Conference on Tuberculosis*, 1921, p.80. Tuberculosis deaths, at early ages particularly, were probably considerably under-reported.

[14] I provide this table and table III as indications of trends rather than as sets of precise measurements. I have compiled them from a variety of sources, the Registrar-General's *Reports* for England and Wales, Scotland and Ireland, Sir Robert Philips' 'The Causes of the Decline in Tuberculosis Mortality',*BMJ*, 28 Apr. 1928, p.701, and the *United Nations Demographic Yearbooks*. I have ignored changes in definition of 'other forms of tuberculosis', and Northern Ireland. The user should remember the warning of the Registrar-General for Ireland in 1894: 'There are considerable difficulties encountered in dealing accurately with the statistics of deaths from phthisis as many persons affected by phthisis have their lives terminated by other forms of disease, especially ... bronchitis or pneumonia'. Many of the returns vary in the 'provisional' figures they present, sometimes for years on end. A few contain calculations that are internally inconsistent or clearly arithmetically wrong. Where the data permit, I have recalculated them.

[15]Benjamin Phillips, 'The Prevalence and Alleged Increase of Scrofula', *Journal of the Statistical Society*, vol. ix, 1846, pp.152-4.

[16]H. Timbrell Bulstrode, *Report on Sanatoria for Consumption*, 1908, p.33.

[17]Dorothy J. Dow and W. Ernest Lloyd, 'Tuberculosis Mortality in Children', *Brompton Hospital Reports*, vol.i, 1932, p.39.

[18] *75th annual report of the Registrar-General for England and Wales, BPP* 1913, vol.xvii, p.lxxviii.

[19] Dow and Lloyd, *Brompton Hospital Reports*, vol.1, 1932, pp.25, 49.

[20] C. Fraser Brockington, *The Health Of The Community*, 1954, p.259.

[21] Henry Clutterbuck, *An inquiry into the Seat and Nature of Fever* , second ed. 1825, p.195; Clay in *Lancet*, 9 Jan. 1841, p.554; James Copland, *Consumption And Bronchitis*, 1861.

[22] Mr Thornton (Margate), *Lancet*, 25 May 1889, p.1035; William Knight Treves, (Margate) *Lancet*, 22 Sept. 1889, p.634.

[23] Phthisis death rates per one million by age groups, England and Wales, *Lancet*, 27 July 1901, p.233.

[24] N.B. Capon, in *Proc. Roy. Soc. Medicine*, vol.xxxiii, pt. II 1940, p.619; Peter Underwood and Zdenka Underwood, 'New Spells for Old ... in ... Yemen ... ', in J.F. Stanley and R.A. Joske, (eds.), *Changing Disease Patterns and Human Behaviour*, 1980, p.286; see also Kenneth F. Kiple and Virginia Himmelsteib King, *Another Dimension to the Black Diaspora*, Cambridge 1981, p.139.

[25] Frederick J. Brown, 'The First Food of Infancy', *Journal of Public Health and Sanitary Review*, vol.11, Mar. 1856, p.59.

[26] e.g. Walter Johnson, *The Domestic Management Of Children*, 1857, pp.75-6; George Black, *The Young Wife's Advice Book*, n.d. [1880?]. pp.96-7; Joshua Waddington in *Lancet*, 24 Dec. 1842, p.471.

[27] Thomas R. Forbes, 'Mortality Books for 1820 to 1849 from the Parish of St. Bride, Fleet Street, London', *Journal of the History of Medicine*, vol.27, 1972, p.24.

[28] F.B. Smith, *The People's Health 1830-1910*, 1979, p.69.

[29] 'The Death-Rate of England', *Sanitary Review*, vol.iv, Oct. 1858, p.224.

[30] J.B. Russell, 'Influence of the Friendly Societies' Act upon Uncertified Deaths', *Glasgow Medical Journal*, vol.x, 1878, pp.559-60; G.B. Longstaff, *Lancet*, 14 Apr. 1883, p.638; Hugh R. Jones, 'The Perils and Protection of Infant Life', *Journal of the Royal Statistical Society*, vol.Lvii, 1894, pp.28-30.

[31] J.M. McPhail (Middlesbrough), *BMJ*, 7 Feb. 1931, p.239.

[32] Octavius Sturges in *Lancet*, 17 Nov. 1888, p.991; Louis Cobbett, *The Causes of Tuberculosis*, Cambridge 1917, pp.10-11; James Spence et. al., *A Thousand Families in Newcastle upon Tyne*, Oxford 1954, p.63.

[33] D.J. Gair Johnson in *BMJ*, 24 Aug. 1929, p.335.

[34] J. Middleton Martin, MOH Gloucestershire, in *BMJ*, 9 Jan. 1932, p.72.

[35] Spence, *A Thousand Families in Newcastle upon Tyne*, pp.65-7; F.J.W. Miller, S.D.M. Court et al., *Growing up in Newcastle upon Tyne* , Oxford 1960, pp.114-7.

[36] *BMJ*, 16 May 1925, p.945.

[37]Leonard P. Ayres, *Open-Air Schools*, New York 1911, pp.3-8; Edward J. Morton (Assistant School Doctor, London County Council), 'Open-Air Schools', in Charles E. Hecht (ed.), *Rearing An Imperial Race*, 1913, pp.196-8.

[38]Mrs D.M. Power Sweeney, (Organizer (?) London Open-Air School, Upper Holloway), *Transactions of NAPT, 1912*, pp.139-48.

[39]*The Child*, Dec. 1927, pp.44-6.

[40]*The Child*, June 1927, p.266.

[41]Descriptions of Birley House and Shrewsbury House - open air schools of London County Council, *Tuberculosis Year Book 1913-1914*, pp.358-9; *The Child*, vol.iv, Dec. 1913, p.202.

[42]D.O. Holme (Organizer of Elementary Schools, Norwich), in Hecht, *Imperial Race*, pp.219-21.

[43]D.M. Taylor (Medical Officer of Health for Halifax), *Tuberculosis Year Book 1913-1914*, pp.130-1.

[44]Holme, in Hecht, *Imperial Race*, p.219.

[45]*The Child*, Aug. 1919, p.520; Halliday Sutherland recalls the school in the Regent's Park band rotunda in *The Arches Of The Years*, 1933, pp.209-10.

[46]*The Child*, June 1927, pp.260-1.

[47]John E. Gorst, *The Children of the Nation*, 1906, p.110.

[48]Taylor in *Tuberculosis Year Book 1913-1914*, p.130-1; W. Bolton Tomson, *Some Methods for the Prevention of Tuberculosis*, 1929, p.97.

[49]William Baker (Hon. Director, Barnardo's Homes), 'The Boys' Garden City', *The Child*, Oct. 1912, pp.60-4.

[50]H.J. Gauvain, 'Tuberculous Cripples', in T.N. Kelynack, (ed.) *Defective Children*, 1915, p.119.

[51]Benjamin Moore, *The Dawn Of The Health Age*, 1911, p.11.

[52]G. Gregory Kayne, *The Control Of Tuberculosis In England*, 1937, p.10; Thomas Reid, *An Essay on the Nature ... of the Phthisis Pulmonalis*, 1785, pp.4-7.

[53]Registrar-General, quoted in *Lancet*, 29 Aug. 1896, p.626; Dr H. Old, 'Statement ... on Wales' to Ministry of Health, 1927, PRO MH96/1111.

[54]Gunnar Dahlberg, 'Mortality From Tuberculosis In Some Countries', *British Journal of Social Medicine*, vol.iv, 1949, pp.224-7; Reginald Dudfield, 'Note on the Mortality from Tuberculosis 1851-1905', *Journal of the Royal Statistical Society*, vol.lxx, 1907, p.457.

[55]Old, 'Statement ... ' 1927, PRO MH96/1111.

[56]H. Handford, 'Menstruation and Phthisis', *BMJ*, 22 Jan. 1887, p.153.

[57]Geoffrey Beven, 'The Effects of Pregnancy on Pulmonary Tuberculosis', *Tubercle*, vol.xxxiii, 1952, pp.18-19.

[58]William Thomson, *The Germ Theory Of Disease*, Melbourne 1882, pp.27-8.

[59]J. Andrew in *BMJ*, 12 Apr. 1884, p.709.

[60]W. Burton Wood in *BMJ*, 25 Mar. 1933, p.509.

[61]John Guy, *Pulmonary Tuberculosis*, Edinburgh 1923, p.12.

[62]Bulstrode, *Report*, pp.45-6; Moore, *Health Age*, pp.160-1.

[63]Harold S. Scurfield, (former MOH for Sheffield) in *Transactions of the National Association   for the Prevention of Tuberculosis ... 1923*, (hereafter *NAPT)* ,pp.155-68.

[64] Edwards Crisp in *Transactions of the St. Andrews Graduates' Association* , 1867, p.113; W.A. Guy in *First Report of the Commissioners on the State of Large Towns,* , *BPP*, 1844, vol. xvii, Qs. 5560-4.

[65]C.R. Drysdale in *Lancet*, 8 Aug. 1896, pp.427-9; *Report of MOH to London County Council*, 1909, p.56; Guy, *Pulmonary Tuberculosis*, pp.7-8; Walter Pagel et al., *Pulmonary Tuberculosis*, Oxford 1964, p.475.

[66]Sir John Robertson (Professor Public Health, Univ. Birmingham), in *BMJ* 23 June 1934, p.1136.

[67]Noel A. Humphreys, 'Class Mortality Statistics', *Journal of the Royal Statistical Society*, vol.L, 1887, p.273; *51st ... Report of the Registrar-General for Ireland, 1914, BPP* , 1914-16, vol.ix, p.xxviii.

[68]*Transactions of the NAPT, 1931*, pp.34-5.

[69]Destreé and Gallmaerts in *Lancet* , 2 Aug. 1890, p.245; Bulstrode, *Report*, pp.70-4; David M. Kissen, *Emotional Factors in Pulmonary Tuberculosis*, 1958, pp.10-13.

2 ETIOLOGIES

Etiological narratives of phthisis, scrofula and other tubercular maladies had a simple mechanistic logic. The process of disease began with upset of the normal balance and flow of fluids in the body, manifested as inflammation, set going by putrefaction within the body or by physical injury. Putrefaction within the body might be ascribed to the introduction into the bloodstream of external decayed matter which continued to oxidise and thereby disseminate poisons within the system. Sooner or later these poisons might attack the tissues of the lungs or other organs or joints and begin to 'consume' them. The consumed tissue might then begin to be deposited as tubercles within the lungs or other parts of the body. Tubercles were rounded nodules resembling seeds two to three millimetres in diameter: they might be fibroid, or caseated, or soft and indeterminate, and usually they were pale yellowish-grey in colour. They could be found during dissection of the lungs of known consumptives, or at the sites of inflammation in joints or bone cases, or, among scrofulous victims, in the neck and other lymph glands or organs through the body. Their presence in these diverse conditions implied that a common degenerative process had occurred, but tubercle did not prove that the various maladies had common origins or courses. Persons of general education had a vague grasp of Laënnec's claims for the 'unity' of tubercular phenomena but they easily accommodated his hypothesis to the common sense observation that the phenomena were merely secondary occurrences of little diagnostic value.

In 1842, for example, a representative gathering of ordinary medical practitioners in London had agreed that tubercles were final deposits of congealed and accreted detritus born partly from external putrescent matter and partly from the decay of poisoned tissues. They further agreed that the process could develop independently of poisons inhaled or ingested because post mortem evidence showed that deposition might begin in the stomach, where digestion left 'morbid effluvia'.[1]

Tradition and common observation also explained why some individuals or families rather than others became consumptive. These unfortunates exhibited the tubercular diathesis or physical predisposition to the affliction. They had a scrawny torso, flat or concave narrow chest, fair freckled skin, red or 'very pale hair and eyes', irregularly harsh instead of silky breathing, and a high probability that their parents and elder kin had had similar characteristics and had been phthisics. Their narrow chests and laboured breathing indicated that such cases had weak circulatory systems, likely to prove incapable of flushing the poisons and preventing deposition.[2]

Tubercles were also commonly found in slaughtered cattle. They too were subject to the tubercular diathesis. The scraggy offspring of scraggy parents, when weakened by bad hay and dirty water and dank overcrowded stabling, suffered attenuation of their eliminatory processes   with the result that the effluvium, the 'virus', accumulated in their stomachs and udders and might be conveyed in their milk and flesh to vulnerable human stomachs. The 'virus', the oxidising potentially destructive matter, was apparently contagious. Foul cowsheds usually housed contiguous, inferior beasts producing low yields of milk which putrefied quicker than milk from healthier animals. Careful consumers preferred to have milk from a sound, single cow because the chances of ingesting tainted milk were reduced. Consumptives who could afford it sometimes were ordered asses' milk as a strengthening diet, because asses were not subject to the tubercular diathesis. Jane Austen's Lady Denham was prepared to supply asses' milk to consumptive sojourners in Sanditon.[3]

Tubercular phenomena were easily accommodated within a Newtonian frame of mass, weight, proximity, gravity and the predispositions created by their interaction. In 1862 Dr Henry Silvester, of Clapham, advised his lay audience that 'in scrofulous disease of the hip-joint, where the patient is compelled to recline on one side...for a considerable time, it is found that whichever side happens to be reclined upon, it is that which is the more disposed to deposit.' Gravity was also at work in the distribution of tubercles in the lung. Post mortems showed that they were usually 'first' deposited, that is, found only in the upper parts: this occurred because the detritus floated to the surface of the circulatory system and was stranded there because of 'inadequate aeration'.[4]

The indefinite range of tubercular phenomena together with the simple sequential understanding of their occurrence encouraged the promiscuous attribution of first causes. All baffling illnesses beget this kind of dogmatising, and not only in the nineteenth century - think of contemporary debates about cancer and insanity - but tuberculosis was distinct in evoking so many diverse, untested and untestable explications. Dr James Copland's list of fourteen causes offers a representative sample from 1861. A few derived from clinical knowledge but most were moral inferences drawn from the belief that tubercular illnesses were culpable deviations from a normal moral, healthy state. Copland cited first, 'ill-regulated studies, amusements, and exercises, in both sexes'. These, as his contemporary, Dr Peter Eade explained in 1869, reduced that 'nervous power' which controlled cell growth. A constitution weakened by excitement allowed anarchic cell proliferation which in turn eased the destructive progress, accumulated effluvia and accelerated the deposition of tubercle. Even strong, healthy people became susceptible to consumption during periods of 'depraved or depressed, or irregular nervous power', brought on by anxiety or mental overwork, or poverty and intemperance. 'The tumid puffy upper lip' and 'the prominent pouting of this part during a paroxysm of acute hysteria' were 'familiar symptoms' of 'tuberculous cachexia'. Copland's catch-all listing of 'intense or prolonged mental exertions', 'depressing mental emotions', 'nostalgia' and 'disappointed hopes and affections' contributed in the same way. 'Improper clothing in respect of the several regions of the body' and 'cold rooms' induced consumption because they lowered normal body heat. Immodest dress in women particularly exposed the respiratory system. Such dress, especially if it became wet, simultaneously hastened the loss of nervous electrical force and the onset of exhaustion. 'Improper' constraints on the trunk, 'supports, stays', hampered breathing and thereby efficient aeration of the system. The sudden rise in incidence of phthisis among women after age fifteen might be ascribed partly to their subjecting their bodies to newly severe tight lacing.

Three of Copland's causes related to the observed link between certain occupations and high phthisis mortality. 'Trades which are injurious by preventing exercise in the open air', 'occupations in which dust or other irritating matters are inhaled, and 'occupations which are exposed to great vicissitudes of temperature and weather'. There were good grounds for all of these assertions and I shall return to them later.

Copland's remaining three causes were moral-physical ones: 'premature or excessive sexual indulgence'; masturbation; and celibacy. Excessive sexual indulgence weakened the body's resistance to putrefying influences. Celibacy induced masturbation which again weakened the body and led to consumption.[5] Catholic nunneries and seminaries in France were well known to have high consumption rates.[6] In Protestant England the temptation to masturbate began with horse riding. Copland knew of 'no more certain means of exciting females to this vice'.[7] His Brompton Hospital colleague, Dr Edward Smith, reinforced these views in 1862 with the finding that among 600 male patients, 11.6 per cent 'had committed sexual abuse', 18.2 per cent had 'been addicted to masturbation', 22 per cent had 'suffered from voluntary emissions', 16 per cent had syphilis and nearly 30 per cent admitted to having 'led a bad life'. L. Key was a typical case. He was a clerk, single 'aged 22' when he came to Brompton. Five years earlier he had had a haemoptysis. Seven years ago, at school, he had masturbated. He owned to 'frequent spermatorrhoea' two or three years ago. Key was now emaciated, with poor appetite, 'a white and frothy condition of the tongue, with short inspiration and night cough. He was very nervous, and had all the appearance of phthisis'. Indeed, his moral history proved the diagnosis. After one more visit to Smith, he disappeared.[8]

Moral culpability also explained the similarity between the consumptive diathesis and the bodily weaknesses inherited from a parent with the 'syphilitic taint'. Dr Smith observed that a delicate child raised upon poor food and exposed by its immoral parents to deleterious pursuits such as street trading was more likely to become scrofulous than a child with equal 'delicacy of glandular organization' but reared 'properly' in a comfortable household. Smith revealed in 1862 that he and his colleagues had found syphilis to be common among parents of scrofulous children, while scrofulous non-syphilitic parents seemed rarely to have openly scrofulous children.[9] George Meredith had already blamed a syphilitic father for a consumptive daughter in *The Ordeal of Richard Feverel* in 1859. In 1882, the year of the discovery of the bacillus, Dr T. Henry Green of Brompton announced his discovery of a third 'distinctly syphilitic' type of phthisis, to be set beside 'chronic basic pneumonia phthisis' and the inflammatory disorganisation of lung phthisis.[10] The theory was popular on the Continent, too. As late as 1912 Carl Spengler of Davos, the proponent of I.K. [Immunkörper] vaccine therapy, endorsed the view of his British followers that syphilis was intimately involved with tuberculosis and claimed to have grown syphilis germs from tuberculosis sputum. Both taints increased the amount of effluvial degenerative matter in the bloodstream and soft tissues.[11]

Other pustular affections could also harm the system. In 1858 Dr William Addison of Maidstone attributed the development of tubercle in a lady aged eighteen to an attack of measles six years earlier. From that time she had suffered sore throats, colds and a regular 'a hem'. Three years after the measles she had had whooping cough. Soon afterwards she became emaciated and her hair fell out. She felt chilled; everything she touched had to be warmed. Addison employed percussion and auscultation to diagnose consumption. She died soon after the diagnosis, following unspecified treatments. Her rank precluded a post mortem. At the time of the measles, when Addison first examined her, she had apparently showed no phthisic diathesis, although when reviewing the case, he remarked that she must have had it in a disguised form because he had learned subsequently that two of the young lady's aunts had died of consumption. Hence the family diathesis had enabled the measles to 'originate' the tubercles 'notwithstanding the absence of all signs'.[12]

Alcoholism was also involved as a moral etiological factor, especially when it violated middle class conservative norms. Dr Charles Drysdale, the Malthusian campaigner and early social Darwinist, declared in 1867 that 'drunkenness cause[d] a rapid form of tubercular phthisis, and that in the strongest persons, such as navigators and sailors'.[13] A decade later, the sanitarian and temperance campaigner, Dr Benjamin Richardson, elaborated this insight by discovering a new form of 'alcoholic phthisis'.[14] Certainly drunkenness and phthisis often went together. Dr J.B. Bradbury, physician to Addenbrooke's Hospital in Cambridge, announced in 1871 that 'a morbid delicacy of the walls of the blood-vessels of the lungs...induced by... intemperate habits' led to pulmonary disease which led to haemoptysis. This indubitable sequence reinforced his opinion that 'blood-spitting' did '*not*' cause phthisis while drunkenness unquestionably did. His intemperate patient had been spitting up to a quarter-pint of blood at a time over nine months. Bradbury had first tried to stop the haemoptysis with gallic acid. This failed and he added acetate of lead to the dose. That failed. He added Dover's Powder [opium and ipecuanha] to induce vomiting and 'thereby check the bleeding'; but the powder 'proved rebellious to the acetate of lead and the mixture of gallic and sulphuric acids which the patient was...taking'. After three months on Bradbury's beverages the patient died - weakened, Bradbury opined, by his old dissipations.[15]

The first critical investigation of these assumptions was published in 1886. Dr Isambard Owen, of the Collective Investigation Committee of the BMA, found that 50 per cent of his (presumably male) phthisical patients at St George's Hospital could be regarded, 'on their own showing' as excessive drinkers, averaging daily over four pints of beer or their equivalent. The percentage of heavy drinkers among the non-phthisical patients was a still remarkable 33.5; while 'the temperate class' formed 41.5 per cent among the general patients and only 23 per cent of the phthisics.[16] The findings of later investigations tallied with Owen's, although each seems to have been pursued in ignorance of what had gone before. James Whyte of the United Kingdom Alliance asserted in 1889 that insured male working class Rechabites aged between 25 and 55 had over the period 1879-83 less than half the consumption death rate of the non-abstaining Foresters, who in turn had rates slightly under the general mortality level of the comparable English population.[17] Through to 1963 researchers reported that heavy drinkers - now defined at two or more pints of beer daily - were over-represented to about 100 per cent among severe tuberculosis hospital cases.[18] The causes of this linkage have yet to be determined. Dr H.T. Bulstrode suggested in 1908 that the high tuberculosis rate among barmen and others in the trade implied both that the tuberculous might take to drink and that the ensuing addiction reduced the money available for food and shelter.[19] Recently other workers have suggested that active tuberculosis presents as a late breakdown in elderly individuals as a result of other diseases which lower resistance, especially alcoholism and diabetes.[20] Moralising assertions have been shaded by clinical pathological ones, but the correlation persists. Reinfection might also be exacerbated by inhaling bacteria in the mouth while in a drunken stupor.

But throughout doctors agree that alcoholic consumptives only turn up when their disease is advanced and that they remain uncooperative patients.

Another minatory etiology, the traditional assertion that consumption was 'the result of breathing foul air' was vigorously promoted by Florence Nightingale in the 1850s and 1860s. The fundamental vacuity of her argument was masked by a confident plausibility. Foul air, in her view, was air 'contaminated by the breath of other persons'. It was abundantly produced by overcrowding and thereby enlarged the risks of phthisis, especially in sleeping quarters at night when the 'atmosphere is close and foul' and 'the system is more peculiarly disposed to its effects'. The idea went back to some fragmentary, obscure assertions by Aristotle. Nightingale and her friends conceived of the disease being generated de novo in the lungs by bad air.[21] The first big international health and welfare conference in London in 1862 endorsed Miss Nightingale's declaration and by the mid 1860s the author of the article on 'Sanitary Science' in *Chambers Encyclopaedia* was able to praise his century for having 'placed on unquestioned authority' the old hypothesis that phthisis originated 'in breathing an atmosphere contaminated by respiration'.[22]

The new indubitability of the theory rested upon a notional closed system akin to those predicting finite, exhaustible coal and iron reserves which haunted educated Victorians from the 1860s. The pullulating town masses breathed and re-breathed air that was not renewed at the same rate and thereby condemned themselves and their fellow countrymen to an ever more 'vitiated atmosphere' reduced in oxygen and thickened with effete carbon ready for deposition and mischief in the lungs. Statistics proved it, Dr Edwards Crisp told the British Association in 1868. London's consumption mortality rate was 24 per 1000; Westmorland's was 18 per 1000; the crowded West Riding had a rate of 24 per 1000 while the North Riding's rate was 19 per 1000. Thinly-peopled districts had an overall rate of 17 per 1000; large towns had a rate of 28 per 1000.[23]

Crisp also adduced a particular proof in the destruction of a cheesemonger's family. Their sitting room was above the shop where the cheeses lay. The room's air was 'vitiated' by the palpable emanations from below. Four of the five children had died from phthisis or tubercular meningitis, while the fifth was only 'comparatively well'. He had survived, Crisp explained, 'because he got aerated on a voyage to South Africa'.[24]

Henry MacCormac, the Belfast medical polymath, also held the bad air theory to be 'as true as that the stars shine in Heaven'. He declared that, on first principles, consumption must be rife in Iceland because the inhabitants had to breathe each other's spoiled air while immured together through their winters. Thereby he damaged the bad air theory. A proud Icelander rebuffed MacCormac in 1869 with the artful claim that his homeland had no 'indigenous' consumption and that the rate was low. Henceforth the theory stood as ancillary to other causes said to be implicated in phthisis.[25] But it remained a potent, attractive idea because it indicated a course of action. Florence Nightingale was vindicated when the consumption rate in the army fell after the barracks had been ventilated and enlarged.[26]   Hirsch's authoritative *Handbook of Geographical...Pathology*, of 1887 emphasised bad air etiology.[27] Arthur Ransome, a leading consumption specialist, urged it through the 1890s and persuaded one influential lay member of the Royal Commission on Tuberculosis, Lord Basing, of its truth in 1896. Dr John Tatham enshrined it in his supplement to the Registrar-General's report of the following year. Thereafter the theory faded away, to be revived a decade later when reformers associated it anew with   bad housing.[28]

Sanitary priorities fueled a like theory about the phthisic-inducing qualities of damp soils. It too had its heyday in the 1860s. The theory came from the United States, where Dr H.I. Bowditch had popularised it in 1862. In 1864 Mr A.B. Middleton had outlined to the British Association the evil miasmic consequences of the humidity and nastiness of the atmosphere produced by canals and cesspools. He asserted that the phthisis rate in his town, Salisbury, had fallen rapidly after main drainage and sewage works had lowered the water level by, he said, four to five feet. The medical profession and local authorities really took notice after Dr George Buchanan published an extensive set of correlations between soil dampness and phthisis mortality in the Registrar-General's report for 1868. Salisbury, Ely, Rugby and Banbury had all recorded falls in phthisis mortality rates between 41 and 49 per cent from 1859 to 1866 while 'much' or 'some' drying had occurred. By sad contrast, Alnwick, Brynmawr and Chelmsford recorded either increased phthisis rates or no change, and 'no

drying'.[29] Sanitarians used Buchanan's figures throughout the
1870s in their campaigns for drainage schemes. But in 1879 Dr
Charles Kelly, the Medical Officer of Health for West Sussex,
damaged the correlation with his report that phthisis in his
rural district had substantially declined while the soil remained
as damp as ever. Moreover, mortality rates over longer periods
showed no clear trends. Petworth, with the highest rate in the
1860s, and Steyning with the lowest, were equally ill-drained
and remained so while their death rates were reversed in the
1870s (and reversed again in the 1880s). A few dedicated
sanitarians, including Dr Richard Thorne Thorne, an inspector
in the medical department of the Privy Council, continued to
press a fall in phthisis mortality as a reason for spending rates
on drainage, but this cause was lost.[30] By the late 1880s doctors
and reformers were thinking in terms of complex multiple
antecedents rather than single causes.

These single sequence etiologies are bizarre mainly for the
hectoring assertiveness which possessed their advocates. The
arena was open because no one had a clear idea of contagion. In
general, Catholic southern Europe acted upon the belief that
consumption was infectious; opinion in France had long been
divided - Cullen and Laënnec had said that it was not - while
most progressive, scientific doctors in the United Kingdom and
Protestant Germany were sure that it was not spread by
infection.   The isolation and fumigation procedures
traditionally imposed in Mediterranean countries seemed to be
superstitious legacies. Sir James Clark, the court physician and
influential authority on phthisis, who treated the dying
consumptive Chopin in 1848, rejected the Italian hospital
practice of maintaining separate consumption wards as cruel
and useless and 'due to the obsolete idea of consumption being
contagious'.[31]   Certainly it did not seem to be readily
communicated like measles or smallpox from a sufferer to a
healthy person. Yet it was also 'common observation', Dr W.H.
Wiltshire told the Medical Society of London in 1844, 'that
young persons sleeping with old ones lost much of their vital
power...[and] in phthisis there was a low state of vitality, similar
to that which existed in old age; might not a healthy person
sleeping with a phthisical patient lose some of his vitality?' that
is, the phthisis virus was 'contagious'.[32] In the 1860s only one
doctor, the humble Dr C.R. Bree of Colchester, replied to a
questionnaire admitting to a belief in contagion of some kind.

Inherited predisposition was not a sufficient answer, Bree thought, because over 36 years he had known many relatives of phthisics who had slept with the patient afterwards die of phthisis even where, as with wives or husbands, there was no blood relationship. 'If the tubercular element is so minute', he ventured, 'as to be conveyed by the ovum to the offspring, why should it not be thrown off by sweat, and be absorbed by the skin?'. His eminent brethren ignored his contribution, while they reiterated their beliefs in hereditary and moral degeneracy as causative agents.[33]

The anti-contagionists were rallying because they faced two powerful challenges to their belief. The first came from the brilliantly original and courageous Dr William Budd, who had done so much to explain the distribution of cholera infection in 1849 and the 1850s and to define typhoid fever. Budd argued from the sudden appearance of consumption among native peoples in places newly colonised by Europeans that the consumption must have been introduced and that it must be catching. Tuberculosis was distinctive only in that it was slow to develop. His case was both too well documented and too much against prevailing doctrine to be gainsaid, so it passed with little debate; but it must have unsettled Budd's contemporaries, because they continued to refer to it, usually to dismiss it, for the next twenty years.[34] As with his work on cholera, he never received his due in his lifetime.

Budd's paper was also obscured by the row which erupted in 1867 over the researches of J.A. Villemin, a French army surgeon. He had found that human and bovine tuberculosis could be transmitted by injecting rabbits, dogs and other subjects with tuberculous matter from humans and cows. Many of the injected beasts and birds developed tubercles. His discoveries threatened beliefs in the structural deposit sequence of consumption and the tubercular diathesis as a predisposing condition. Condescending enemies among his fellow countrymen, Pidoux and Colin for example, German rivals, led by Virchow, Cohnheim and Frankel, joined British sceptics headed by Burdon-Sanderson, the eminent physiologist, in asserting that Villemin's experiments only reinforced their dominant view that consumption was 'due to the entrance of dead and inspissated pus into the circulation'.[35] Villemin's work implied that tubercles were essentially uniform in structure and they were an integral, concurrent element in the disease process. However, dissectors more experienced than Villemin knew that tubercles varied in structure according to their mode of deposition, that they could occur independently of other symptoms of tubercular affliction, and that their variation proved that they were a residual product of tissue decay and therefore not communicated from one person to another. Burdon-Sanderson explained that Villemin's injections had merely initiated and accelerated the process of inflammation, the production of pus and its deposition.[36]

Virchow saw his life's work on cell structure threatened by the new claims. He and his disciples rallied to defend the view that tubercles were mere 'knots of tissue', pieces of 'inflammatory consolidation', 'deposits', and not 'growths' as in cancer. They asserted that Villemin's work simply proved that tubercles in guinea pigs might beget further decay manifested as new tubercles, particularly because guinea pigs were notoriously predisposed to the production of pus and tubercular deposits. His findings did not prove the existence of a particular tuberculous poison.[37] His detractors ignored Villemin's experiments with other animals and birds. Dr Edwards Crisp, of the North London Hospital for Consumption, agreed that Villemin's theory rested upon the untenable assumption 'that the body cannot generate a poison like tubercle'. Crisp boasted of having dissected many tubercles and often finding 'worms' in them which had been seeded with the first deposit of effluvium.[38] Fundamentally, Villemin's discovery threatened to make existing medical knowledge and practice irrelevant to an intriguing and profitable disease. British doctors continued to dismiss his results for the next two decades. Attempts to repeat his results mostly failed. The ubiquity and comparative torpidity of the bacillus and its near relations makes it a difficult organism to investigate, even in modern laboratories. Villemin had got it right by genius, good technique and good fortune. He was to die disregarded.

Indeed, the reaction to Villemin revived the old idea that phthisis was the ultimate result of other lung inflammations, pneumonia, pleurisy and bronchitis, producing phlegm which degenerated into pus. This commonly observed sequence made sense to laity and doctors alike, against Laënnec's opinion that the illnesses were distinct. The seamstresses in Anne Marsh-Caldwell's *Lettice Arnold* (1850) had kept their workroom windows shut against the damp air which brought colds and thence phthisis. 'They all dreaded', their creator explained, '...taking cold; those fatal coughs which every season thinned the ranks... were invariably attributed to some particular occasion when they had "taken cold"'.[39] Professor A.T. Thomson of University College London had expounded the same belief in 1834: 'continued cough...in cases where...diathesis exists...might bring on a phthisis'.[40]

The sterile debate about the origin and structure of tubercles, briefly interrupted by the Villemin row, continued through the 1870s. Doctors contested the differences between 'catarrhal pneumonia'. 'broncho-pneumonia' and 'alveolar catarrh' and their declensions into 'lobular phthisis', 'fibroid phthisis' and 'pneumonic phthisis' and thence to acute miliary phthisis, that is, phthisis marked by rapid advance and widespread growth of tubercles through the body. The issue remained structural. The 'overgrowth of the ...adenoid tissue' activated by inflammation, might liquefy, soften and be expectorated, or settle and caseate, or grow fibroid. Whatever eventuated, Burdon-Sanderson explained, the lungs and bronchial passages became constricted and thereby a new degenerative process of fever, digestive upsets and emaciation was instigated.[41] Consumption was a late secondary sequence, not a primary disease entity.

Meanwhile, medical opinion about the possible contagiousness of phthisis remained vague and contradictory. By the late 1870s some doctors were toying with the idea that phthisis might be transmitted if one susceptible person inhaled 'fine particles of tuberculous sputa, atomised into the air by the patient's cough'.[42] In 1878 Tappeiner reported from Meran his experiment of keeping dogs in a chamber into which fine particles of tuberculous sputa were blown. All the dogs displayed miliary tuberculosis. Doctors writing in the *Lancet* dismissed Tappeiner's results as not proving anything about human consumption because the dogs' phthisis was 'artificially' induced.[43] The British key argument in resistance to contagion theory was the claim (subsequently shown to be false, even within its own assumptions) by Brompton Hospital men that no doctor, nurse or porter had contracted phthisis 'at Brompton'.[44] In 1883, six months after Koch's announcement, 34 out of 38 respondents to a questionnaire from the Cambridge Medical Society about the communicability of phthisis declared the disease to be 'constitutional' or hereditary, but not infectious. If it were infectious, there would be more consumption about and the death rate would be stable or even rising, rather than falling.[45] Four years after Koch the eminent Mr Thomas Meeres declared that he had never met with a case that could be traced to infection and in 1890 the *British Medical Journal* neutrally reported the deep division within the Paris Academy of Medicine over the alleged infectiousness of phthisis. The one clear fact, according to the British delegates to the International Congress on Tuberculosis in Berlin in 1899, was that 'phthisis ... (was) not "catching" in the popular sense of the word'.[46] The turn of opinion on the spread of the disease did not come until about 1905. Nevertheless, doctors had consistently advised marriage partners to sleep separately when one of them developed phthisis. Families who could afford the materials and the room transfers were advised to burn sulphur daily in the patient's bedroom. Still, the risk seemed slight. There appeared to be few straightforward instances of wives or husbands taking the disease from their spouse; the phthisis deaths of spouses after the phthisis deaths of their partners were explained by the additional tiredness and disruption imposed by the presence of the dying partner which had triggered the inflammatory process and its phthisic outcome. Of 6167 recent cases at Brompton to the mid 1860s only 106 had involved marriage partners and each of these cases could be explained by 'hereditary predisposition'.[47]

Doctors and laity clung to the hereditary explanation because it made sense of the otherwise inexplicable distribution of the disease and it upheld medical authority within the family. Sir William Jenner, physician to the Queen, declared in 1870 that diathetic or tuberculous parents almost invariably transmitted the 'morbid tendency' to their offspring and, moreover, the participation of both in the act of transmission heightened the tendency, 'to a degree exceeding the sum of the tendencies of the parents', just as occurred with insanity. In cases where only one parent was tuberculous Sir William had observed that fathers transmitted the tendency with a greater destructive power than mothers.[48] From about 1870 it seems to have become usual for engaged couples with a tuberculous background to consult their medical adviser, who in turn advised against marriage when the threat was obvious. In *Marion Fay*, Trollope, who had a tragically extensive acquaintance with tuberculosis in his own family, has his heroine flee from her lover once she discovers she is phthisic.

Jenner's doleful opinion matched that of Dr Charles Drysdale, who proved the 'extremely hereditary', non-contagious nature of phthisis by producing the indisputable fact that three-fourths of patients among the upper classes admitted to a tuberculous parent or grand-parent. His remark in 1882 that doctors must treat phthisis by the 'choice of parents' is an early thrust towards the eugenic faith that flourished after the turn of the century, engendered in part by anxieties about tuberculosis.[49]

During the 1860s doctors had begun to publish statistics proving the traditional belief that consumptive parents were distinctly likely to have consumptive offspring. It followed that the children 'were predisposed' and predictably would exhibit the diathesis. Dr Edward Smith told the British Association in 1862 that of 1000 Brompton patients, 54 per cent had lost their father from phthisis, 46 per cent their mother, and 28 per cent had lost both. Almost a quarter of the 1000 had also lost brothers or sisters from phthisis and over 9 per cent had lost aunts and uncles. The primacy of the hereditary factor was proved by the low percentage - 'only 14.3 per cent' - who had 'been insufficiently nourished' and might therefore have been precipitated into disease by want.[50] The widespread German opinion that phthisis might not be hereditary and that such a sequence had yet to be proved, was anathematised in Britain.[51] Through the 1880s life assurance offices rejected proposals for the children of consumptive parents because 'phthisis and insanity gather force through the generations'.[52] In opposition to French medical belief that the germ was transmitted with the spermatic fluid, British doctors held that the 'family predisposition' was communicated with the ovum.[53] But Landouzy showed in the mid 1880s that the seminal vesicles of tubercular patients contained bacilli and the British fell silent, only to revive in 1892 when Birch, Hirschfeld and Schmal grew tubercle in a guinea pig injected with material from an apparently non-tubercular foetus removed from a dead consumptive mother.[54]

Through the 1890s, however, British medical faith in the hereditary principle began to weaken once the germ theory of contagion began to overshadow it. As Dr Arthur Ransome pointed out in 1890, the social implications of the hereditary theory were horrid. If some 'gemmules' of tuberculosis were implanted in the race and liable to be transmitted through the generations, to break out unpredictably, doctors and laity must 'despair of ever casting out this plague' and the possibility of preventing marriage between consumptives would have to be seriously entertained. Medical assistance would be condemned for ever to mere palliation.[55]

This prospect induced a new interpretation of the statistics. Dr Robert Philip rejoiced in 1892 that 'only 23.3 per cent' of 1000 Edinburgh consumptives showed a definite history of family 'taint'. The fact that 'children' were 'not born tuberculous in any sense', according to Dr James Niven, Medical Officer of Health for of Manchester, in 1897, renewed the doctors' charter to press for better ventilation and less overcrowding. Converts to the sanatorium movement also began to insist that 'tuberculosis was not hereditary in any sense'.[56]

In 1907 this optimistic movement was temporarily halted by a seemingly powerful restatement of the hereditary case. The statistician Karl Pearson publicised, amongst his 'studies in national deterioration', figures which suggested that simple infection could not account for the incidence of consumption within families, especially when children with two consumptive parents were more likely to have the disease than children with one and much more likely than children with neither parent consumptive. Infection theory, Pearson declared, revealed 'an anti-social disregard for national eugenics'.[57] His findings and subsequent work into the 1920s were based upon unstated numbers of Belfast families, possibly around 400. His evidence seems to have been gathered for him by medical practitioners from patients' testimony. Pearson's confidence in the conclusions he derived from this evidential quicksand is startling, but nobody appears to have queried it at the time. Moreover, the central, obvious flaw in his reasoning, the failure to account for possible infection, leaves Pearson in this instance at least an opinionated and bad statistician. A disregarded 22 per cent of his families had a tuberculosis death without either parent being recorded as tuberculous.[58] But his uncomplicated message appealed to would-be interventionists. The Destitution Conference of 1911 proceeded upon his assumptions. As Sidney and Beatrice Webb warned the delegates: there was a proven 'family "class atmosphere"' which nurtured the 'grand parade of the tuberculous, the syphilitic...the uncivilized, the undisciplined'.[59] Public money would be better spent on inculcating selective parentage than building sanatoria. Geoffrey Drage, a social Imperialistic busybody, wanted the money to be spent on 'restricted farms' to house defective families whose reproduction of 'drunkenness, consumption, insanity and suicide' would be 'controlled'.[60] School medical officers countered by claiming that they could spend the money better on the schools, identifying and isolating defectives and risks. Dr A.D. Edwards, schools medical officer for Bournemouth, investigated over 10,000 children to 1914 and found proof of hereditary taint in the fact that 'ailing children' were 40 per cent more likely to have relatives with tuberculosis than 'non-ailing children'. The ailing required special schools and their parents required investigation.[61]

These beliefs never became paramount, so far as tuberculosis was concerned, because the medical profession had so large a stake in palliative sanatoriums. But they lingered in the eugenics movement and Major Leonard Darwin was still preaching birth control and voluntary sterilization as remedies for 'hereditary predisposition' into the 1930s.[62] In the United States, however, hereditarian ideas were much more influential and research programmes devoted to exemplifying them continued into the 1950s. The highpoint came in 1943 when Kallman and Reismir reported a longitudinal study of twins purporting to reveal an 87.3 per cent tuberculosis morbidity rate among identical twins compared with 11.9 per cent among half-siblings. In those simple days before Sir Cyril Burt's false studies of twins were exposed, their findings were regarded very seriously.[63] Present authorities are much more cautious. Maurice Lefford proposes that 'genetically determined variation in susceptibility is difficult to establish in man because of the importance of environmental factors. The primary determinants of any infection disease are related to duration and intensity of exposure to the pathogenic agent'.[64]

Doctors and laity clung to the identification of diathesis and symptoms with the disease process as not only reasonable in itself, but because it provided the only acceptable rationale of management. Infection was strictly untreatable. Submission to it would entail intolerable fumigatory and isolation measures and the resigned, ignorant apathy which prevailed in Mediterranean countries.

Scrofula was also commonly believed to be hereditary. Scrofulous children were observed to come frequently from 'consumptive stock'. The swellings and ulcers represented the efflorescence of a diathesis indicated by 'delicacy of glandular organization' often exacerbated by an 'hereditary...syphilitic taint'.[65] Exposure to cold or humidity, usually from dwelling on wet soil, improper diet and, from the 1880s onwards, enlarged tonsils or adenoids and pigeon-chestedness, could lead to inadequate cleansing of the blood which brought on the scrofula.[66] As experiments with rabbits had shown in the early 1840s (they were kept in cold, wet dark cages and fed only green food), this sluggishness in the circulation could lead to the deposit of tubercles, although scrofula was not ordinarily linked to other forms of tuberculosis in medical and lay understanding until Edwardian times, twenty years after Koch.[67]

Scrofula was attacked with the usual armentarium against inflammations. Throughout the century infusions of gentian, lime water washings, lead ointments, hot bread or yeast poultices were applied externally as counter-inflammatory irritants, sometimes singly, sometimes in varying permutations, sometimes serially, over weeks, months, years, with no striking improvements. Iodine was popular with doctors and patients after the French had become enthused with it in the early 1830s. It was taken orally, rubbed on, given in baths, in various strengths between one half to one grain per pound of distilled water, with a dish of muriate of soda. Tincture of gentian was also given internally. John Savory recommended it in 1840, to be taken together with iodine and four to six grain mercurial pills. He noted that such doses had been known to cause 'serious derangement of the nervous system', but declared that the good results outweighed the dangers.[68] Dr Charles Clay in Manchester in 1841 reported 'decided improvement' in patients with 'scrofulous ulcers' after three weeks of iodine in three ounce doses, gentian in seven grain doses taken together three times a day, reinforced by bread poultices night and morning.[69] A generation later Professor McCall Anderson of Glasgow healed a ten year old girl suffering from 'tubercular peritonitis', 'a dull lung' and 'decline of the bowels' with juniper drops and cream of tartar to 'reduce the swelling'. He maintained this regime for a fortnight but the child continued to waste. So he added pancreatic emulsion (prepared from pigs' pancreas) to the mix, two drops in milk twice a day, but after four days this showed no good results. He then added cod liver oil, half an ounce three times a day and after a short but unspecified period he dismissed the girl as 'well', although she still had a slight dullness at the apex of the left lung. Anderson instructed her to persevere with the treatment.[70] And that is the last we hear of her.

Cod liver oil had become a prime restorative around the 1840s. It nauseated many patients, but they readily agreed with their medical advisers that it did them good. Dr Theophilus Thompson of Brompton Hospital prescribed it for all his patients in the 1850s because, he said, it combined with the albuminous element in the chyle (milky fluid in the small intestine composed mainly of tissue fluid and fat absorbed from food) 'so as to form the healthy chyle - granules which feed the blood' - a shaky argument in modern physiological terms. Thompson also recommended cod liver oil for external use, particularly when patients found difficulty in swallowing it. He instanced a woman patient, aged twenty, who had lost weight throughout the two years he had treated her with 'tonics', but who had gained weight after two months of rubbing with a liniment composed of three ounces of cod liver oil, one ounce of aromatic ammonia, half a drachm of oil of lavender and five grains of opium, applied to the chest and back, night and morning.[71]

These regimens suggest why many scrofulous cases put up with their condition and avoided doctors. Victims procrastinated in seeking help and tended to abandon treatments if the ointments did not succeed immediately. It was a lucky patient whose treatment coincided with a remission; although it is possible that the iodine and lead ointments controlled some secondary infections. Cod liver oil retained its popularity. It was rated 'most efficient' in Squire's *Companion to the British Pharmacopoeca* (1915) and by 1933 had joined the national health subsidy list.[72] Scott's Emulsion and similar patent preparations continued into the present.

Patients whose kin could afford it had since the eighteenth century gone to the seaside to inhale the salt air and bathe, or journeyed to Malvern, Buxton or the Isle of Wight to take the mineral waters. Specialist infirmaries opened to cater for the visitors. The leading institution was the Margate Infirmary of 1791, a charity, later to become the Royal Sea Bathing Hospital. The standard therapy at these places embraced 'pure air', 'nutritious diet', salt water bathing and rest, with iron concoctions given internally to strengthen the physique and purify the blood.   Cases of tuberculosis of the joints were leeched to reduce the swelling.   The rest and improved diet must have made the sufferers' lives easier, especially the 'necessitous' free cases, but none of these treatments could remove the disfigurements and disabilities.[73]   Tim Linkinwater's room-bound neighbour in *Nicholas Nickleby* personified thousands of children through the nineteenth and earlier twentieth century who were never able to play with their fellows.

The passive management of phthisis combined warmth with food and rest.   Active treatments included the usual repeated doses of iodine, gentian and cod liver oil.   Until the 1860s medical attendants generally bled the patient, on the assumption that they were withdrawing bad blood likely to deposit further tubercle and that haemoptysis resulted from a superfluity of blood.   Admittedly, bleeding 'lowered' the patient, but this could be countered with doses of sulphuric acid in tinctures of around two drops per hundred in hundred drop doses.   Dr Copland of Brompton was still bleeding consumptives in the 1860s, but the practice was becoming unfashionable and Copland only bled 'healthy looking specimens'.   He combined the bleedings with emetics, usually tartrate of antimony in milk, 'to clear the digestion'.[74]

Haemoptysis demanded especially drastic action.   Copland instructed his students to bleed the patient, 'healthy-looking' or not, then give a dose or two of two grains of tartrate of antimony, and, 'as soon as nausea commences', give two grains of copper sulphate, and a nutmeg size electuary of quinine, sulphurous sublimate, potassium nitrate and antimony sulphate, kneaded with gum, together with doses of aniseed water 'for the cough'.   He also told them that hydrocyanic acid was 'most useful' and that a mixture of boracic acid and dilute phosphoric acid was 'of much service'.   Creosote was best for asthenic types of phthisis and Copland had often ordered the patient's room to be impregnated with it.   Blood-spitting types of phthisis could be alleviated with lead acetate, especially when it was combined with opium, ipecuanha and acetic acid.   Copland boasted of individual cases and groups of cases which had been variously 'benefited' by his ministrations but, like his colleagues, eminent and lowly, he showed no conception of controlled experiments over time.[75]   Indeed such experiments would have been pointless, because they would have revealed that his nostrums did not work and thereby caused much distress. He and his colleagues never reported bad results. Creosote was still being recommended in the 1920s. Koch had shown that it destroyed the bacillus in vitro, but it had been only once, so far as I know, subjected to controlled experiment, by Flint in New York in the late 1880s, and then only to find patients' tolerance of maximum short-term dosages.[76]

Good results were broadcast. Mr Edgar Spilsbury of Walsall had successfully treated four phthisics by rubbing lard into their bodies to 'feed'the skin. Each had put on weight and two were 'completely cured' after nine months. Spilsbury had noticed that butchers and their families were remarkably exempt from consumption and attributed their immunity to regular contact with animal fat. His observation was not as absurd as it appears: subsequent investigations reveal that butchers had a low phthisis mortality rate among occupational groups.[77] Between the 1860s and the 1920s doctors were intermittently keen on prescribing Chaulmoogra oil both internally and externally. It was a foul smelling, foul tasting brownish mess from Burma. Patients were nauseated by it, but often persevered in the faith that a treatment so vile and exotic must do them good.[78] In 1862 Dr John Hastings was administering boa-constrictor excreta 'with great success'. Half a teaspoonful in a gallon of water (it would not dissolve) formed an unguent which, when rubbed into the patient's chest, gave 'instantaneous relief'.[79] Twenty years later Dr Joseph Pick announced aluminium and its compounds to be 'a most effective remedy'. He mixed thirteen grammes of metallic aluminium and aluminium hydrate into 60 pills and prescribed three each day. It worked as an antiseptic astringent which dried the throat.[80] Dr A Broster placed his faith in a mixture of Indian hemp, quinine, mercury, beef tea and cod liver oil. In 1871 after five weeks on this concoction a 'far gone' woman of 27 was restored to being 'only delicate'.[81] At Glasgow Infirmary, Hitchin Infirmary and elsewhere between the 1850s and 1880s, the patients were exposed to the usual round of bleeding, blistering, phosphoric acid, ether, digitalis, and the great reviver, copious doses of brandy, four ounces at a time. The brandy was taken with ergot, to stimulate the patient, especially after cupping. In 1891, Dr C.T. Williams, a leading consumption specialist, still relied upon arsenic and quinine, seconded by aconite and digitalis, stimulants countered by anodynes, reinforced by 'counter-irritation' to the chest derived from cartharides blisters, aided by an 'expectorant' made from ammonium carbonate, antimonial wine and an equal amount of about four to five minims of aconite, topped with three to five grains of quinine. Williams, like his colleagues, was therapeutically eclectic while proclaiming his proprietorship of particular procedures he happened to be using at particular times.[82] His was an art that never attained an experimental level. It was instead a self-deceiving, self-promoting exercise that doubtless cheered his patients but did not help their life chances.

Throughout the century doctors had also sought to get at the seat of the disease in the lungs with various kinds of inhalations. Dr John Ferriar in the late eighteenth century had pumped in 'hydrocarbonate air', with 'no effect'.[83] Iodine vapour became fashionable from the 1830s, by analogy with the benefit scrofulous victims gained from breathing sea air and air enlivened with the iodine emanations from sea-weed. In the later 1830s, Dr Reid Clanny of Sunderland moved on to sulphuretted hydrogen and coal gas, after observing that pitmen who had breathed a lot of both were notably free from phthisis. He claimed a triumph with Ann Robinson, into whom he pumped twelve cubic inches of gas four times a day for six days and then increased the dosage to twenty cubic inches. After a fortnight 'all symptoms disappeared'. But a rival practitioner informed the *Lancet* that Robinson had never been phthisic. She was a 'cony cutter' and like others in her trade merely suffered from a constant bronchitis caused by the fur and dust.[84] The rationale of the treatment had two parts: the gas expanded the bronchii and thereby enlivened the circulatory system, while the active constituent in the gas, iodine, sulphuretted hydrogen, creosote, carbolic acid in the 1860s following Lister, sulphurous acid and any of several other astringents, was believed to act as a 'stimulant' upon the 'indolent masses of tubercle' and thereby promote their 'absorption'.[85] From the 1860s the theory incorporated the notion that antiseptic gases inhibited the process of putrefaction.[86]

The paraphernalia became increasingly elaborate, especially after antiseptic pursuits spread in the late 1860s. Patients absorbed gas through the mouth, they lay immersed in gas-filled rooms for hours, they had it pumped into their rectums. Some practitioners, such as the irregular Dr Robert Hunter, made fortunes at a guinea for the first pumping and a five pound fee for regular monthly refills. He claimed to aerate the body with oxygen to burn up the carbon which smothered combustion and thereby allowed the deposition of tubercle.[87]

There was no statistical or experimental foundation for the practice. In 1883 Dr A.H. Hassall, the microscopist, zoologist and founder of the Royal National Hospital for Consumption, reported that carbolic acid did not vaporise sufficiently to enter the lungs. Often inhalation of expired air contained no carbolic acid. Creosote was more volatile in boiling water, but most of it remained in the sponge of the inhaling device. Iodine, by contrast, was so readily absorbed into the body tissues that it disappeared after one hour and, Hassall argued, thereby lost its antiseptic properties. There was no evidence that it ever reached the lungs. A few years later he demonstrated that practically none of the antiseptic gases added to the inhalation medium of boiling water or hot air entered the rectum.[88] Apparently no one noticed his criticisms. Burney Yeo at Kings College Hospital persisted with his trials of carbolic acid, sulphuretted hydrogen, eucalyptus, and terpinol and claimed 'astonishing success' when they were administered through the rectum, whence the gases were 'sure' to enter the lungs.[89] Humbler practitioners at Ventnor, in the London suburbs, and in hospitals throughout the nation pressed on. Patients found 'comfort' in the procedure, although it was painful and rendered them dizzy and 'tipsy'. Their spit was less viscid and they had the assurance that the antiseptics were killing the bacilli inside them. 'Vapores' entered the *British Pharmacopoeia* in 1888.[90] The German discovery during the same year that the germ could live only at temperatures between 38° and 41° C gave a fresh impetus to setting patients to inhale superheated air at up to 150° C or pumping it into their rectums. Some doctors mixed aniline and iron with the vapourising mixture, following the Russian, Kremianski. The iron was said to reduce the tendency of patients to turn blue.[91] Dr Wilberforce Smith of London had one patient inhale carbonic acid for 18 months by means of putting his head into a 'large inhaler made from an ordinary hat box in which flannel charged with carbolic acid was suspended'. The outcome was 'successful'.[92] Suddenly in the mid 1890s inhalation became unfashionable amongst orthodox practitioners and their clients, although there had been no recent scandal or compelling demonstration of its inutility. Possibly the clients and their doctors recognised the procedures as coarse. Looking back, a *Lancet* writer reflected that 'it seems hard to believe that this treatment should ever have been widely accepted, and the results that were alleged to follow its application are a curious commentary upon the fallacious character ... of many therapeutic theories'.[93] Quacks continued to find buyers. One was still peddling inhalation contraptions to unregistered practitioners and sanatorium directors in 1935.[94]

The rural populace handled phthisis less destructively than the doctors. The disease was considered infectious and sufferers were frequently isolated and made to sleep alone.[95] In the Scottish Highlands, during the first half of the century at least, consumptives were massaged by 'muscular old women' to 'open out the chest'. The patient was seated on a stool, the woman rubbed her hands in butter and, from behind, swept her hands downwards and backwards, pressing her little fingers into the lower rib cavities and pushing in sideways to deploy the xiphoid cartilege (at the lower end of the sternum). By contrast with the diet which doctors ordered until about 1910 - a little white meat or fish, weak tea, gruel, arrow-root, sago and a little bread, to prevent the build-up of blood and thereby haemoptysis - Highlanders fed phthisics cream and abundant warm milk and ox-blood in black puddings.[96] Consumptives and scrofula victims joined other sick people in visiting seventh sons on seven successive days. The sufferer fasted before each visit; the healer washed the affected part with water from a well facing north, while uttering incantations and spitting into the well, presumably to transfer the evil. Then the patient had a hearty meal.[97] Throughout Great Britain patients sought to inhale the warm breath of a healthy beast. In Suffolk in the 1850s it had to be a stallion, in Herefordshire a piebald, in Scotland a cow or sheep. The effluvium of maggoty meat was believed to be counter-tuberculous until about World War I, while the eating of live snails and snake excrement was also accepted as prophylactic. In Ireland consumptives ate great mullein - *verbascum thapsus* - boiled in milk and strained. One Dublin doctor who tried it reported that it eased the cough.[98]

Koch's announcement in April 1882 that tuberculosis was a communicable disease caused by bacilli only began to affect the management of tuberculosis in the 1890s. He demonstrated brilliantly with a series of animal experiments that scrofula and other forms of tuberculosis were infective and that they originated from a specific microorganism, and he inferred that the disease was propagated by infection from one body to another and in no other way. The glory remains his, although his fellow countryman, K.H. Baumgartner, now forgotten, published very similar findings about the bacillus (although he did not exclude hereditary transmission) four days after Koch.[99] The other forgotten contributor is William Thomson of Melbourne, whose *Germ Theory of Disease* was also published in April 1882 in that city. Thomson by courageously independent observation and ratiocination had argued since 1876 that the fact that the prevalence of consumption among young Australians subject to none of the usually cited causes, diathesis, climate, wet soils and so on, could be explained only by infection from newly arrived phthisics who expelled a specific disease-causing microorganism with their breath and that this organism was inhaled by hitherto healthy persons. His hypothesis, Thomson claimed, unriddled the higher female death rates, particularly among domestic servants and other indoor workers, who inhaled dust suffused with dried sputum containing the microorganism, and the generally higher rates in towns. Thomson's work passed almost unnoticed in Europe, which was unfortunate because he had adumbrated a workable environmental preventive method which otherwise took almost twenty years to evolve.[100]

The dominant men in British and French tuberculosis circles resisted Koch as their elders had resisted Villemin. His findings devalued current therapeutic practices and overturned traditional structural comprehension of the disease. The French declared themselves unable to replicate his results. In the United States Dr Schmidt dismissed Koch's bacilli as fatty globules soluable in boiling water and Dr Rollin Grigg scouted them as mere fibrin filaments with no pathological properties. In England Dr William Dale told a BMA meeting in mid 1883 that the bacteria were a by-product of degenerated tubercle.[101] In 1886 Dr Sinclair Coghill announced that 'bodies' identical with the bacilli were common in the joints of 'apparently healthy individuals of a particular type' and that these bodies only became pathological after the diathesis induced morbid conditions or was 'excited by syphilis'.[102] After vainly trying for twelve months to repeat Koch's experiments the eminent Watson Cheyne rejected Koch's claims. He leaned to an explanation reminiscent of Burdon-Sanderson's when dismissing Villemin, that the act of injecting tubercular pus induced disease manifestations which were distinct from real pathological events in everyday life. Two years after Koch he was arguing strongly, with widespread provincial agreement, that phthisis must 'be generated by pyaemic matter' rather than the tuberculosis bacillus.[103]   Less distinguished practitioners, like Dr W.J. Simpson, Medical Officer of Health for Aberdeen, revealed their bewilderment by asking why, if bacilli were 'everywhere', phthisis was not universal. Simpson could not see how bacilli could be prime causes of disease: they must be 'merely concomitants'.[104]   The Leeds and West Riding Medico-Chirurgical Society dismissed Koch's specific bacilli as 'medical curiosities' in 1884 and predicted that they would soon be 'altogether laid aside'.[105]   Support for Koch from younger doctors was deplored.[106]   General acceptance of germ causation of tuberculosis by infection did not come in Britain until after 1890.[107]

One basic source of resistance to the idea was repugnance to its social implications. As the advocate of dry climate therapy, Dr J. Henry Bennet, argued, in late 1884, 'its general adoption would lead to much that is distressing to the patients, to their relatives and to society in general'. A phthisic would have to be treated like a medieval leper 'separated from his family, to be isolated, shut up ... refused admission into hospitals and asylums ... his clothes should be destroyed, and whether he die or recover, the home ... should be burnt'. Bennet took comfort, he said, in the belief that Koch could not be right and that explanation in terms of the 'pre-breathed air' was both true and enjoined comparatively benign preventive and therapeutic regimens that preserved personal liberty.[108]

Meanwhile Vignal in Paris had demonstrated that bacilli in sputa might be ground under foot, dried out, moistened and dried up to eight times and if moistened again still grow and kill a guinea pig.[109]   Brompton Hospital began to disinfect its spittoons, although they were still only emptied 'two or three times a day'.[110]   In 1886 the French Hygiene Council issued the first public orders against spitting.[111]   In 1893 British doctors began to demand the compulsory notification of the disease and the construction of isolation hospitals in the countryside.[112] The new therapeutic regime feared by Bennet was closing in.

NOTES

[1]Sir C. Scudamore, Dr Carswell and others in *Lancet* , 29 Oct. 1842, pp.157-60.

[2]T. Henry Green, *Lancet*, 1 July 1882, p.1065. Gauvain, 'Tuberculous Cripples', in Kelynack (ed.), *Defective Children*, p.118.

[3]Jacob Hare, *Lancet*, 29 October 1842, p.160; editorial, *Lancet*, 22 May 1880, p.813.

[4]Henry R. Silvester, *The Physiological Method of Treating Consumption*, 1862, pp.4, 15.

[5]James Copland, *Consumption* , pp.121-2, 145-9; Peter Eade, 'Aetiology of Phthisis', *BMJ*, 12 Mar. 1869, p.234.

[6]Edwards Crisp, 'On Tubercular Affections...', *Transactions of the St. Andrews Medical Graduates' Association, 1867*, p.120.
7Copland, *Consumption*, p.149.

[8]*Lancet*, 5 Apr. 1862, pp.355-6; *BMJ*, 20 Mar. 1858, p.221.

[9]*Lancet*, 5 Apr. 1862, p.356; 'A Statistical Inquiry into...1000 Consumptive Persons', *Report of BAAS, 1862*, pp.174-5.

[10]*Lancet*, 20 May 1882, p.813.

[11]Walter H. Fearis, *The Treatment of Tuberculosis by means of... (IK) Therapy*, 1912, p.22.

[12]*BMJ*, 15 May 1858, p.390.

[13]Drysdale in *Transactions of the St Andrews Medical Graduates' Association, 1867*, p.141.

[14]G. Sims Woodhead in T.N. Kelynack (ed.), *The Drink Problem of To-Day*, 1916 (first pub. 1907), p.59.

[15]*Lancet*, 28 Oct. 1871, pp.602-4.

[16]*BMJ*, 20 Mar. 1886, p.550.

[17]*BMJ*, 16 Nov. 1889, p.1139.

[18]J.G. Lewis and D.A. Chamberlain (Brompton Hospital), 'Alcohol Consumption And Smoking Habits In Male Patients With Pulmonary Tuberculosis', *British Journal of Preventive and Social Medicine* , vol.17, 1963, pp.150-1;

[19]Bulstrode, *Report*, p.86.

[20]J.G. Lewis, *Tubercle*, vol. XLII, 1961, p.380; M.W. McNicol, 'Tuberculosis', in D.L. Miller and R.D.T. Farmer (eds), *Epidemiology of Diseases*, Oxford 1982, p.32.

[21]Florence Nightingale, *Notes on Matters Affecting the Health...of the British Army...*, 1858, p.501.

[22]Florence Nightingale, 'Army Sanitary Administration...' in *Congrès International de Bienfaisance 1862*, tome II, p.104; Anon. 'Sanitary Science', *Chambers Encyclopaedia*, p.716, n.d. [1860s].

[23]Edwards Crisp, 'On the Statistics of Pulmonary Consumption...', *BAAS Report 1868*, pp.158.

[24] Edwards Crisp, 'On Tubercular Affections...', *Transactions...St Andrews...Association*, 1867, p.119.

[25]*BMJ*, 16, 30 Jan., 13 Feb. 1869, pp.60-1, 110, 154; Arthur Leared, quoting Hjaltelin, in *BMJ*, 28 Aug. 1869, pp.255-6. Professor W.T. Gairdner announced the relegation of the theory in *BMJ*, 11 Oct. 1884, p.702.

[26][Andrew Wynter], 'Lodging, Food, and Dress of Soldiers', *Quarterly Review*, vol. 105, Jan.-Apr. 1859, p.172; 'Correspondence relating to Barracks Improvements, etc', *BPP*, 1857-58, vol. xxxvii, p.214; Andrew Clark, *The Real Significance of the Proposed Barracks Loan*, 1890, pp.3-5.

[27]Hirsch, *A Handbook of Geographical and Historical Pathology* , translated by Charles Creighton, second ed., 2 vols, 1885; *BMJ*, 8 Jan. 1887, p.70.

[28]Ransome in *BMJ*, 8 Mar. 1890, p.526; Ransome and Basing in evidence to Royal Commission on Tuberculosis, Qs 1272-78, 1319-22, *BPP*, 1896, vol. xlvi. Tatham, 'Supplement', *BPP*, 1897, vol. xxi, p. xcix. Mrs Robert Henrey was still popularising the bad air theory in *The Little Madeleine* in 1953, p.31.

[29]R. Douglas Powell in *BMJ*, 11 Oct. 1884, p.698; W.D. Wilks in *BMJ*, 15 Nov. 1884, p.992; George Buchanan, supplement to 10th annual registrar-general's report, *BPP*, 1868, vol. J. Andrew's analysis of varying drying rates is in *Lancet*, 19 Apr. 1884, p.696.

[30]Kelly's findings are outlined in *BMJ*, 23 Oct. 1880, p.674; R. Thorne Thorne, *The Progress of Preventive Medicine during the Victorian Era*, 1888, pp.47-50.

[31]E. Long, *A History of the Therapy of Tuberculosis and The Case of Frederic Chopin*, Lawrence, 1956, p.27.

[32]*Lancet*, 2 Mar. 1844, p.774.

[33]*Transactions...St Andrews...Association, 1867*, pp.118-43.

[34]*Lancet*, 12 Oct. 1867. for dismissals, see editorial, *BMJ*, 6 Jan. 1883, p.21; and Cambridge Medical Society's survey, 13 Jan. 1883, p.77, 3 Mar. 1883, p.415.

[35]C.R. Drysdale, '...Some Disputed Points In The Nature And Antecedents Of Tuberculosis', *Transactions...St Andrews...Association*, 1867, pp.134-5; *Lancet*, 18 July 1868, pp.88-9; 23 Jan. 1869, p.132.

[36]J. Burdon-Sanderson, 'Recent Researches as to the Artificial Production of Tubercle', *BMJ*, 4 Sept. 1869, p.274.

[37]*Lancet*, 4 Apr. 1868, p.431.

[38]*Transactions...St Andrews...Association*, 1867, pp.118, 127-8.

[39]Quoted in Myron Brightfield, *Victorian England in its novels, 1840-1870*, Los Angeles 1971, vol.ii, p.128.

[40]*Lancet*, 27 Dec. 1834, p.484.

[41]Andrew Clark, at Medical Society of London, 'On the Influence of Pleurisy on the Production of Phthisis', *Lancet*, 23 Oct. 1869, p.573; James E. Pollock, senior physician, Brompton, *Lancet*, 1 Apr. 1876, p.487; Burdon-Sanderson, *Lancet*, 18 Mar. 1876, pp.413-4.

[42]*Lancet*, 23 Nov. 1878, pp.741-2.

[43]Reginald E. Thompson in *Lancet*, 6 Nov. 1880, p.727.

[44]C. Theodore Williams (Brompton), *BMJ*, 30 Sept. 1882, p.619; I. Burney Yeo in *BMJ*, 17 June 1882, p.895.

[45]*Lancet*, 24 Feb. 1883, p.323; *BMJ*, 13 Jan. 1883, p.77.

[46]Meeres in *BMJ*, 20 Mar. 1886, p.550; *BMJ*, 1 Feb. 1890, p.265; Sir Herbert Maxwell and P.H. Pye-Smith, 'Report of...Delegates to International Tuberculosis Conference, Berlin', *BPP*, vol.xlv, pp.6-7.

[47]Bulstrode, *Report*, quoting Niven (1905) and Weber (1899?), pp.70-4; Ernest G. Pope, Karl Pearson and Ethel M. Elderton, 'A Second Study Of The Statistics Of Pulmonary Tuberculosis: Marital Infection', *Drapers' Company Research Memoirs*, 1908, p.15.

[48]*Lancet*, 23 July 1870, p.118.

[49]*BMJ*, 30 Sept. 1882, p.626.

[50]'A Statistical Enquiry into...the Constitution in 1000 Consumptive Persons', *Report of BAAS*, 1862, pp.174-5; see also Copland, *Consumption*, p.123.

[51]Felix Niemeyer, *Clinical Lectures on Pulmonary Consumption*, 1870, pp.19-20; C.R. Drysdale in *BMJ*, 30 Sept. 1882, p.621.

[52]Reginald E. Thompson, *The Different Aspects of Family Phthisis in Relation to Heredity and Life-Assurance*, 1884.

[53]R. Douglas Powell (Brompton) in *BMJ*, 11 Oct. 1884, p.701; W.T. Gairdner (Glasgow) in *BMJ*, 25 Oct. 1884, p.835; Fernet in *Lancet*, 17 Jan. 1885, p.124.

[54]*Lancet*, 4 June 1887, p.1141; *Lancet*, 12 Mar. 1892, p.599.

[55]*BMJ*, 22 Mar. 1890, p.648.

[56]*BMJ*, 23 July 1892, quoting Philip, *A Thousand Cases...*, p.181; cf. J. Edward Squire, *The Hygienic Prevention of Consumption*, 1893, p.28. Niven in *Medical Chronicle*, Apr.-Sept. 1897, pp.1-2; James A. Gibson, *The Nordrach Treatment*, 1901, p.21.

[57]Karl Pearson, 'A First Study Of The Statistics Of Pulmonary Tuberculosis', in *Studies In National Deterioration*, 1907, pp.11-12.

[58]Charles Goring, 'On The Inheritance Of The Diathesis of Phthisis and Insanity...Based Upon...1500 Criminals', *Studies In National Deterioration*, 1909, p.15; W. Palin Elderton and Sidney J. Perry, 'The Mortality Of The Tuberculous', *Studies In National Deterioration*, 1913; Percy Stocks and Mary N. Karn, 'Fresh Evidence on the Inheritance Factor in Tuberculosis', *Annals of Eugenics*, vols. ii, iii, 1927-8; G.R. Searle, 'Eugenics and Class', in Charles Webster (ed.), *Biology, Medicine and Society 1840-1940*, Cambridge 1981, p.225.

[59]*National Conference on The Prevention Of Destitution*, 1911, p.63.

[60]Geoffrey Drage, MA, *The State And The Poor* [1914], p.68.

[61]*The Child*, Dec. 1914, pp.155-6.

[62]Major Leonard Darwin, *What Is Eugenics?* 1928; *BMJ*, editorial, 14 Mar. 1925, p.517.

[63]Marc Daniels et al., *Tuberculosis In Young Adults*, 1948, p.158; F. Macfarlane Burnet, *Natural History of Infectious Disease*, second ed., Cambridge, 1953, pp.198-9, 297; Charles L. Dana et al (eds), *Contributions To Medical And Biological Research*, 2 vols., New York, 1919, vol. i, p.409; Ruth Rice Puffer, *Familial Susceptibility To Tuberculosis*, Cambridge, Mass. 1944, pp.5-10; A.W. Anderson, B. Benjamin et al., 'Control Of Tuberculosis Importance Of Heredity And Environment', *British Journal of Preventive & Social Medicine*, vol.ii, 1957.

[64]Lefford, 'Immunology of Mycobacterium tuberculosis', in Andre J.Nahmias and Richard J. O'Reilly, *Immunology of human infection*, New York 1981, vol.1, p.349.

[65]W.H. Ross, 'Phthisis: Its Origin and Arrest', *BMJ*, 11 Sept. 1858, p.769.

[66]Philip B. Hynes, 'Scrofula', *Lancet*, 3 June 1843, pp.343-4; August Hirsch, *Handbook of Geographical And Historical Pathology*, second ed. 1885, vol. ii, p.627; William K. Treves (Margate), *Lancet*, 23 Sept. 1889, p.633.

[67]Ayres, *Lancet*, 3 June 1843, p.343; Frederick Treves, *Lancet*, 25 May 1889, p.1035; John E. Gorst, *The Children Of The Nation* , 1906, p.110. Memorandum by E.J. Steegman (?) n.d. (1908 or later?), Astor Papers, Reading University Library MS 1066/1/1042.

[68]John Savory, *A Companion to the Medicine Chest*, second ed., 1840, pp.83.

[69]Charles Clay (Manchester Dispensary), *Lancet*, 9 Jan. 1841, p.554.

[70]*Lancet*, 3 Mar. 1877, p.303.

[71]Theophilus Thompson, *Clinical Lectures on Pulmonary Consumption*, cf. William Farrer on patients being nauseated,*The Times*, 1 Jan. 1873.

[72]BMA, *National Formulary for National Health Insurance Purposes*, second ed., 1933, p.8; the formulae for Scott's Emulsion and its competitors are given in *Lancet*, 2 Feb. 1924, pp.256-7.

[73]Bertram Thornton (Physician to Margate Sea Bathing Infirmary), *Lancet*, 31 Aug. 1889, p.456.

[74]A.T. Thomson (North London Consumption Hospital), *Lancet*, 7 Feb. 1835, p.671.

[75]Copland, *Consumption*, pp.221-3.

[76]Guy, *Tuberculosis*; p.252; *Lancet*, 30 Aug. 1890, p.455.

[77]*Lancet*, 12 Dec. 1835, pp.446-7.

[78]I. Burney Yeo, *Practitioner*, vol.xxii, 1879, pp.240-7; G.H. Murray and H.H. Dale,' Report to Medical Research Council on infections of codeine and chaulmoogra oil', 25 Sept. 1917, Astor Papers, Reading University Library, MS 1066/1/1042.

[79]*Medical Circular*, 19 Mar. 1862, p.210.

[80]*Lancet*, 3 May 1884, p.815.

[81]*Lancet*, 14 Jan. 1871, p.46.

[82]*BMJ*, 28 Mar. 1891, p.683.

83John Ferriar, *Medical Histories and Reflections*, 2 vols, 1795, vol.ii, pp.232-9.

84*Lancet*, 29 Apr., 6 May 1837, pp.186, 221.

85T. Wilson in *Lancet*, 26 Feb. 1842, p.749; Copland, *Consumption*, p.336.

86Peter Eade (Norwich Hospital), *Lancet*, 6 Oct. 1877, p.514; I. Burney Yeo (King's College Hospital), *BMJ*, 1 July 1882, p.7.

87Charles J.B. Williams, *Memoirs of Life And Work*, 1884, pp.333-6.

88*Lancet*, 5 May 1883, p.765; 2 July 1887, p.10.

89*Lancet*, 16 Apr. 1887, pp.761-3.

90James M. Williamson (Ventnor), *Lancet*, 23 Apr. 1887, p.850; Owen Pritchard (London), *Lancet*, 24 Sept. 1887, pp.605-6; R.J. Lea, *Lancet*, 28 Jan. 1888, p.197.

91*Lancet*, 29 Sept. 1888, p.628; 1 June 1889, p.1102.

92*Lancet*, 3 Mar. 1894, p.543.

93*Lancet*, 9 June 1894, p.1458.

94 David Fingard to Minister of Health, July 1935, PRO MH55/151.

95Dr H.D. Littlejohn to Royal Commission on Tuberculosis, Qs. 1483-5, *BPP* 1896, vol.xlvi.

96Rev. D.T. Masson, 'An Old Highland Form...', *BMJ*, 20 Apr. 1889, p.881.

97'Scrofula Cure', *Medical Magazine*, Nov. 1907, p.656.

98Wayland D. Hand, 'Folk Medical Inhalants in Respiratory Disorders', *Medical History*, vol. xii, 1968, p.157; R.P. Colson, 'Phthisis and Physic', *Practitioner*, vol. iii, 1869, pp.90-2; F.J.B. Quinland (St Vincent's Hospital, Dublin), *BMJ*, 27 Jan. 1883, p.149; Pamela Horn, quoting reminiscences of Walter Rose, born 1871 in Haddenham, Bucks, on dread of consumption and eating live snails as a prophylactic, in *Victorian Country Child*, Kineton, 1974, p.174.

99Robert Saundby, 'Recent Researches on Tubercle', *Practitioner*, vol.xxix, 1882, p.180.

100Thomson, *Germ Theory*, pp.8-27. His work was reviewed only, so far as I could find, in the *Practitioner*, vol.xxxi, 1883, p.121, where the anonymous reviewer deemed it 'remarkable'. The *Lancet* caught up with his work on 27 Sept. 1884, p.548, and R.D. Powell of Brompton acknowledged it in *BMJ*, 11 Oct. 1884, p.700.

101William Dale, address to Earl Anglian BMA, *BMJ*, 30 June 1883; cf. Hirsch, *Handbook* (1885), as translated by Charles Creighton. Koch's 'so-called bacillus of tubercle...has no warrant whatsoever'. Vol. ii, p.637.

102*BMJ*, 20 Mar. 1886, pp.550-1.

103*Lancet*, 28 July 1883; *BMJ*, 11 Oct. 1884, p.699.

104 *BMJ*, 16 Dec. 1882, p.1213.

105*BMJ*, 5 Apr. 1884, p.672; *Lancet*, 26 Apr. 1884, p.758, 23 Aug. 1884, p.3111.

106J. Henry Bennet, *BMJ*, 11 Oct. 1884, p.704.

[107]Eg *Lancet* editorial, extolling Baumgartner's resurrection of the inheritance notion, 7 July 1888, p.27.

[108]*BMJ*, 11 Oct. 1884, pp.704-5.

[109]*BMJ*, 18 Aug. 1883, p.340.

[110]C. Theodore Williams in *BMJ*, 30 Sept. 1882, p.619.

[111]*BMJ*, 20 Mar. 1886, p.564.

[112]Dr Chaplin at Hunterian Society, *Lancet*, 13 May 1893, p.1139.

3 RESPONSES

Koch's discovery promised antidotes and preventives. Pasteur had shown the way with an attenuated germ protective against animal anthrax. Doctors and sufferers could believe that the old unhopeful, self-fulfilling miasmic and diathetic etiologies were entering eclipse.

From August 1890 rumours spread that Koch in Berlin had developed an anti-tuberculosis vaccine. By late autumn patients and doctors were hurrying to Germany. Koch, importuned by visitors and pressed by his government sponsors and patriotic colleagues, announced on 13 November that he had indeed made the breakthrough. His audience was ecstatic. It was the first sensational international scientific occasion in history. Doctors jostled for access to Koch's laboratories and for samples of the fluid. Phthisics competed for admission to his clinics. Reporters milled about the meetings and the clinics. Lord Lister, among the luminaries who arrived to be convinced, immediately nominated his niece for the treatment. Koch warned that his announcement had been made prematurely and that more work was necessary, but his reservations were ignored. He withheld the formula partly for these scientific reasons, and partly because his official employers wanted to monopolise it for the glory and profit of the Fatherland. The Germans had joined the French in making the new bacteriology a nationalist trophy.[1]

Koch reported that injections of his vaccine into guinea pigs at foci infected four to six weeks earlier produced necrosis of the skin at the second inoculation points. This skin then sloughed, leaving a superficial ulceration which healed quickly and completely. None of the usual tuberculous nodules appeared at the sites of the second injections and there was no spread of infection from them. He had made over 1000 trials. To the present there are no conclusive explanations of the phenomenon. Koch had proceeded to clinical trials on humans. By 22 November his colleagues claimed to have cured fourteen cases of facial lupus, three of scrofula, eighteen joint and bone and four laryngeal cases. He warned that the active life of his fluids was still undetermined - probably only a matter of days - and that dosages were still unfixed. The impact of the vaccine upon phthisics was less dramatic, but encouraging nonetheless. They lost their cough and expectoration, after an initial increase following the first injection. Their sputa became mucoid and their bacilli count diminished. Night sweating ceased. Patients gained weight. After four to six weeks 'early stage' patients could be 'regarded as cured'. Koch had tried his remedy on himself. It had produced a 'horrid reaction' with a rise in temperature, vomiting and lassitude over several days. He was probably suffering a severe positive reaction from an overdose of what was almost certainly a wildly variable preparation. Koch asserted that his vaccine selected and worked only on living tubercular tissue and that it could therefore be given in large and increasing doses, beginning perhaps at two to eight milligrammes and rising to 500 times that dose within three weeks. His assertion was to harm the reputation of his fluid while the side effects were to distress thousands of patients.[2]

His tuberculin (subsequently labelled Old Tuberculin) contained, he revealed later, proteins from killed bacilli from his guinea pigs concentrated in a filtrate of the ox bile and glycerine medium in which the bacilli had been cultured. Doctors hurried home with samples of the mystic fluid to analyse and test on their patients. The samples must have been diverse. Koch enjoyed extraordinary luck with his first batches. Meanwhile, French medical leaders dismissed his work as unproven and the Royal College of Physicians refused to endorse a 'secret remedy'.[3] By Christmas, enthusiasm in Britain had cooled and disillusionment spread. Eight cases at the City of London Chest Hospital showed no improvement, excepting one lupus victim. Eleven subjects at King's College Hospital, after a fortnight's trial, showed no progress. Koch's miraculous results simply were not being repeated. Nobody suggested that the trial period was too short and that the vaccine might have been too old or unstable. Grumblers like Dr W.S. Richmond, who had declared that British doctors had no right to inject into patients a secret foreign fluid with nasty side-effects, enjoyed their schadenfreude.[4]

Eight months of further trials only confirmed the original disappointments. Watson Cheyne, who had been beaten by Koch in the vaccine race, experimented at King's College Hospital with a range of dosages between two and eight milligrammes at up to three injections a day. The injections caused great inflammation and soreness which lasted up to three weeks. He treated 38 cases of lupus and bone and joint tuberculosis for around six weeks each. All had 'improved' and the improvement had lasted for two months after the treatment ended. None was 'cured'. But Watson Cheyne had already encountered the drawbacks that were to dog tuberculin therapy for the next forty years. Continuous treatment was almost 'debarred', as one British doctor complained, because the vaccine was so costly. Once patients realised that it was not a miracle cure they evaded it because of the pain, fever, headaches, and 'general depression' it induced. Others refused it outright because they saw it as yet another medical vaccination which intruded germs into their already infected bodies. Patients who took the course lost weight during the first fortnight and were 'pulled down'. Other patients agreed with Watson Cheyne in blaming tuberculin injections for arousing cross infections which we might now reasonably attribute to unclean procedures.[5] While they were 'down' patients were probably liable to the virulent influenzas which were sweeping Europe during the early trials of Koch's remedy.

By 1892 senior British medical opinion had turned decisively against tuberculin. At Brompton Hospital Dr Theodore Williams had tried it 'systematically' for four months on 30 early cases, 28 of them consumptives: fifteen 'improved', one remained 'stationary' and twelve became 'worse', including three deaths. He and his colleagues concluded that the injections aggravated fever and did not reduce the number of bacilli in the sputa. The two remaining lupus cases first improved markedly and then quietly deteriorated, even before the injections ceased. At Brompton even submissive patients were provoked by 'alarmist reports in the newspapers' into refusing to continue the trials. Elsewhere in the country doctors and patients were abandoning tuberculin, as reports recorded 'no effect' or retrogression.[6] Tuberculin remained unfashionable in Britain excepting among a few votaries.

The faithful claimed results that were almost as wonderful as Koch's original cures. Two of the most active, R.W. Philip in Edinburgh and W. Camac Wilkinson in London, were typical in having been personally converted by Koch in the late 1880s and in their dedication to making tuberculin succeed. Both were also typical of their embattled faction in being arrogant and pugnacious, and in possessing first-rate organising capacities.

They proclaimed tuberculin as the one therapy that met the special difficulties of poor patients, without saying why.

Philip and Wilkinson were never friends but they were united in presenting tuberculin as an invaluable agent in diagnosis, against the majority of their colleagues who neither used it nor wanted to know about it. The enthusiasts were right, but Wilkinson damaged the cause by characterising all positive reactions as conclusive signs of active tuberculosis.

Their second certitude was that tuberculin was an unfailing cure for early consumption. They experimented for decades with dosages, having recognised in the 1890s that individual responses varied widely. By 1912 Wilkinson was starting with 1/1000 of a milligramme and then rapidly increasing the dosage, given twice a week. Even well-disposed colleagues thought his doses dangerously high. Dr Butler Harris followed German standards in beginning at 1/50,000 of a milligramme. The possibility of using so low a dose made it easy for homeopaths to adopt the fluid, and orthodox contempt for the treatment was thereby reinforced. The smaller doses reduced the incidence of fever and general discomfort. There is no reason to doubt Philip's claim in 1913 that tuberculin 'contained' local lesions, although he produced no detailed proofs. He was reserved about its impact on phthisis, but again there is a lot of anecdotal evidence that patients in the hands of such men as Philip and Wilkinson did enjoy notable remissions.[7]

Outside their clinics the therapeutic status of tuberculin was to remain indeterminate. The elusive nature of tuberculosis made it impossible to devise conclusive trials. Even so, modes of administration were never standardised. Some doctors gave it only intravenously in minute doses, others gave large doses intradermally or orally. Some gave it only to feverish advanced cases, some only as a last resort to terminal victims, others only to 'early' non-febrile patients. Few poor patients were on it for more than a few weeks because it was so expensive. The cost of the standard emulsion prepared by Messrs Meister, Lucius and Brüning usually limited it to private patients and they disliked treatments based on injections. Dispensaries sometimes produced their own cheaper tuberculin, but there was no agreed way of fractionating the fluid or monitoring its shelf life. The quality must have varied enormously. The newer preparations of PPD tuberculin (purified protein derivative) were also not securely standardised. Moreover, there was no set procedure for taking temperatures. The side effects of over-large doses were so brutal and uncertain that a consistent 50 per cent of patients gave up after the first injection.[8]

It is a measure of medical antagonism to tuberculin that only four ambitious tests of it were mounted in Britain. From 1898 to 1913 Dr Nathan Raw treated 640 cases at the Mill Road Infirmary. He used both Old Tuberculin and Koch's new 'human' strain, in varying doses up to 1/1000 milligramme increasing up to 1/100 milligramme over twelve weeks, injected in the forearm of mild, early chronic sufferers. He concluded generally that although tuberculin did not cure, it did 'arrest' the disease.[9] He never published an analytic statement of his procedures and results. Dr Noel Bardswell, at the well-endowed King Edward VII sanatorium at Midhurst, gave 154 patients unspecified doses of tuberculin between late 1911 and mid 1913. He reported that 64 per cent were 'much improved', 17 per cent were 'stationary or worse' and 32 per cent lost 'bacilli'. These results look good but Bardswell, who was to become an implacable and influential opponent of tuberculin, qualified them with the observation that the cases which did best were 'early' and these usually did best whatever the therapy. A few, he asserted later, had been given placebos. Bardswell helped to confirm the National Association for the Prevention of Tuberculosis, the leading medical-lay national pressure group, in its rejection of tuberculin.[10] Suggestions that British troops be inoculated with tuberculin during the Great War were blocked by the tuberculosis specialists.[11]

The two other normative investigations of tuberculin were conducted by the Ministry of Health under lay political pressure, applied through Lord Astor who had a long standing interest. Each study concentrated upon the combative, self-advertising Dr Camac Wilkinson and his dispensary. Between 1919 and 1921 the ministry officials found that Wilkinson's records were skewed to show only good results: he did not list drop-outs who amounted to nearly one-third of his patients. The outcome was inconclusive: some cases 'improved markedly' while others were 'positively harmed' by the injections. The report was never published, although the gist of it was leaked to the hostile *British Medical Journal,* and thereby became the more damaging because hearsay versions of it made tuberculin sound wholly useless and even dangerous. Camac Wilkinson, who had extraordinary powers over his patients, those who stayed at least, meanwhile became increasingly paranoid and harmful to his cause.[12] In June 1924 a second trial (there had been an earlier, inconclusive one about 1920-1 which had been reported seemingly only by word of mouth) was arranged at the Edward VII sanatorium. Thirty-one severe cases began a 29 weeks course of Old Tuberculin: 26 completed the trial and the outcome was unclear, with twelve 'stationary', another five 'quiescent' one 'worse' and thirteen 'improved' or 'much improved'. Less than three years later one-third of them were dead and nearly all the rest were 'not doing well'. There were also 35 controls selected at the outset but their fate is not recorded.[13] The anti-tuberculin forces were jubilant: at the 1932 annual meeting of the BMA, in Camac Wilkinson's presence, Dr F.G. Chandler dismissed tuberculin, like antiphlogistine, 'as one of the ingenious errors of the human mind'. Textbook writers moved from mentioning tuberculin curtly and neutrally, to misquoting the Edward VII trials and advising strongly against its use.[14]

Yet individualists like Camac Wilkinson continued to rely on it. In 1927 Dr William Stobie at the Radcliffe Infirmary, Oxford ventilated a basic reason that had remained unspoken in the controversy. Tuberculin could be supplied to regular working class attenders at local dispensaries while they continued in employment and thereby it bred antagonisms between dispensary doctors and general practitioners. 'Tuberculin was not a cure for starvation', but it did suppress the sputum and perhaps most importantly, it nerved patients to fight on. By permitting them to continue in their homes and employment it also probably helped sustain the family income and thereby preserve a better standard of nutrition and warmth.[15] Like other therapies of the period, tuberculin appeared to work best for ambulatory patients who might expect remissions in the normal course of living carefully, but tuberculin's protagonists also claimed that it dried up ugly lupus manifestations and scrofulous ulcers and that it sometimes eased tuberculous joints and these claims were rarely contested by the anti-tuberculin doctors. But patients often resigned themselves to it only when their condition became desperate.[16]

Between 1887 and the late 1930s Philip and his wealthy wife and a few devoted followers ran dispensaries in Edinburgh, Dundee, Paddington and other places. Wilkinson's separate Tuberculin Dispensary League, backed by a clutch of aristocratic ladies, operated at least six free clinics between 1910 and 1927 in respectable working class districts such as Kensington and Euston Road and in Portsmouth.[17] But they were always hard up and beset by local general practitioners, tuberculosis officers and sanatorium promoters who all regarded them as stealers of patients.

The tuberculin debacle made British tuberculosis authorities suspicious of other vaccines. As each was announced and celebrated in its nation of origin, British doctors tried it, briefly and desultorily, found the results inconclusively poor, and rejected it. Maragliano's serum killed bacilli under laboratory conditions in 1895 but it seemed ineffective elsewhere. A few British doctors continued to try it on patients until after 1920. Marmorek's vaccine, appearing in 1903, enjoyed a fleeting vogue and was discarded. Carl Spengler in Davos around 1920-1 advertised his IK serum - Immunkörper - made from, he said, the red corpuscles of rabbits which had been injected with human and bovine tuberculosis and had retained in their blood the toxins secreted by the bacilli. These, when injected into human patients, had both a preventive and restorative effect, because the red corpuscles activated the recipient's erythrocytes (Spengler and his disciples apparently thought they were distinct entities) to generate 'immune substances'. His English publicists claimed 100 per cent cure rates with stage I and II cases. Spengler had a strong following in Davos and won adherents in Britain, mostly among lay sufferers and fringe medical professionals, but even they had largely abandoned IK therapy by the early 1920s. Their allegiance swung to Friedmann's vaccine produced from turtles, which was exotic and expensive and enjoyed strong support in Weimar Germany and in Hungary. In 1934 the *Lancet* revealed as bogus claims of Friedmann's German and Hungarian colleagues for magnificent cure rates.[18]

The failure of vaccine therapy, in Britain at least, permitted the voluntary general hospitals to continue their neglect of tuberculosis, after their flurry of interest in tuberculin. They routinely excluded phthisics because they could not afford beds for chronic cases, who also posed heavy nursing liabilities, and because terminal cases confounded the hospitals' purpose as restorative institutions. Consumptives were admitted 'only', as Dr Roodhouse Gloyne revealed of the 1930s, 'in small numbers either undiagnosed or for acute emergencies such as haemoptysis, or for teaching purposes'.[19] Bone cases however, began to find ready admission in the 1920s as their numbers declined and they became interesting to surgeons.

There were also four hospitals in London devoted to consumption and chest ailments: Brompton, the oldest, founded in 1842, the City of London Hospital for Chest Diseases begun by Quakers in 1848, the North London Hospital for Consumption (1860s), and the Royal National Hospital for Chest Diseases. Brompton with a nominal 330 or so beds in the 1880s was much the largest, followed by the City of London with a nominal 160, the North London with about 40 and the Royal National with around 26.[20] These, the only specialist hospitals in the kingdom, indeed in Europe, between them housed about 1000 in patients a year at a time when the registered phthisis death totals in England and Wales ran at over 50,000 a year. Proud medical contemporaries claimed that these institutions exercised a decisive impact on the reduced British death-rate as compared with that of the Continent, but a closer look at their bed ratios and procedures suggests that in this respect these hospitals were ineffectual.[21]

Each required patients to present subscribers' tickets and, Brompton excepted, adhered to the general hospital rule limiting inmates to short stays 'to prevent', as the City of London reassured subscribers in 1858, 'its becoming a refuge for the incurable'. Their letters entitled the recipient to two months treatment only.[22] The North London was a doctors' racket. Until at least the mid 1880s no records were kept, physicians were appointed for life, large grants from the Hospital Sunday Fund went unaccounted for, in-patients were turned over quickly and instructed to continue their treatments as private patients of the Hospital physicians, while intending out-patients were directed to the physicians' private houses.[23]

Brompton was the leading hospital. About half of its nominal beds were reserved for pulmonary patients, but until the 1890s at least, nearly half of these beds were secretly empty for want of funds and nurses and the same was true of its fellow hospitals.[24] Hitherto scholars have accepted statements of numbers of general hospital beds at face value and found the totals astonishingly small, given the traditional historical claims for their contribution to the public health: this new evidence should lead us to re-examine the figures and perhaps reduce the effective bed numbers and thereby bring further into question the role of hospitals in the nineteenth century.

Shortage of funds worsened an already hard regimen. The buildings until the 1880s were makeshift and the new buildings were stuffy and dingy. From the early 1860s when some doctors were converted to fresh air theories, some wards were unheated and were 'ventilated with pure fresh air' throughout the year.[25] Even so, live bacilli were found in the hospital air vents in 1890.[26] Spittle was emptied untreated into the drains until the mid 1890s, when it was burned in the basement, while sputum vessels were disinfected with carbolic fluid only from about 1896.[27] Erysipelas and sore throat were endemic until at least the 1880s and there had been notably severe outbreaks in 1869 and 1875.[28] Bedding was not disinfected until after 1900.[29] Inmates were fed on the standard hospital fare of meat soups, puddings, potatoes, bread and milk (unboiled until the twentieth century), reinforced by cod-liver oil, arsenic, hypophosphites, and atropine and strychnine in doses up to 30 minims to alleviate the night sweats. Some physicians intermittently prescribed antiseptic or hot air inhalations: 'many [were] materially benefited' Brompton reported annually. In 1897 a non-Brompton tuberculosis specialist alleged a 'cure' rate of 4 per cent.[30] Brompton's figures are evasive: I have calculated a death-rate of around 13 per cent of annual admissions for the 1880s, but it could well be much higher.

The great majority of Brompton's patients only got as far as the out-patient department. By the 1880s about 300 were attending per day and about 200 managed to come before a doctor. Out-patients were required to bring a subscriber's letter, which might have taken them or their kinsfolk weeks to procure, entitling the bearer to three months' attendance. This requirement seems to have lapsed around the time of the Great War; by the 1930s the rules required each out-patient to present a ticket signed by the lady almoner. Beyond that formality the system remained unchanged. The note was scrutinised by the porter, and the case's name registered. Then the cases and their relatives sat waiting, snuffling in the dim, stuffy hall, shuffling along the benches, coughing, hawking, intermittently disappearing down a corridor upon a sharp summons to a test or examination.[31] Except for the increased number of tests he underwent, the five or six year old lower-middle-class John

Osborne's experience in the 1930s doubtless rehearsed that of thousands before and after him.   Osborne's father was consumptive, his elder sister had died of tubercular meningitis when two years old, and he was regarded as 'delicate'. Young Osborne and his family were caught in the round-ups that followed notification, a subject to which I shall return.   His mother brought him, as directed, to Brompton once a month. The visit

> took all day, from about nine o'clock ... at the end of the afternoon ...   The porter ... acted like a policeman. I felt I ... was there because of some unknown transgression ... We sat on long, dark refectory-like benches and prepared to wait ... in this dim, bustling crypt [with an] ... overpowering smell ... like no other ...   [The Scots sister] would make me take off my shirt almost immediately on arrival and I would be forced to walk without dawdling around the ... corridors to my various X-rays and tests, and return to our bench wearing only my shorts ...
> We had nothing to eat all day, as my mother obviously thought that to bring sandwiches ... would have been ... like munching ... during Evensong. She had a reverential ... attitude to medicine ... very common at the time, and believed ... that doctors, exclusively were ... people who drove their own motor cars.
> Shivering, hungry, largely ignored for hours ... the last visit of the afternoon was ... always to Dr Henderson ... she thumped away at my tinny ... body impatiently ... Eventually throwing me a barley sugar, she would sit and write her report ... My mother, doubtful and bewildered, would lead me off to the dispensary [probably for bottles of cod-liver oil, and opium-based cough mixture] ... At last ... I was allowed to put on my clothes ... My release was not complete until the ... interview with the Lady Almoner. I did not mind this so much because ... I knew that I had got my ticket, at least for the next three months. My mother [accepted] ... it with smiles and nods of understanding and all from a very posh lady in overalls.[32]

Possibly young Osborne was inspected at Brompton by Clive Fitts, a young doctor intending to specialise in tuberculosis. He, unlike Osborne, found Brompton a friendly, useful place. 'All the physicians have been very kind to me', he reassured his mother, '[each] ... has ... offered me the use of his cases to write a paper, or to do some research on.'[33]   Mr Osborne's autobiography suggests that his survival owes little to Brompton; perhaps the impulse to write *Look Back In Anger* owes rather more.

Consumptives, scrofula and lupus cases must have comprised a large proportion of the regulars at the old charitable and contributory dispensaries. Officials found them unsatisfactory patients, desultory in attendance and near impossible to heal. Typically, Dr Hughes Wiltshire of the London Fore Street Dispensary complained in 1842 that his phthisis cases were irregular attenders and irresponsible takers of the medicines he ordered. They also, he knew, neglected his rule for low diets at home. In his experience Parisian patients were much more obedient. The leaching and cupping below the clavicle that he employed to counter haemoptyses were done at the Dispensary, but Wiltshire despaired of patients obeying at home his directions to rub tartrate of antimony on the affected side of their chests and to take their one-quarter gram doses of extract of belladonna (atropine) three times daily to dry up their coughs. The antimonial counter-irritant could provoke cruel eruptions and the atropine could induce convulsions and disturbed vision.   'Systematic poisoning' had occurred, Wiltshire mused, even when the patient claimed to have taken less than the prescribed dosage.[34]   Nonetheless the general dispensaries were never short of consumptive attenders who expected to be given drastic medication while they continued to live at home and to work while they were able.   The dispensaries were cheap or even free and the system allowed patients that self-determination-indiscipline- that Dr Wiltshire deplored.

The popularity of the general dispensary and the vested interest many general practitioners had in its contributory arrangements inhibited the development of specialist institutions.   Dr Robert Philip's Royal Victoria Dispensary, founded in Edinburgh in 1887, remained unique for almost twenty years.   Its potentialities as a model were further circumscribed by Philip's commitment to tuberculin.[35]

The specialist dispensaries began to develop suddenly after about 1909, as sanatorium promoters and Poor Law authorities realised that they needed a network of recruiting, marshalling units within the community. 'All the tuberculous material of the district' could be summoned, Dr D.J. Williamson told the Destitution Conference in 1911, and '...sorted out for appropriate treatment'.[36] The patient could expect to be diagnosed, tested, receive cod-liver oil and advice about home hygiene and diet, and have his or her contacts traced. 'Early' cases could be listed for entry to a sanatorium, interesting cases be recommended to Brompton or another specialist hospital and advanced cases instructed to guard their cough and their spitting. Some dispensaries were free, but most before 1914 charged a fee smaller than that levied by the local general practitioners, usually sixpence a visit, medicine included. Attenders at the Philip private dispensaries needed letters of recommendation from subscribers or practitioners and were required to join the dispensary provident scheme. Domiciliary patients insured under the National Insurance Act and those discharged from sanatoria and still on their sanatorium benefit under the Act could legally be treated at dispensaries, but private practitioners insisted throughout that such cases had to be handled by them; dispensary officers, when they discovered a patient to be on benefit, usually directed the case back to a private colleague.[37]

Tuberculosis dispensaries were above all recording, investigative institutions. Each attender was required to provide the fullest possible details about his or her antecedents and family. Philip had conceived the system as a sorting, isolating mechanism rather than a curative resource. The presiding doctors were young graduates, on £500-£700 a year. The nurses were similarly inexperienced and cheaply obtained. They were expected to process about 30 to 35 cases a session, allowing each about six minutes. Dispensaries usually opened for three hours at 2 p.m. on Tuesdays and Fridays. Frequent calls to open outside working hours were largely ignored, partly because the dispensary was designed to regulate the family and contacts at least as much as the original sufferer, and they could be visited during working hours. Philip's great invention was the 'march past'. The information in the patient's record enabled a nurse or volunteer lady health visitor promptly to inspect the patient's dwelling. She gave instructions about the isolation of the patient, separate sleeping arrangements, ventilation, the cleansing of the patient's bedding and eating utensils, drinking more milk and cod liver oil and cleansing the household. She then reported to the doctor, who was supposed to visit the family 'with a view to gaining a thorough knowledge of the ...surroundings of the patient he is treating, and seeing that his instructions are being carried out, but more especially with a view to seeing the other members of the household'. Guided by the patient's record and the visitor's report, he conducted a 'march past', looking for susceptibles who were told to report for examination.[38] In Scotland the dispensary officers could legally enter a dwelling under a Scottish Local Government Board ruling declaring tuberculosis to be an infectious disease but the English Board had refused to create this power: doctors in England entered houses and conducted 'march pasts' without legal authority but I have found no instance of their being openly defied.[39] However, English officials appear to have been less intrusive than their Scottish counterparts: Philip chided them for 'laziness'.[40]

The laziness was possibly encouraged by passive resistance from families. A few English medical leaders had been calling for compulsory notification of tuberculosis since the early 1890s and local authorities with vigorous medical officers of health in Sheffield, Manchester, Brighton and Liverpool had introduced voluntary notification between 1892 and 1903. Progressive Sheffield secured a local act of parliament making notification compulsory from 1904. Theoretically, voluntary notification required the patient's consent. This in practice, as Dr Arthur Newsholme, Medical Officer of Health for Brighton, admitted in 1903, 'limited the operation of...notification...chiefly to...the poorer classes, and particularly those treated in connection with the poor law, or in public hospitals and dispensaries'. These patients lacked the power to prevent themselves being labelled and they were, Newsholme said, grateful for the free fumigation of their rooms and free spittoons and paper handkerchiefs.[41] Doctors rarely notified patients 'at the top of the ladder, lest they prove vexatious'.[42]

Newsholme and his northern allies were ahead of their colleagues. Tuberculosis was no ordinary infectious disease. Many doctors dreaded committing themselves and their patients when diagnosis was peculiarly difficult, prognosis was uncertain and the pattern of infection was unverifiable and ubiquitous.   Compulsory notification also daunted local authorities because it entailed isolation hospitals, removal from employment and schools for indefinitely long periods and widespread home fumigation. Tuberculosis had been a striking omission from the Infectious Diseases (Notification) Act of 1889. The English central government moved first where it was cheapest, by requiring Poor Law Medical Officers in 1908 to report their cases to their local Medical Officer of Health. The rapid spread of dispensaries during 1909-10 enabled the government to extend compulsory notification to all patients in voluntary hospitals and dispensaries and finally, after a recommendation from the progressive Royal Commission on Tuberculosis, all cases became notifiable from 1912. Practitioners were to receive one shilling per notification. Each notification was to stand for three months, when it was supposed to be reviewed. The compulsory isolation that usually accompanied notification of infectious disease was never enforced on consumptives.

After 1912 more practitioners settled for passive resistance. Some notified without telling the patient, enabling him or her to remain unstigmatised and thereby continue to hold a job.[43] Others only notified if the consumption seemed 'active', some only on proof of bacilli in the sputum, while compassionate doctors often waited until the case was clearly terminal.[44] Patients avoided doctors often known as keen notifiers and turned to practitioners with more complaisant reputations.[45] The Local Government Boards and subsequently the Ministry of Health nagged the profession but notification never worked efficiently. Between 1915 and 1918 in England and Wales 19 per cent of deaths certified as resulting from tuberculosis had not been notified and 27 per cent more tuberculosis deaths had occurred within three months of notification. Even after the Ministry tightened the rules in 1920, 87 per cent of tuberculosis deaths in Barnsley were cases previously unnotified or notified only within six months of death. The proportion in Paddington up to 1921 was about 37 per cent and in Bath around 50 per cent.[46] These figures understate the situation because non-pulmonary tuberculosis notifications, whose victims were commonly under age or never in employment, were believed to have much nearer complete coverage.[47] In 1927, 47 per cent of London tuberculosis deaths had passed either unnotified or notified within three months of death.[48] The Ministry continued to reprove and cajole but in 1942-3 8 per cent of consumption deaths in England and Wales passed unnotified and an additional 42 per cent had occurred within a year of notification.[49] Notification rates were still 'unsatisfactory' the authorities said, in 1961.[50] Despite the high claims of its advocates and the hours of paperwork that it involved notification did not, as it had done with other diseases, contribute greatly to the reduction of tuberculosis.

Notification did, however, confer great power on dispensary, hospital and municipal officials over families like the Osbornes. But the thousands of people mobilised into regular attendances, home investigations and 'march pasts' quickly imposed intolerable burdens on the charitable dispensaries. By 1911 dispensary advocates were divided between those who wished to preserve their independence and realists who asserted that the system could develop only if it were municipalised. The Dundee Dispensary was already municipalised by 1911 but it provided a warning of what the tuberculosis controllers feared; the corporation undertook to subsidise the Dispensary only on condition that notification remained voluntary with the implication that a patient's consent might be required.[51] Municipalisation also involved inspection by the Local Government Boards, and many of the charitable dispensaries were ill-managed and badly housed.   Above all, municipalisation threatened the powers of dispensary officers, committee members and volunteer lady visitors to interfere in the lives of tuberculosis families. The movement's promoters had close ties with the Charity Organization Society and their dispensaries adhered to the Society's rules forbidding 'material relief' except through the Society, while cases who could afford private treatment were sent to get it. Dispensaries were created to check out-patient abuses, not foment them. 'No case should in any circumstance be attended by a dispensary who is already under treatment elsewhere...Such cases are immediately sent back to their own doctors', and no non-tuberculous case was to be entertained. These were to be directed immediately to private doctors or the general hospitals.[52]

Medical advocates of municipalisation had no quarrel with these procedures. They simply wanted to make them work. As Dr Harold Scurfield, Medical Officer of Health for Sheffield, declared in 1911, only officials backed by local authority could do 'full investigatory and notification work'.[53] After the Local Government Board accepted an interim recommendation from Waldorf Astor's Royal Commission in May 1912, dispensaries moved on to the rates during the next decade. The transition was impelled by rising costs, inadequate voluntary support and the access by local authorities to central government bloc grants. Charitable dispensaries which resolved to keep their independence lingered on at the edge of bankruptcy. Patients' provident funds, donations and sixpenny attendance charges, regardless of how many patients were processed, could not cover the minimum of £1152 a year the average dispensary needed in 1912 to survive. The chief medical officer cost £500 or more, his assistant £300, two nurses £100 each, a clerk-dispenser £100 and a porter £52. Beyond that were rent, maintenance and bulk purchases of cod liver oil and malt extract.[54] Expenses rose with technological developments. Manchester's showpiece new dispensary in 1913 cost £800 for its building, £150 for X-ray apparatus, £120 for a bacteriological laboratory. By 1918 the average dispensary cost £1500 a year. Doctors' salaries had risen to £650 a year, nurses' wages to £150. Drugs and appliances doubled in price during the War.[55] Nonetheless, municipalisation underwrote an expansion from 442 recognised dispensaries in Great Britain in 1922 to 482 in 1938 recording almost 111,000 new cases a year.[56]

Tight budgets meant dingy premises. Ratepayers resented dispensaries, which seemed to pander to weaklings and to achieve little against a ubiquitous, intractable disease. Consumptives, ailing, complaining, unpredictably feeble, always threatening infection, aroused little compassion in the healthy. Local practitioners disliked dispensaries because they stole patients. Medical Officers of Health distrusted them because they were effectively outside their jurisdiction, and yet hurt their budget. County tuberculosis officers preferred dealing with the more medically reputable sanatoria. Yet dispensaries, together with hospital out-patient wards, were the main providers of diagnosis and support, such as it was, but practitioners and ratepayers joined to keep dispensaries in check. Many were installed in basements of buildings housing the better esteemed maternity and school clinics.[57] Chorlton-upon-Medlock dispensary in Manchester in the 1920s was ill-lit, in a busy street: auscultations proceeded between breaks in the traffic.[58] Battersea's rooms in the Baths had no screened areas for disrobing and no space for the all important records.[59] A proposal in 1925 to buy a site in Lincoln Grove, Manchester, for a new dispensary was blocked by local ratepayers who argued that a consumption den in the neighbourhood would congregate undesirables and reduce property values.[60] Local hostility to their gaining better premises kept North Islington in 'temporary' unsuitable premises for two decades between the Wars.[61]

Until the 1920s dispensaries opened only during professional hours. Thereafter a few, principally in Lancashire, opened for an hour or two at 6 p.m. Patients normally could not make precise appointments. Amid the waiting and shuffling, 'recording came first.' A new patient presented his or her note from a local general practitioner, Poor Law or health official, or lady almoner. Cases without a letter or those who admitted to receiving treatment elsewhere, especially if a private practitioner was involved, were turned away. Then the case's name and address and next of kin were recorded. The case was enrolled in the dispensary's provident fund and undertook to pay sixpence per visit. The patient then stripped to his or her vest, was weighed, and waited to be called to be ausculated or X-rayed. The results were entered on standard forms with four diagrams to be completed on the state of the lungs at admission and discharge. Usually a new case was given a tuberculin test; occasionally, in the better establishments, some sputum was taken for testing. After the normal five minute encounter with the doctor, the patient received a thermometer and temperature chart from the nurse and instruction in taking his or her temperature twice daily and recording it. The patient might also get instructions about eating more eggs and milk and sleeping alone in an airy room. Then came the reward of the visit, from the patient's viewpoint: a free bottle of cod liver oil and another of Virol (a sweet, brown malt-based viscous tonic). Doctors said that patients would not come regularly unless they got their bottles. The nurse often accompanied the gifts with a dressing down for not keeping the temperature chart properly and breaking hygiene rules at home, and working too hard. The average case attended fortnightly or monthly for about six to eight months, until he or she enjoyed a remission, gave up, or became too ill or ashamed to come. Meanwhile a nurse, health visitor or even a doctor was supposed to have inspected the case's habitation and given orders about rearranging family life. The orders changed little between 1906 and 1952. The case had to have separate, marked utensils. Cracked crockery had to be thrown out. All spitting onto the floor had to cease: it had to be done into a spittoon or into the fire. The case was not to fondle or kiss other members of the family, children particularly. The case was to sleep separately, preferably behind a partition if a whole room could not be spared. Windows were to be opened. Food masticated properly. Onions not added to every dish. The dwelling was to be fumigated and dust in corners and behind beds swept up. Dr Duncan Forbes, Medical Officer of Health in Brighton, instructed his visitors to order the case to sleep with his or her face turned away if the family could not afford a separate bed, or to sleep with his or her head at the opposite end of the bed. The sputum flask was supposed to be boiled for ten minutes daily and its contents burned. Food scraps were to be burned and all utensils were to be boiled after use. Bed clothes had to be kept separate and boiled at home. The person attending the patient had to don a special overall on entering the room, to be kept in the case's room. In practice the case's life was easier, if no more hopeful, because the system worked poorly:

> G.W. (male) 35, phthisis...has a wife and four children. He was a brassfounder, and first fell ill in October 1906, when he went to a charitable dispensary. He says that his chest was not examined, but that the doctor knew what was the matter by looking at him. He continued at work until sixteen weeks ago, and now [1909] attends the dispensary of a general hospital. He gets cod-liver oil and cough mixture. He has a heavy spit. During the day he spits into the fire, and at night into a chamber pot. No sanitary officer has called...He and his wife and a baby...sleep in the bed.[62]

The dispensary visitor might also lend the sufferer a shelter to occupy in the open air. Visitors could recommend cases to local charities or Poor Law officials for extra food, bedding or clothing. Above all, the visitor scrutinised 'contacts' - the rest of the family, accessible kin, neighbours, workmates or schoolfellows. Likely cases were ordered to the dispensary and tests. A thorough 'march past' could desolate a family. The inspections and directives had no legal authority : that would have required amendments to the Sanitary Acts, which never eventuated. Ordinary 'contacts' knew that they could ignore the directives of the health visitor and not be legally liable.[63]

Their response was to lie low. The dispensary busybodies might never get around to them. Voluntary visitors were rare; beyond fear of infection and the poor kudos attached to direct tuberculosis work, they were discouraged by professionals because they 'lacked tact'. Their cases appear also to have resented them, together with bossy lady almoners. Orders to sweep up, dust corners and sprinkle disinfectant were rebuffed with the claim that it would upset the landlord. Cases also resisted orders to sleep in separate beds because that seemed less fond, was colder, especially for the sufferer, and meant extra outlay on blankets. Visitors had to 'insist' on shelters being used because cases were 'terrified' of sleeping outdoors and 'object[ed]' to being seen in a deck chair in...an open space'. 'It ain't the game, miss. I ain't ill, and the fellows will all come round and think I was doing the toff'. Not surprisingly patients 'dropped out' at the first sign of getting better.[64] Despite the setbacks, many senior doctors were keen to keep the volunteers at work. If voluntary effort failed, Dr Charles Grey warned in 1911, the state would step in and regulate doctors as well as patients.[65] But it turned out that the central and local authorities were more than willing to leave local care to unsupervised agencies, meagrely subsidised at £2 per 1000 population to 1930, and thereafter to £5 per 1000.[66]

Dispensary nurses were always too few and rarely stayed long. The work was arduous, unrewarding and relatively ill-paid at about £130 a year in 1920. Staff shortages and 'lack of appreciation of the importance of the work', according to the Ministry of Health inspector, meant that Deptford Dispensary only 'followed up' ten per cent of 'contacts' around 1920. Two-thirds of Deptford's notifications arrived within six months of death. In the mid 1930s metropolitan borough dispensaries examined only about 2.5 persons for every tuberculosis death and county borough dispensaries only about 1.8. In 1936 only 5.6 per cent of these contacts were diagnosed as tuberculous.[67] Half-consciously perhaps, dispensary officers sensed that the 'march past', much vaunted by Sir Robert Philip and the tuberculosis hierarchs, produced results wholly incommensurate with the intrusion and misery it involved.

Dispensary doctors were usually impecunious new graduates who took the posts as interim jobs while they worked as assistants and scraped towards a private practice outside the service. The dispensary normally required their attention for two mornings or afternoons a week. Their appointed task was to diagnose, but not to treat. Once diagnosed, their client was to be referred to a general practitioner who normally held aloof

from them. Home visiting was time-consuming and conferred
a local reputation for officiousness. Tuberculosis doctors had
low professional esteem. They formed a Tuberculosis Officers'
Association about 1920 to press for a diploma and higher
allowances, claims that the General Medical Council had
rejected. The existing Tuberculosis Society composed of
sanatorium directors and medical officers of health rebuffed
their pleas for affiliation. The British Medical Association
proved lukewarm when their salaries were cut in the mid 1920s
to under £500 and again in 1931.[68]

Even the nurses in dispensaries were contumacious. They
made their headquarters the town hall or school health clinic,
rather than the poky dispensary. They kept patients to
themselves and withheld records from the doctors, a stratagem
that was helped by the convention which precluded transfer of a
case's record when he or she changed residence. Private
practitioners also hung on to their records, not least because
they were uncertain in their treatments.[69] Many patients must
have drifted from one doctor to another, one dispensary to the
next, one out-patients' ward to the next, resigned to the
knowledge that the authorities were too much at odds to find
them out. However, families were 'scared' of dispensary
officers. Fifty per cent of tuberculosis deaths between 1915 and
1925 in West Monmouth, for instance, occurred among
sufferers unknown to a dispensary.[70]

The other arm of the ideal dispensary was the after care
committee, composed of voluntary workers with ex officio
dispensary functionaries. They were modelled on the district
committees of the Charity Organization Society and were
intended to assess payment for treatment of uninsured cases,
review visitors' reports on cases' home conditions, make grants
in aid of food and clothing and find employment for ambulant
cases. But charitable workers avoided the 'embarrassing'
tuberculosis arena. The cores of the committees remained the
local tuberculosis officers and hospital almoners, together with
the occasional compassionate alderman. Trades unions and
friendly societies held aloof. Amid high unemployment the
unions opposed underpayment of wages and part-time work
and setting skilled workers to unskilled jobs, while the societies'
rule against disbursement of benefits if a member was receiving
wages led them to concentrate upon sanatorium treatment.[71]

It was 'exceptional' for an after care committee to try to find work for an ex-patient. Until 1944, legislation discouraged it. The 1924 National Health Insurance Act paid a sickness benefit of 15s to 17s a week up to 26 weeks, and thereafter a disablement benefit of 7s 6d to 8s 6d, provided the recipient did not receive wages.   The Employment Sub-Committee of the Joint Tuberculosis Council had, to 1926 at least, never met.[72] Within factories and offices, workers adamantly opposed employment of 'lungers', while employers readily quoted their employees' objections when rebuffing approaches from consumptives and care committees. Consumptives were quickly dismissed when they began to miss days and were found out. Few employers held the job open when an employee departed for a sanatorium. Occasionally a kindly dispensary doctor would omit to take a sputum test or X-ray of a likely case still holding a job in order not to have to notify the 'marked man' and jeopardise his chance of keeping it.   Ambulant working patients who were diagnosed positive or notified, and sacked, were known to return to their trade under assumed names.[73]

Care committees were directed to meet weekly, like the best district committees of the old Charity Organization Society. But most were moribund.   Bethnal Green committee met only about four or five times (they were not sure which) during 1920 and achieved 'little useful work'. Hackney met only monthly. The only active committee in Wales between the Wars was Anglesey. Until 1937 they were legally precluded from engaging clerical assistance.[74]   Patients too disregarded the committees. The maximum weekly allowance was still only 12s in 1942: there were no loadings for low incomes or numbers of dependents. 'Our sympathy goes out', the National Association stalwarts Harley Williams and Irene Harbert wrote in 1945, 'to health visitors, almoners and social workers who are called upon ... to perform miracles on behalf of some tuberculous person, who does not seem to have the will or capacity to help himself'.[75] Only Grimsby, Rochdale and Blackpool consistently ordered maximum or near-maximum allowances.   In other towns patients preferred to try the public assistance or unemployed assistance boards, who had no stigma of disease and were readier to give - only dubiously legally - an extra nourishment allowance for eggs, butter, malt extract and cod-liver oil on presentation of a note from the tuberculosis officer.[76]

One benign outcome of after care defeatism was the failure in Britain of the French boarding-out movement. Belief in the hereditary nature of phthisis was traditional in France, and germ theory was readily accommodated in the 1880s as merely a more immediate means of transmission between predisposed parents and offspring. If the germ was not transmitted at conception it was, French medical authorities agreed, conveyed in mother's milk. It followed that the traditional French practice of wet-nursing infants of weak mothers and fathers had a fresh justification.[77] By the 1880s French doctors were removing infants at birth from tuberculous mothers and sending them to sound Catholic peasant families. Their justification lay in the terrible estimated death-rate of one in four infant deaths attributed to tuberculosis, amounting to over 2000 annually in Paris.[78] In 1903 the fostering system was regularised as l'Oeuvre Grancher, named after a French pediatrician. After the carnage of the Great War the French government adopted the scheme with a 60 per cent subsidy amounting to 61.4 million francs in 1924-5, although it was still run as a private charity. The babies were removed without the mother, who was masked during the birth, seeing or holding her child. The sources are silent on whether her permission was sought or required, but the use of the word 'selected' by hospital officials suggests that permission might have been a formality.

They remain in their peasant family - so P.F. Armand-Delille commended the scheme to an international conference in 1921 - under the supervision of the country doctor, as long as it is necessary for the disappearance of contagion in their ... family. This disappearance becomes sometimes ... a cure, but more often the death of the tuberculous parent.

That demands an average of three years. But if the healthy parent, after the death of the tuberculous one, does not ask for the children to return home, we leave them in the country up to ... 13, when they have completed their schooling.

At that age, either we give back the children to the parents to be sent to earn their living, or we place them in the country, especially in farms, as servants ... The children ... grow up honest and of good character.

The scheme was relatively cheap, 400 francs a year per child before the War, 1200 after it, compared with 7000 francs for a year's sanatorium stay. It was helping to maintain the French countryside with healthy stock because 50 per cent of the children stayed on the farms.[79] By 1925, 2300 infants had been removed from diseased, radical Paris. Calmette of the Baudelocque Clinic claimed that the Grancher scheme had reduced infant tuberculosis mortality in the maternity ward from 33 per cent in 1923 to 7 per cent in 1926.[80]

L'Oeuvre Grancher, with its competitor, Placement Familial des Touts-Petits, launched in 1920 by Dr E. Rist, a rival to Armand-Delille and Calmette in the French tuberculosis hierarchy, were run with 'unvarying precision'. 'The separation between mother and child [was] absolute.' In rare instances where the doctors deemed it necessary that a mother should nurse her child, 'this [was] carried out in isolated rooms in the sister's presence. The mother [wore] a surgical mask ... and ... gown so that the infant is never in contact'. After a BCG injection and a Wasserman test, the infants were despatched into the far countryside, where parents could not visit them. Parents who retrieved their children in under two years had to surrender the costs of their clothes and travel expenses. Rist's Placement Familial preferred small farmers and market gardeners or remote convents as foster parents: the farmers were 'keen to have children able ... to appreciate country pursuits'; while the convents were 'good at preventing parental visits'.[81] Armand-Delille and Rist boasted very low tuberculosis death rates among their separated children. But they never admitted, or apparently ever applied their vaunted precision to figures which suggested by 1935 a death-rate among them 'appreciably higher than the general infantile mortality', from causes other than tuberculosis.[82] The Grancher system was adopted in Belgium, Algeria and Quebec and was still processing 7000 French children in 1955, 'with complete success', according to Armand-Delille.[83]

In Britain L'Oeuvre Grancher was tried at Hastings, Plymouth and in Shropshire. But they lacked the official backing and money to do the job properly; and as Dr Letitia Fairfield, senior medical officer of the London County Council complained in 1931, 'the scheme was gravely interfered with by lack of co-operation ... [from] tuberculous parents'.[84]

Hastings Tuberculosis Care Committee, led by the enthusiastic W. Bolton Tomson, boarded out older, failing children 'with people of their own class' during the summer months between about 1925 and 1930.[85] The Plymouth Hospital committee and the London County Council copied the Hastings' plan late in 1925 but apparently few children were ever involved. 'Parents ... [refused] to allow their children to be sent away', and the doctors had no legal power to force them.[86] A more humane scheme was launched in Shropshire by Arthur C. Watkin, the county tuberculosis officer, in 1933. The children of tuberculous mothers were housed in a 'county home for babies' while their mothers stayed for up to one year at a sanatorium, and at the end of that time 'the parents [were] persuaded ... to send the child to relatives or to a public assistance institution'.[87] By 1935 this system, together with the Hastings and Plymouth ventures, had separated 2500 children annually, allegedly with 'excellent' results although there appear to be no reliable figures.[88] But apparently they were collapsing before the War largely ended them.   Researchers at the Lymanhurst Health Centre in Minnesota showed in 1935 that, so far as tuberculosis was concerned, children who remained at home with tuberculous parents had the same chances of later morbidity as children who were separated. Moreover, doctors had begun to realise that the costs were high. In 1940 Dr Reginald Lightwood told a receptive Royal Society of Medicine about the American findings and added that separation and 'institutional treatment ... of ... infants might be more dangerous than the disease'.[89] He omitted to add that the danger was compounded by the diversion of scarce money to administrators concerned with a tiny percentage of the population at risk.[90]

If the care committees found tuberculous parents intractable, they had small success with male breadwinners.   The committees were hamstrung by the refusal of the Ministries of Health and Labour to define 'fitness for work', or to adopt the helpfully elastic German notion of 'arbeitsfähigkeit' - recovery of working powers - as a guide to pension entitlements. By 1910 only about one-third of sanatorium ex-patients had found employment, generally at a lower status and wage than they had known, and this proportion seems to have remained the same until the Second World War.[91] Between 1909 and 1951 males found jobs as rent collectors, railway bookstall keepers, rabbit breeders, canvassers, rat catchers, under-gardeners in public parks, night watchmen and pre-eminently, in a new outdoor, learnable skill requiring little physical effort, as motor car chauffeurs. The increase of traffic in the 1930s created the first posts - eagerly monopolised by consumptives - as 'motor watchers', car-park attendants. Opportunities were few for females - home knitting and mending, home laundering, shop cashiers and prostitution.[92] Lungers who found a job tried to hide their cough and weakness. However, spitting on to the floor in factories - and in hospital waiting rooms - was apparently acceptable until at least 1914. According to Duncan Forbes, Medical Officer of Health for Brighton, 'tailors, shoemakers, iron founders, upholsterers ... can spit ... without any notice being taken ... while the use of a spit-bottle might lead to suspicion, and ... dismissal', but domestic servants and charwomen were instantly dismissed if they were caught, as were shop assistants.[93] A discharged Frimley patient told his sanatorium mentors in 1909 that he was

being everywhere congratulated on my very fit appearance - Unfortunately however misfortune seems to be dogging my footsteps ... My employer is an extremely nervous man and he has just taken his only son into the business and he is so terrified at the thought of infection that he cannot think of taking me back - He is kind enough to say that it is a very great blow to him ... but he has a brother in law a Dr ... & no matter what I say or ask him to enquire about he is genuinely in terror ... I am to have a month's salary ... in order to look around & find something ... Of course without trying to let it worry me in any way - I mustn't let it do that - it is a considerable task to know what to set one's hand to especially to find something at an adequate salary to support myself - wife & 2 children ... it is wonderful what an inconvenient place home is to carry out the treatment esp. with children...[94]

Employers, rightly, did not trust sanatorium or dispensary certificates and most were brutally frank:

Dear Mr. H.
... I am instructed by my Directors to tell you that they regret they are unable to make a vacancy for you.

Speaking personally I am ... convinced, in spite of what your Medical Superintendent says, that you would be exceedingly foolish to come back again, if you had an opportunity. I return herewith Mr. Paterson's certificate ... [95]

In 1926 the Holborn Workshop for Tuberculous Persons began to employ 23 men. But the venture, said to be the first of its kind in England, did not flourish. The government refused to allow national insurance funds to be diverted to it, and private insurers declared that they could not support 'experiments'.[96] The Workshop appears to have closed before 1928, when the Central Fund for the Industrial Welfare of Tuberculous Persons opened the sheltered Spero Workshops, mainly for skilled men, copied from the Altro Workshop in New York. But amid worsening unemployment, the idea did not spread and the Spero venture struggled.[97] A Leeds committee employed 42 men 'at varying periods' during 1934 at a 'Factory in the Field', preparing firewood, making brushes, and attempting job printing but the enterprise soon lapsed.[98] Remploy did not begin until 1943. It was said to have been helped by the Disabled Persons (Employment) Act of 1944, which required employers of more than twenty persons to reserve 3 per cent of posts for disabled persons, but its relation to Remploy is unclear and there is little evidence that consumptives gained from the Act.[99] The limit of about one-third of discharged male patients in reasonably regular employment three years after discharge seems to have remained constant to the 1950s. In 1951 27 per cent of Frimley male patients released in 1949 were reported to have jobs, at a time of full employment. Only 13 per cent of female ex-patients had 'returned to housework'. One of the few employers to act decisively upon the 1944 Act was the Austin Car works in Birmingham. They took on 60 male consumptives, 26 of whom were still working uninterruptedly in 1950 and earning wages equivalent to their unhandicapped workmates. After the streptomycin/PAS revolution of the early 1950s about 47 per cent of unskilled male consumptives and 40 per cent of the unskilled females discharged from institutions remained unemployed.[100] Welfare workers were fond of referring to tuberculosis in the 1930s and 1940s as a 'disease of discouragement'.

The one imaginative attempt to create special employment for tuberculous patients was the village settlement movement, led by Papworth in Cambridgeshire. The precursors to the movement were the labour colonies for the unemployed. Hollesley Bay colony in Suffolk, for instance, had by 1908 become restricted to tuberculous unemployed, while the Garden City run by the Trinity College Oxford Settlement was also concentrating upon consumptives. Both projects taught agriculture and tried to sustain themselves by selling their produce. Hollesley Bay inmates rose at 5.45 a.m., began work at 6.30 a.m., and then worked 8.30 to 12 and 1 p.m.. until 5. Inefficient men left or were discharged, able men were retained.[101]

In 1920 the tuberculous unemployed were reinforced by 40,000 ex-servicemen diagnosed as phthisic, 3000 of whom were judged sufficiently well to enter a village settlement. The Astor Inter-Departmental Committee recommended expenditure of £1 million from the exchequer (to be repaid by local corporations over five years) for a projected 250 settlements, but by 1920 the government had provided only £25,000. Delay helped the treasury: of 430 London consumptives demobilised in 1918, 60 per cent were dead by May 1920. The Labour Government of 1924 promised another £20,000, gave £2,500, and there it ended. This was the easier to do because few ex-service consumptives survived, gas victims especially, and those who did were mostly too sick to cope with what Professor Lyle Cummins described as the 'chill efficiency of the village settlement'.[102]

The money was intended to rescue projects that were already failing. Cumberland Tuberculosis Council, for instance, had in 1919 bought Englethwaite Hall Estate for £5,000. It was suitably far from temptations: six miles from Carlisle and nearly a mile from the nearest village. It was also remote from possible markets. The Council boasted that their Estate was 'run on strictly commercial lines' with a market garden, joinery shed, boot repairs and clog-making, and in 1921, a projected poultry yard. But receipts permitted only 25 of the prospective 100 patients to be installed. The Council had intended to train each inmate for three months and then release him to take up a small holding but already the venture was dependent upon a nucleus of indispensible long-term residents. Englethwaite Hall lingered through the 1920s and apparently collapsed about 1929.[103]

No local authority entirely accepted the government's offer. Cheshire County Council took a loan after it was given Wrenbury Hall by the Red Cross and the Order of St John of Jerusalem. Fifty men on soldiers' pensions and Ministry of Health insurance benefits were in residence by 1924. They earned twopence per hour while they worked with pigs, poultry and cattle. Most were able to maintain a 25 hour week. Two men learned to mend boots and were permitted to keep 25 per cent of their takings. By 1923-4 the inmates had reduced the annual loss on the colony by £1,000 down to £4,000, shared by the Ministry of Pensions and the County Council. 'Expensive instruction' was not provided but the authorities hoped that '"key" men' would stay on. Evidence is scarce, but it appears that Wrenbury Hall did not prosper.[104]

Preston Hall village at Aylesford in Kent began about 1920 as a private venture under its first director, Dr T.L. Bonar. He filled it with ex-service pensioners; rumours of scandals soon led the British Legion to intervene. Bonar's institution, like all tuberculosis establishments, was under-capitalised. By October 1921 the inmates were subsisting on tea, bread, margarine, dripping and herrings. Thefts from the canteen were endemic. The men's canteen welfare fund also mysteriously vanished. Half the 1921 admissions had left or were wanting to go. Many beds were unfilled. The rough board huts were not weatherproof. Rain entered through the unblockable ventilation spaces under the roofs and snow blew in to cover the stretchers and floor. Cups were chipped and lacked handles. Lavatories were 'disgraceful': the workshops contained two for 100 men which blocked every morning. Spitting passed unrebuked and sputum flasks were scarce. Patients were required to spend at least four hours daily at shoemaking, game and poultry keeping, pig farming and cabinet making. James Smith, an inmate, told the chairman of the British Legion in 1924 that Bonar thought 'more about his pigs than he does his patients, at least he tells you so'. Bonar defended his method to various inspectors by listing the prizes won by the Hall pigs and carnations. He had made the colony survive. From 165 young men in 1921, the village grew to 555 men, women and children in 1924 to 654 people in 1928, comprising 131 incapacitated inmates in the sanatorium and 122 settlers, 100 of them married with families.

Bonar was ruthless. Patients rarely saw him because they were afraid of his dog. His assistant was formally titled the 'Discipline Doctor'. The numbers grew because Bonar ensured that good men could not leave. Grumblers and incompetents were expelled before their six months or two years was up, which prevented their receiving their special tuberculosis pension at either 100 per cent at six months or 50 per cent at eighteen months because they had defaulted on their course of training. Settlers were required by 1924 to work a 44 hour week for 15s, less 2s 6d for lighting and rent. Only men on 100 per cent pensions were permitted to stay and be enrolled for courses. Their pension of 19s a week went direct to Bonar. He also pocketed the national training bonus of 5s payable at every 40 hours' satisfactory progress and got away with it because he never issued progress reports to the men. One admission discovered to be a part-pensioner was summarily discharged. The patients' Welfare Committee humbly asked that he be reinstated, at least to retain his pension. Bonar demanded an apology, dismissed the Committee and threatened them with expulsion. Bonar's chosen instructors were ill-paid botchers. Less than half of the men discharged in the 1920s ever got a job, let alone one in the trade they trained for. One trainee in rural carpentry was never shown how to sharpen tools. The poultry men were restricted to watering the birds and cleaning the pens. A request for tuition in rearing chicks was rejected. When one poultry trainee, William Sainsbury, dared in 1924 to ask about reproduction among fowls he received a 'sarcastic' reply which appalled him. The rural carpenters' worked in the open air, on the ground, without benches. The bending and kneeling made them wheeze.

The men lightened the weekly round with surreptitious gambling. They were entertained by, among others, the Comrades Concert Party. There was also a boxing tournament in 1924, the takings of which were misappropriated by the organiser. He escaped prosecution and was appointed entertainments officer by Bonar. He and his dog made patients 'afraid to complain'; a Ministry of Health inspector reported, in August 1924, that Bonar lacked the 'personal touch'. He departed soon afterwards, with his ill-gotten gains, leaving Preston Hall near insolvent.[105]

The new medical superintendent was Major Hamilton. He had to cut costs and raise output. He stopped buying coal and set the men to felling oaks with a crosscut saw and splitting the logs with an axe. The fire-wood was reserved for warming water for the pigs' meals. Brave W.A. Thompson complained to the Ministry of Pensions that the heavy work was enfeebling the men. The Ministry promptly passed on his name to Hamilton. Thompson was discharged within the week, his complaints uninvestigated. He would 'never make a pig farmer', Hamilton confided to the Ministry, and he was a grumbler. He had asked for new false teeth, after he had broken a set during a fit of coughing, but the major refused. Thompson had already enjoyed £6 15s 0d worth of dental work and merited no more indulgence.[106]

By 1928 Hamilton had departed and the new director, J.B. McDougall, had created a quiescent village of 390 cottage residents. Nearly all the ex-servicemen were gone. McDougall had discharged two-thirds of the existing inmates as 'inefficient', 'efficient but temperamentally unsuited', or for 'disciplinary reasons'. Younger civilian consumptives were more amenable than old soldiers who believed society owed them something. McDougall introduced the making of fibre suit cases and the keeping of angora rabbits. Preston Hall made its first profit. And then it burned down. The British Legion rebuilt it at the cost of £100,000 as a garden village, with a miniature street of shops, cottages, village hall, spaced workshops, sanatorium, medical and administrative headquarters.[107] Through the 1930s Preston Hall, assisted by a settler's brilliant marketing of soap, continued as a relatively prosperous haven for around 150 settlers and their families, doctors and nurses, many of whom were also consumptive, together making a community of about 650 souls.[108]

They lived careful, grey lives, threatened by a relapse rate of 50 per cent.[109] A, aged 36 in 1933, had arrived in 1927, and learned printing during a year in the sanatorium. He then settled in the village as a compositor on wages. A was 'steady, sober ... the ideal type of settler'. He was sputum positive, but lost only about seven days a year and earned £133. B was 47 in 1933. He had been a clerk before joining the army, from which he had been invalided out in 1917 after haemoptysis, on a 100 per cent pension. B entered the sanatorium in 1918 but was restive and left to sell insurance for two years, and then struggled through the 1920s doing 'short spells as a clerk with various organisations interspersed with short spells in the sanatorium'. About 1931 he returned to Preston Hall sanatorium and then settled as a clerk in the travel goods department. He remained unmarried and 'looked after himself ... socially ... fairly well'. He was diseased in both lungs and sputum positive. C was a former Navy man aged 37 in 1933. He suffered frequent relapses, yet he had become adept at printing and head of the shop. He was married, with a healthy teenage daughter. 'His social life [was] limited to ... his own house. He is a keen student of his work and takes the greatest care of his physical condition.' He lost a third of each year from illness, but still earned £98 a year. Both his lungs were damaged and he was sputum positive in 1933. D, aged 34, had been a warehouseman before he joined the army, was wounded in France, and discharged B3. He developed chest symptoms in 1920, but worked as a carman until 1928 when he collapsed. Next year he entered Preston Hall. His sputum registered negative in 1931. Possibly D, like many other institutionalised patients, was not tuberculous at all. But in the village he was only a 'handyman' with 'poor earning capacity'. He was also a barely tolerated settler: 'socially, he [was] from a lower social category', demonstrated by his 'poorly administered ... domestic sphere'. He and his wife (?) lived rent free. Nonetheless, Preston Hall was not losing too much on D. By 1933 local authorities and the Legion were contributing £118 per year per inmate. The settler who invented the soap scheme received £200 a year to 1942 while netting the estate £4,000.[110]

The showpiece among village settlements was Papworth, twelve miles from Cambridge. It began in 1915 as a consumptive 'garden city', providing long, cheap stays against the short, expensive ineffectual ones in sanatoria. Its founders rejected sanatorial pretensions to cure and predicated their institution on lifelong infection and the necessity for containing infection and living orderly lives. The Director, Pendrill Varrier-Jones, sought to break the destructive round of sanatorium stays, immediate employment upon discharge, break-down, unemployment, dispensary attendance and return to the sanatorium.[111]

Papworth flourished partly because it was backed by some formidable professorial wives and partly because Varrier-Jones possessed abundant enthusiasm, energy, imagination and charm. He secured the future of his creation by exploiting the sanatorium benefit provision in the National Insurance Act to pay cash sickness benefit to settlers, even though they were 'employed', on the ground that their employment was part of their treatment.[112] From the outset he admitted only patients diagnosed as being in the first or second stages; sceptics wondered whether some admissions with useful skills had ever been tuberculous. Inmates were accepted initially for one year of six months' treatment and six months' training. The treatment was 'holistic'; lots of eggs, milk, cocoa, porridge and potatoes, tuberculin injections and fresh air and sunlight. Patients occupied demountable shelters linked by telephones and bells. Varrier-Jones' chosen site at Papworth St Everard was a hamlet remote from 'Kinema and Public House'.[113] Necessarily, because the inhabitants of Papworth St. Agnes, one and a half miles away, kept the lungers at a distance and unanimously protested in 1921 against a diocesan move to amalgamate their parishes, which would have permitted the settlers to attend their church.[114] Villagers along the Papworth-Cambridge bus route were said also to have pressed the service to neglect St Everard.[115]

The venture began with agriculture and commercial gardening but Varrier-Jones soon realised that returns were too low and tardy to cover wages, let alone capital outlays. He turned to factory production, making portmanteaux. Later the settlers expanded to furniture making (purchased by Cambridge and Oxford colleges - the travel goods were patronised by the royal family) and a printery. Turnover rose from £410 in 1918 to £85,000 in 1930 to £100,000 in 1938. The declared profit in 1929 was £65,000. Financially, Papworth was a success.[116]

Varrier-Jones was a paternalistic overlord, abetted by his formidable matron, Miss K.L. Borne. 'In the interests of the settlement', he vetted 'the frequency, length and character' of the entertainments and picture shows in the village hall. He rigorously controlled leave passes. In 1929 one frequently shown film was based on Papworth itself. It wove 'health propaganda ... into the texture of a romantic story'.[117]

In that year women were admitted for the first time. Their wing, provided by a private gift of £20,000, was made of asbestos sheeting with 'ruberoid' roofing erected by Papworth Industries Ltd. It was 'some distance' from the mens' hostel, but the authorities also had 'a tumulus ... heaped up between the two buildings ... to assist in maintaining necessary segregation'. Nonetheless, the 1930s saw several marriages between inmates.[118] In 1933 Papworth housed 50 women patients, not counting the nurses who were usually consumptives themselves, aged between 16 and 25. Ten of the women had been domestic servants, and the rest had been predominantly clerks, nurses and factory hands. Over half of them had already lost more than two of their family from tuberculosis. Directed by Matron Borne, they formed the core of the subordinate nursing, cleaning and clerical staff. Papworth and the sanatoria benefited from being able to use highly trained, mature nurses who had become consumptive. Generally, they had reached a level in their former employment which made their post pensionable, but once they were diagnosed as tuberculous they lost their job and pension because nurses' unreformed pension schemes, until about the mid 1930s, excluded tuberculosis as a ground for disablement payments. Equally, Papworth and the sanatoria became havens for highly competent rejected nurses. They partially supplied the shortage of healthy nurses created by the lower wages, the stigma of the job and fear of infection.[119]

The orderly lines of shelters were true to the garden city ideal at least in being elemental. False teeth froze to their tumblers, boots froze to the floor. Varrier-Jones and the Matron expelled 'grousers'. Visiting committees were not left alone with patients and were said to have been regaled with special meals which were represented as typical. One grouser was dismissed in 1921 because he was 'too ill to benefit from training' and had complained that it took him two minutes of exhausting walking to get from his chalet in a field to the nearest WC. Other potential scandals, including a probably wrong amputation of an inmate's leg, were hushed up in connivance with the Ministry of Health. Varrier-Jones always successfully resisted calls to report on patients to outside authority.[120]

Many were called, but of 193 admissions between 1917 and 1927 Varrier-Jones chose only twenty to settle. To 1929 only about 7 per cent of discharged trainees had 'succeeded', presumably in remaining active and in maintaining themselves and their families by paid employment. Varrier-Jones had early abandoned attempts to find jobs for discharged trainees. Patients who were expelled or left early were not 'followed-up'.[121] Papworth was not, as the village newsletter, *The Colonist*, boasted in 1929, 'a solution for a world-wide problem'. On the ground that it was 'no real solution', London County Council decided against establishing a similar settlement.[122]   Nonetheless, settlements modelled on Papworth were created at Peamount near Dublin, in 1918, to produce chicken houses, and in Holland, which had several by 1939 including the showpiece Berg-en-bosch which produced luxury toys. The Breslau colony opened in 1929 and specialised in joinery, especially coffins. Its director, E.M. Brieger, fled to Papworth in 1933 and the Nazis suppressed it in 1935.[123]

Chosen Papworth settlers and their families enjoyed a full communal life: a choice of local Protestant denominational worship, book club, boy scouts, cricket, a horticultural society and a tennis club. As Varrier-Jones told the king when he visited in 1926, Papworth served those 'prepared to give more than they get'.[124]   Some thought they got somewhat less. 'Nora' recalled of her time about 1940 that she

> didn't really get on well with Sir Pendrill ... I never felt I could take my troubles to him ... I never really got to know Miss Borne. One didn't, she hardly ever spoke to us ... I don't think she or Sir Pendrill would have taken kindly to any criticism of Papworth.
>
> 'Nora' married another inmate, but for some unstated reason 'had' to live apart from her husband in the village for the first eighteen months in 1944-5. But she never left:
>
> I didn't have the nerve to leave years ago. I wouldn't want to leave now [mid 1970s?] Papworth gave me security and independence.[125]

In 1944 Dr Brieger published a 25 year survey of 244 Papworth families. His information is not standardised and is often difficult to interpret. Brieger himself concluded that about one-third of pulmonary patients had enjoyed considerable healing. Another third had deteriorated. The rest wavered between short remissions and wretched relapses. Significantly, his figures tally with Varrier-Jones' vision of Papworth as a haven of life-long treatment. But Brieger excluded from his calculations an unstated number of families who 'left' early and disappeared beyond the 'follow up', especially when the patient member of the family died. Even among amicably discharged patients, follow up seems to have been desultory, abetted by passive resistance from healed patients and their families who wanted to live undisturbed. Brieger's lists also reinforce the earlier allegations that some useful colonists might never have had active tuberculosis. Patients with skills were most likely to survive and colonise, while bad, unskilled cases were prominent among the leavers. Carpenters, clerks, gardeners, labourers, engineers and printers were the largest groups with stated prior occupations among the colonists.

His brief case histories confirm 'Nora's' testimony to guarded hopes, imprisoning anxieties, cool gratitude and baulked lives. The two following case histories are typical of the whole, which vary only in details. Family 63 comprised a tuberculous positive husband and a wife with inactive foci. They had no children. He had been born in 1903 and had been a waiter. In 1926 he had suffered a haemoptysis and been notified. He was sputum positive when admitted to Papworth in 1928 and for some months he was stricken with repeated haemoptyses. Next year he was discharged and found work as a carpenter, but he was readmitted in 1931. He colonised in 1932 and occupied a village cottage. He was frequently off work. X-rays revealed a cavity in his upper left lobe. In 1935 he left again, remained at home in Croydon for several months, and then returned to carpentry. But in January 1936 he was admitted to the Croydon Public Health Hospital with influenza and bronchitis, and positive sputum. He was transferred to the Croydon Borough Sanatorium where he remained until August 1936. He then returned to work 'on and off' until July 1937, when he was compelled to rest at home, until he was readmitted to the Croydon Hospital in March 1938. X-rays now showed cavitations in both lungs and displacement of the heart and mediastinum. He was returned to the Sanatorium in October 1938 and that is the last we hear of him, let alone his wife.

Family 148 comprised a consumptive former musician, ex-soldier, and after his demobilisation and first haemoptysis in 1920, pensioner, with wife and child. He was born in 1882. He entered a sanatorium in 1925 and was subsequently in that year admitted to Papworth. His sputum was negative throughout his stay. He colonised in 1931, but his wife and child never moved into the village. She apparently refused examination. Their child attended the Village clinic once, in 1927. The man left in 1938, and disappeared into the world of 'no comments'.[126]

After the Second World War Papworth was enlarged again.[127] It is now, after drug therapy has reduced the number of consumptive colonists, a major centre for chest surgery and the rehabilitation of the physically disabled.

NOTES

[1]There is a good account in the *Daily News* from 12 Nov. 1890. Lister's endorsement is reported in the *Lancet*, 3 Dec. 1890, pp.1257-8.

[2]*Lancet*, 22 Nov. 1890, pp.1085-6.

[3]*Lancet*, 29 Nov. 1890, p.1173; *BMJ*, 30 Aug. 1890, p.514.

[4]*Lancet*, 20 Dec. 1890, pp.1350-1; 8 Aug. 1891, p.283.

[5]*Lancet*, 8, 15 Aug., 14 Nov. 1891, pp.183, 349, 1110.

[6]*Lancet*, 2 Jan. 1892, p.40; I. Burney Yeo in *BMJ*, 16 Jan. 1892, p.109.

[7]W. Camac Wilkinson, *Treatment of Consumption*, 1908. There is a representative statement of Philip's beliefs in *Transactions of NAPT, 1913*, pp.100-4.

[8]Discussion of 'Vaccine Therapy', *Proc. Royal Society of Medicine*, vol.iii, 1910, pp.129-209.

[9]*Proc. Royal Society of Medicine*, vol.v, pt.III, 1911-12, p.75; *Transactions of NAPT, 1913*, pp.60-6.

[10]*Transactions of NAPT, 1913*, pp.82-9.

[11]E.g. Louis Cobbett of Cambridge, in *Lancet*, 24 Nov. 1917, p.802.

[12]F.J.H. Coutts, report to Ministry of Health, 14 Aug. 1919; A.S. McNalty, report..., 22 Mar. 1920, 7 Dec. 1920, PRO MH55/148; Coutts, report to MRC, 23 Mar. 1927, PRO MH55/154; W. Camac Wilkinson, *BMJ*, 5 June, 7 Aug. 1926, pp.967, 274-5; 15 Aug. 1931, p.322; editorials, *BMJ*, 3, 17 July 1926, pp.47, 127.

[13]A.S. McNalty(?) reports to Ministry of Health, n.d. (late 1929?), 15 Sept. 1931; 3 Nov. 1933; May 1934; PRO MH 55/149.

[14]*BMJ*, 6 Aug. 1932, p.262; David C. Muthu, *Pulmonary Tuberculosis*, 1922, p.216.

[15]*BMJ*, 12 Mar. 1927, p.490.

[16]John R. Gillespie (Tuberculosis Officer for County Down) in *BMJ*, 3 July 1928, p.35; H. Hyslop Thomson, *BMJ*, 20 Oct. 1926, p.588.

[17]Arthur Latham and C.H. Garland, *The Conquest of Consumption*, 1910, p.159; Sir Robert Philip, in *BMJ*, 2 July 1932, p.3; Annie McCall in *BMJ*, 7 Mar. 1925, on Camac Wilkinson's chain of dispensaries. W. Camac Wilkinson, 'The Tuberculin Dispensary League', in *Tuberculosis Year Book 1913-1914*, pp.378-81.

[18]R.A. Young, *Lancet*, 8 Mar. 1924, p.483; Fearis, *Treatment ... by ...(IK) Therapy*, p.34; Hans Much, *Tuberculosis of Children*, New York 1921, p.55 - on Marmorek; *Lancet*, 22 Sept. 1934, p.664 - on Friedmann.

[19]S. Roodhouse Gloyne, *Social Aspects of Tuberculosis*, 1944, p.113.

[20]*BMJ*, 30 Sept. 1882, p.619; Frederic J. Mouat and H. Saxon Snell, *Hospital Construction and Management*, 1883, vol.II, p.12.

[21]Lawrence F. Flick, *BMJ*, 22 Nov. 1890, p.1202.

[22]Quoted in G. Gregory Kayne, *The Control Of Tuberculosis In England*, 1937, p.34.

[23]*Lancet*, 12 July 1884, p.75.

[24]*Builder*, 3 July 1888, p.459; C. Theodore Williams in *BMJ*, 30 Sept. 1882, p.619. *Brompton Hospital Annual Report*, summarised in *BMJ*, 18 June 1887, p.1368.

[25]I.B. Brown Jr., *Australia for the Consumptive*, 1865, p.10.

[26]Ransome in *BMJ*, 1 Mar. 1890, p.464.

[27]R.D. Powell, (consulting physician, Brompton), to Royal Commission on Tuberculosis, *BPP*, 1896, vol.xlvi, Qs.1198-1203.

[28]Williams in *BMJ*, 30 Sept. 1882, p.619.

[29]Powell to Royal Commission, *BPP*, 1896, vol.xliv, Q.1200.

[30]46th Annual Report, quoted in *BMJ*, 18 June 1887, p.1368; J.A. Lindsay in *BMJ*, 11 Dec. 1897, p.1727.

[31]Cecil Wall (Brompton), in *Transactions of NAPT,1911*, pp.75-8.

[32]John Osborne, *A Better Class Of Person*, 1981, pp.33-4.

[33]Clive Fitts to his mother, 28 Apr. [1933?], Fitts Papers, University of Melbourne Archives.

[34]*Lancet*, 31 Dec. 1842, pp.489-90.

[35]*BMJ*, 2 Apr. 1927, p.641.

[36]*Prevention Of Destitution*, pp.56-7.

[37]J.F. Halls Dally, (Tuberculosis Department of St. Marylebone General Dispensary), *Tuberculosis Year Book 1913-1914*, p.324.

[38]Williamson, in *Prevention Of Destitution* , p.57; Norman Wilson, *Municipal Health Services*, 1946, p.53.

[39]Dr Templeman, (MOH Dundee), in *Prevention Of Destitution*, p.70.

[40]e.g. *BMJ*, 2 July 1932, p.3.

[41]Arthur Newsholme, 'Public Health Authorities In Relation to The Struggle Against Tuberculosis in England', *Journal of Hygiene*, vol.III, 1903, p.454.

[42]P. Varrier-Jones in *BMJ*, 31 Dec. 1927, p.1217.

[43]D. Harold Scurfield (MOH, Sheffield), in *Prevention Of Destitution* , pp.38-9.

[44]Report of Joint Tuberculosis Council to Ministry of Health, Jan. 1929, PRO MH55/157.

[45]George Bankoff, *The Conquest Of Tuberculosis*, 1946, p.170.

[46]G. Lissant Cox, *Transactions of NAPT, 1919*, p.41; Sir George Newman, *BMJ*, 26 Aug. 1922, p.387.

[47] Dr Reginald Dudfield, (MOH Paddington), *BMJ*, 4 Nov. 1922, p.869.

[48] Dr Rose Jordan (Tuberculosis Officer for Lewisham), *BMJ*, 21 Apr. 1928, p.692.

[49] C.H.C. Toussant, *Transactions of NAPT, 1943*, pp.19-20.

[50] W.M. Macleod, 'Notification Rates and the Prevalence of Tuberculosis...In Southampton', *Tubercle*, vol.xlii, 1961, p.297.

[51] Dr Templeman, (MOH Dundee), *Prevention of Destitution*, p.70.

[52] Dr Williamson in *Prevention of Destitution*, pp.58-61.

[53] *Prevention of Destitution*, p.39.

[54] D.J. Williamson, 'Dispensaries...', *Medical Magazine*, Oct. 1912, p.577.

[55] J.E. Chapman, unpublished Reports on 'Dispensaries', Ministry of Health, 1915, 1918. PRO MH52/99, pp.58-61; Manchester City Architects' Office to Local Government Board, 19 Sept. 1913, - on rising costs of new dispensaries, PRO 52/347.

[56] Sir George Newman, *The Building of A Nation's Health*, 1939, p.415.

[57] Moore, *Dawn*, pp.98-101.

[58] Manchester City Council to Ministry of Health, 21 May 1924, PRO MH52/348.

[59] Medical Officer of Health to Battersea Council, Sept. 1924, PRO MH52/145.

[60] F.G.B. Baxendale to [Manchester City Council?], 12 Dec. 1925, PRO MH52/348.

[61] W.E. Snell, (Dispensary Officer for North Islington in late 1920s) 'Changing Aspects of Tuberculosis', *Tubercle*, vol. xxxvii, 1956, p.3.

[62] Duncan Forbes, 'The Sanatorium As An Educational Agency', *Transactions of NAPT,1909*, pp.53-4; John McVail to Royal Commission on the Poor Law, *BPP 1909*, vol. xiii, p.98; Harley Williams and Irene Harbert, *Social Works for the tuberculous, 1945*, pp.19-21; Mrs M. Turner, (Health Visitor Society), *Transactions of NAPT, 1952*, p.371.

[63] Chapman, Report on...Dispensaries, 11 Feb. 1920, PRO MH52/99, pp.19-24.

[64] Miss A.E. Cummins (Lady Almoner at St. Thomas's Hospital), *Transactions of NAPT, 1909*, pp.23-8.

[65] *Transactions of NAPT, 1911*, pp.152-3.

[66] Norman Wilson, *Public Health Services ,1938*, pp.95-101. Ministry of Health, 'Report on After Care in Monmouthshire', PRO MH96/1031.

[67] Chapman, 'Report', 11 Feb. 1920, PRO MH52/99, pp.3-19.

[68] *Lancet*, 20 Oct. 1917, p.593; General Medical Council to Orme Clark, 7 Jan. 1913, copy in Astor Papers, Reading University Library, MS 1066/1/1042; Halliday Sutherland in *BMJ*, 29 May 1920, p.737; J.F.H. Coutts, memorandum, Ministry of Health, 27 June 1931, PRO MH 75/13.

[69] Chapman, Report, pp.16, 33-6. PRO MH52/99. Sir George Newman in *BMJ*, 26 Aug. 1922, p.387; Dickinson Leigh (Tuberculosis Officer for Sunderland), *Transactions of NAPT, 1924*, pp.66-7.

[70]J. Lewis Thomas, *Practitioner*, vol.cxiv, 1925, pp.145-6.

[71]Councillor C.W. Allison, *Transactions of NAPT,1924*, p.70; *BMJ*, 21 Aug. 1926, p.349.

[72]Dr W. Bolton Tomson (Hastings Tuberculosis Care Committee), *BMJ*, 3 July 1926, p.20.

[73]W. Bolton Tomson, *Notes & Suggestions on the Finding of Employment For The Tuberculous*, 1926, pp.6-8; Dr Prest, (Ayrshire Sanatorium), *BMJ*, 9 July 1927, p.63; Eric Wittkower, *A Psychiatrist Looks at Tuberculosis*, second ed., 1955, p.64.

[74]Chapman, 'Report', p.51. PRO MH52/99. Conference Report on After Care in Wales, July 1923, and annotations (1937?) PRO MH96/1030; Dr Emrys Jones to Ministry of Health, 20 May 1938, PRO MH96/1031.

[75]Williams and Harbert, *Social work*, p.1.

[76]Wilson, *Public Health Services*, p.99.

[77]Herman Weber in *Lancet*, 14 Mar. 1885, p.465.

[78]Landouzy in *Revue de Médicine*, reported in *Lancet*, 10 Nov. 1888, p.921.

[79]*Transactions of the Conference of the International Union Against Tuberculosis*, 1921, pp.248-9.

[80]*BMJ*, 7 Nov. 1925, p.866; 18 Dec. 1926, p.1189.

[81]F.G. Bushnell (advocate of a Grancher scheme for Plymouth) in *BMJ*, 10 Aug. 1929, p.279, W. Bolton Tomson, *Some Methods for the Prevention of Tuberculosis*, 1929, pp.16-20.

[82]G. Gregory Kayne, in *BMJ*, 23 Nov. 1935, p.1005.

[83]Armand-Delille, in *Transactions of NAPT, 1955*, p.57.

[84]*Transactions of NAPT, 1931*, p.32.

[85]*BMJ*, 7 Nov. 1925, p.866.

[86]Noel Bardswell in *BMJ*, 23 June 1934, p.1136; Arthur C. Watkin in *BMJ*, 14 Nov. 1925, p.921.

[87]*Lancet*, 23 Sept. 1933, p.719.

[88]*BMJ*, 23 Nov. 1935, p.1005. The 'excellent' results were claimed by Watkin, *BMJ*, 14 Nov. 1935, p.921.

[89]*Proc. Royal Society Medicine*, vol. ii, pt.11, 1940, p.620.

[90]As Marc Daniels and his colleagues gently pointed out in Marc Daniels et al.,*Tuberculosis In Young Adults : report on the Prophit Tuberculosis Survey 1935-1944*, 1948, p. 111.

[91]Bulstrode, *Report*, p.168; A.S.M. Macgregor, (Assistant Medical Officer, Public Health Department, Glasgow), *BMJ*, 26 Aug. 1922, D. Diamond, (Tuberculosis Officer, Kingston-upon-Hull), *Transactions of NAPT, 1938*, p.4.

[92]*Transactions of NAPT, 1924*, P.66.

[93]Duncan Forbes, *Transactions of NAPT, 1909* (at Whitechapel Art Gallery), p.54.

94 —   to Dr Marcus Paterson, 14 May 1909, quoted by P. James Bishop, 'The Marcus Paterson Collection'. *Tubercle*, vol.xlvii, 1967, p.69.

95Quoted by Marcus Paterson, *Auto-Inoculation In Pulmonary Tuberculosis*, 1911, p.222.

96*BMJ*, 24 Oct. 1925, p.760.

97Dr Menzies (Medical Officer of Health for London County Council), *BMJ*, 4 Feb. 1928, p.196; *Lancet*, 26 May 1928, p.1096.

98Wilson, *Public Health Services*, p.104.

99C. Fraser Brockington, *A Short History Of Public Health*, 1956, p.174.

100Neville C. Oswald, 'Brompton Rehabilitation Clinic', *Brompton Hospital Reports*, vol.xx, 1951, p.70; A.A. White (Medical Officer, Austin Car Co.), *Tubercle*, vol.xxxiii, 1952, p.46; A. Barr, 'Employment of Recovered Tuberculous Patients'; 'Employment Of Tuberculous Patients', *British Journal of Preventive & Social Medicine*, vols 9, 10, 1955, 1956, pp.103, 16.

101Bulstrode, *Report*, pp.208-9.

102Bolton Tomson, *Some Methods*, pp.60-8; Cummins in *BMJ*, 26 Aug. 1922, p.368; Ministry of Health memorandum on Treasury decision to end training schemes for tuberculous ex-servicemen, n.d. (23 Feb. 1923?), PRO MH55/166.

103Anonymous report in *BMJ*, 8 Jan. 1921, p.54.

104Lionel J. Picton, *BMJ*, 28 June 1924, p.1150.

105The troubled lives of Preston Hall's inmates and Dr Bonar can be traced in two large Ministry of Health files. PRO MH52/67 AND MH52/71.

106W.A. Thompson to Ministry of Pensions, 20 Jan. 1925; report by Ministry inspector, 15 Jan. 1925. PRO MH52/71. Cf. Mr Allen of the Leeds Tuberculous Ex-Servicemen's Society and Drs Bolton Tomson and Prest in *Transactions of NAPT, 1924*, pp.47-9.

107J.E. Chapman, 'Report on Preston Hall' (to Ministry of Health), 10 Jan. 1928. PRO MH52/73; *BMJ*, 'Preston Hall ... Settlement', 25 Aug. 1928, p.354; *Lancet*, 12 Apr. 1930, p.816.

108F.R.G. Heaf and J.B. McDougall, *Rehabilitating the Tuberculous*, 1945, p.78.

109J.B. McDougall, Private memorandum to Ministry of Health, Sept. 1930, PRO MH57/73.

110J.B. McDougall in *BMJ*, 25 Mar. 1933, pp.505-7; Heaf and McDougall, *Rehabilitating the Tuberculous*, p.78.

111Sir German Woodhead and P.C. Varrier-Jones, *Industrial Colonies and Village Settlements For The Consumptive*, Cambridge 1920, pp.4-5.

112Woodhead and Varrier-Jones, *Industrial Colonies*, p.33. Newman, *Building a Nation's Health*, p.416.

113[D.J. Williamson? Chief Tuberculosis Officer, Portsmouth] Report on Papworth to Ministry of Health, 7 Mar. 1919, PRO MH52/1.

114 D.J. Williamson, Report on Papworth to Ministry of Health, 20 Mar. 1921, PRO MH52/1.

[115]As recalled for the author in 1968 by Mrs G.E. Moore of Cambridge. Patients admitted to Mount Vernon travelled to Hampstead in a private ambulance 'to allay local prejudice' against their using the railway, Bulstrode, *Report*, p.425.

[116]J.F.H. Coutts, Report on Papworth, n.d. (June 1926?), PRO MH52/2; Linda Bryder, 'Papworth Village Settlement - A Unique Experiment in the Treatment and Care of the Tuberculous', *Medical History*, vol.28, 1984, p.379.

[117]J.F.H. Coutts, Report on Papworth to Ministry of Health, 15 June 1929, PRO MH52/3; *BMJ*, 23 Nov. 1929, p.991.

[118]J.F.H. Coutts, Report on Papworth to Ministry of Health, 15 June 1929; P. Varrier-Jones to Minister of Health, 14 June 1932, PRO MH52/3.

[119]Miss K.L. Borne, *Transactions of NAPT, 1933*, p.157; K.L. Borne to *Lancet*, 19 Feb. 1936, Miss Annie Louise Evans, 'Statement', July 1932, PRO MH 52/3.

[120]Bryder, 'Papworth', p.377; T.W. Blake to Ministry of Pensions, c.24 Aug. 1921; George S. Lawley to Enfield Local Tuberculosis Committee, 15 July 1921; A. Salusbury McNalty, 'Report', 13 Sept. 1921; cases of Tommy Course, T. Paine and McIntyre, (1920-1?) discussed in P. Varrier-Jones to County Medical Officer for Middlesex, 13 Sept. 1921. PRO MH 52/5.

[121]*BMJ*, 9 Apr. 1927, p.696; Bolton Tomson, *Some Methods*, pp.71-2.

[122]*The Colonist*, Feb. 1929, p.1; P. Varrier-Jones in *BMJ*, 31 Dec. 1927, p.1218.

[123]*BMJ*, 4 Oct. 1930, p.576; Heaf and McDougall, *Rehabilitating the Tuberculous*, p.92.

[124]*BMJ*, 3 July 1926, p.21.

[125]Rowland Parker, *On The Road*, Papworth 1977, pp.161-2.

[126]E.M. Brieger, *The Papworth Families A 25 Years Survey*, 1944, pp.73,350,495.

[127]Owen Clarke et al, 'Papworth's Results', *Lancet*, 9 Mar. 1957, p.522.

4 SANATORIA

Sanatoria were places of hope deferred. Their rationale was simple. They were medically supervised refuges from the bad air, crowded households and wear of industrial life, set in well-drained, breezy but mild countryside. Consumptives could rest there, freed from business and family cares. They were to be well fed and to take measured exercise. Thereby the lungs might be recuperated to build fibrosis around the points of infection and then wall off the bacilli which could not be killed, and perhaps rebuild old cavities by encouraging further fibrosis. Poor inmates could earn their keep by gardening and housework, private full-paying patients could walk and take carriage rides, all under medical direction. Two beliefs underpinned this rationale. The first was a rarely expressed, vague notion that bustle and poor nutrition either precipitated or exacerbated consumption and that removal to a salubrious environment could cure or arrest the disease. The second belief was founded upon Naegli's proof in 1901 of a much older post mortem observation that tubercular lesions could heal spontaneously. It followed, in retrospect, that such cures must have ensued from otherwise unnoticed changes in the sufferer's way of life: 'tiredness' must have induced the sufferer to rest and to work less hard, which in turn must have led the sufferer to spend more time outdoors where the consequent larger intake of fresh air would have produced a larger appetite and better nutrition. These inferences gave sanatoria in Germany and Britain a new priority among tuberculosis treatments.

The sanatorium vogue had begun in Germany around 1860, inspired by a mixture of traditional cure-taking at spas, nature worship, and a new physiology of lung weakness. The idea was not original. The remarkable George Bodington had created a rudimentary modern sanatorium near Sutton Coldfield in 1840 and fully explained the regime of fresh air and exercise, but his medical contemporaries had scorned his attempts to drill rather than cosset wasted patients and Bodington died in ignominy.[1]

The new respectability of the sanatorium depended upon the assertion developed in the 1850s and 1860s by Austrian and

German physiologists that phthisis was caused by the failure of small weak hearts to circulate the blood forcefully enough to prevent the deposit of tubercles. In 1859 Dr Herman Brehmer implemented the treatments indicated by the new theories at his sanatorium at Goebersdorf in the south German alps. He directed patients to take garden and forest walks elaborately scaled for length and difficulty. Outdoors, nature purified the patient's spirit, indoors, his or her blood and digestive system were cleansed by the water cure. Like many a proprietor of sanatoria after him, Brehmer was a consumptive.[2]

Another German, Peter Dettweiler, at his sanatorium of the mid 1870s at Falkenstein in the Rhineland, reversed Brehmer's practice by ordering long periods of immobility to strengthen the heart and lungs. Brehmer made patients walk up the gradient when starting and come down the gradient when returning. Dettweiler had his patients do the opposite. Beneficent nature in the form of sunlight and fresh air healed the patients as they lay exposed on the liegehallen, sheltered open balconies and dormitories. After a decade, in 1886, Dettweiler claimed impressive results: 1022 patients had remained for more than one month, all of them 'confirmed phthisics'; 132 had departed 'completely cured' not counting a mysterious 72 who were 'cured' also. Dettweiler's figures become even more puzzling when we discover that 12 of the 132 had 'relapsed' after an unstated period and that another 11 of them were 'dead' at the time of counting.[3]

Flaky statistics notwithstanding, German sanatoria practice profoundly influenced British therapeutics. The reasons for exercising or resting were never very clear and most British physicians ordered them both in varying proportions. The institution that probably made the deepest impact upon their handling of their patients was Dr Otto Walther's sanatorium at Nordrach in the Black Forest, which opened about 1889. This abode of spartans was 1500 feet above sea level and exposed to every wind. The patients' liegehallen were compulsorily open day and night, summer and winter, to dissipate the 'impure air' expired by the patients and admit nature's healing sunlight and clean air. Exposure developed the appetite. Walther believed in building bodily resistance by 'overfeeding'. He insisted that each patient daily consume several pints of milk, together with abundant cheese, fat meat, potatoes, butter, bread, sweets and fruit. 'It is amazing', rejoiced an English convert, 'the amount one can eat when forced to'. There were three enormous communal meals each day, accompanied by one hour's prescribed rest before and after. Dr Walther forbade drugs: they were unnatural and 'upset the stomach'. Patients ate in teams, competing to consume the most and gain the most weight. Improving patients were permitted short graduated walks. Otherwise inmates spent their time on couches, commanded to stillness, their minds blank, because 'there [was] nothing so harmful ... as over-exertion in any form, mental or bodily'. Concerts and exciting books were prohibited. Each patient took his or her temperature per rectum four times each day and was responsible for keeping his or her chart. Feverish patients were confined to bed and kept immobile. Lights out and silence arrived at nine each night and the rule was enforced by patrolling nurses. Nordrach housed a maximum of 50 inmates, the limit, Walther considered, for constant supervision. His establishment was expensive but there was always a waiting list. Each entrant had to promise to stay at least six months, to ensure a cure. Walther examined every patient's chest and sputum once a month. I could not discover the reported cure-rate, or indeed if a rate was reported, but Nordrach was famous throughout Britain and Germany. It provided a haven for affluent consumptives obsessed with their misfortune and infatuated with tracing the diurnal variations in their ailment while seeking, through the regime, punishment for having fallen ill.[4]

The regime at Davos, which led the development of the Swiss alpine tuberculosis resorts in the mid 1870s, was more benign. The British began to winter there from about 1877, joining the established Germans, Dutch, Russians and Americans. Davos lay in a sheltered, windless valley 5200 feet high. The invasion of foreign consumptives launched a building boom of inns and hotels about 1880. These chalets had double-glazed windows which were usually closed, central heating, and usually no resident physician or mandatory therapeutic regime. By 1887 the sojourners in the valley numbered over 3000, 30 times the permanent population of two decades earlier. Four new first class hotels catered for English speakers: the Belvedere, L'Angleterre, Victoria and Buol. All were centrally heated; none was ventilated. Swiss phthisics remained more sceptical about the curing powers of dry cold air at high altitudes and alleged low germ content, and apparently stayed in their homes.

During the 1880s developers at St Moritz, formerly an unfashionable spa, Samaden, 'very windy' but brisk, and Pontresina, calm and cold because it was shaded by mountains, began to compete with Davos. In another former impoverished village, Arosa, promoters built outdoor international schools to tap the flow of rich, consumptive children. But Davos held its preeminence until the end of the century. The municipality canalised the river to reduce mists, the hoteliers installed 'proper sewage schemes' and began to cut prices to fill their ever growing numbers of bedrooms clustered in jerry-built chalets behind the main buildings. The graveyard was already 'rapidly filling' by 1887.[5] Clifford Allbutt, the fashionable physician who was among the first to direct his patients to Davos, felt let down: the necessary 'liberal dietary' was being 'sacrificed on the altar of economy'.[6] But the foreigners kept coming, especially during the 1890s after the new railway eliminated the former seven hour trip by diligence which had sunk many a wan phthisic.[7]

Patients expected to find the clean, still, cold altitude exhilarating and healing and many had their expectations fulfilled. John Lowe was a former medical officer of health for Wokingham whose career had ended with a haemorrhage. He had tried English coastal resorts but had continued to lose weight and strength. In about 1887 his eminent colleagues, C. Theodore Williams and Allbutt, advised him to flee to Davos. Within days of his arrival Lowe found his sleep and appetite restored and his fears reduced. He gained a pound in weight each week. After eleven weeks of careful self-management, Lowe could walk sixteen miles a day. He returned to England after nine months with all signs of active phthisis gone, excepting a 'dullness' in both lungs. He was lucky, he believed, because he was an 'early' case, and had held aloof from the dissipations Davos offered. Davos, he remarked, had a bad reputation, unfairly bestowed, because physicians sent hopeless advanced cases in order to be rid of them. And in Davos the hopeless cases had accelerated their decay by plunging into keeping late hours, drinking, gambling and frequenting noisy parties. Lowe had witnessed 'terrible scenes in winter'.[8]

The cold certainly vitiated the weak and the despairing. Another English consumptive doctor, Dr H. Coupland Taylor, found himself perished by the cold and subject to near continual pleurisy. He betook himself to warm Madeira.[9] But Davos and similar resorts throughout the European Alps were to continue to attract consumptives until after the Second World War. One met a good class of people there. Until 1914 the minimal outlay for twelve months at a reputable chalet was £500. Many paid much more at the big hotels and stayed for years. They composed bizarre cosmopolitan assortments of mostly young adults of both sexes isolated at the top of the world. At the outset, at least, they were mostly ambulant, because the hoteliers and presiding physicians preferred not to admit the hopelessly bed-ridden. They wafted through the days and seasons, between huge meals, compulsory temperature checks, rest and exercise periods that came in as the smaller chalets gradually came under German-inspired medical direction in the decade before 1914; out of doors they shopped for expensive warm clothes and room decorations; indoors they played cards, indulged in light reading, concerts, stamp collecting, flirting, and gossip about fellow patients and the staff; they did jigsaw puzzles, enjoyed medical examinations, quarrels and sleigh rides, developing withal an anxious self-regard that fended off boredom. The ambience is memorably caught in Beatrice Harraden's *Ships That Pass in the Night*.[10]

The Swiss sanatoria varied, but in the main until 1939 they were more hotels than hospitals. Their advertisements emphasised the quality and abundance of their tables: meal times and menus were listed, but never therapeutic regimes or cure-rates. The sanatoria doctors, often consumptive themselves, who shared ownership with private investors or the local commune, took all comers and their servants, regardless of whether they had active tuberculosis or not, as Hans Castorp - and Thomas Mann himself - discovered. Prices of rooms varied with the position and the view: poorer patients in the cheaper north-facing dormitories, lying half-clothed exposed to the sunless cold, had a hard time. There were many extras, unadvertised. Meals taken privately in one's room were extra, as was the additional nursing required by bed-bound patients. Periodical disinfection of rooms was also an extra and patients whose money was running out often tried to skimp on it.[11]

At a basic three to ten francs a day Sanatorium Schatzalp at Davos in 1913 was a typical middle-ranking establishment. Breakfast at 7.30 am to 8.30 am comprised coffee, tea, chocolate or cocoa with bread, butter, pastry, honey and preserves. Morning tea at 10 am brought soup, milk, bread and butter.

Dinner at 12.30 pm was a four course offering centred upon meat, potatoes and pudding. Afternoon tea at 4 pm brought tea, coffee, chocolate, with more bread, butter and honey. Supper at 7 pm was another substantial three course meal with meat, vegetables and pudding, and at 9 pm everyone had another glass of milk. In between patients might take gentle exercise at their discretion and plenty of rest. The sanatorium appears not to have had a resident physician. In general, Swiss doctors and the foreigners licensed to practise were easygoing. Concerts, dances and lights out were mildly policed. Sputum flasks were not always insisted upon, especially among ladies in the public rooms. Patients were never coerced, as they were in German and British establishments, into the 'occupational therapy' which burgeoned in the 1920s. The notion, among a nation of cuckoo-clock carvers and watch assemblers, remained entirely foreign.[12]

The First World War cut British ties with the Swiss sanatoria and they were never fully restored. Germans became the predominant national group during and after the war. The Swiss government made its visa requirements tortuous and the exchange rate put Switzerland beyond the range of Britons 'of moderate means'. They increasingly stayed at home.[13] British physicians soon produced a therapeutic rationale for the change. In 1922 Dr John Bain spoke for many of his colleagues when he asserted that the weather at Davos, even in summer, was worse than that of Inverness and that Britons, delicate cases particularly, did better in 'the climate to which they were accustomed'. Bain's patients were doing very well, he said, at South Shields.[14]

From the mid 1920s farsighted Swiss proprietors turned to catering for winter sports enthusiasts who required a different cosseting. Sanatoria which endured did so mostly because their environs were unsuitable for skiing. They became fossilised under-heated, under-staffed retreats, with patients confined to their rooms 'resting', as the cheapest way of handling them.[15] While the *Magic Mountain* is emblematic of Europe in the 1920s, its narrative of day to day life in the sanatorium derives from their heyday before the war. Mann visited Davos in 1912. A.E. Ellis's savage *The Rock* (1958) recounts the tyrannical austerities of the sanatoria in their final decay after the Second World War.

The huge Swiss investment in residential treatment led their medical profession to hold out longer than most against chemotherapy, but by the late 1950s their remaining sanatoria were becoming summer refuges for the new class of chronics and old people wanting to buy care away from it all.

Tuberculosis had served Switzerland well: impoverished mid-alpine valleys had become bonanzas, the drug industry waxed fat and banking institutions had arisen to service the peculiar, often secretive, needs of affluent cosmopolitan sojourners, many of whom lived on remittances. Similarly, the present winter sports and entertainment facilities in Colorado, Nevada and Arizona originated, in many cases, as tuberculosis refuges in the later nineteenth century.

The Nordrach model appealed to many British patients, doctors and philanthropists. They believed that it worked. They liked the authoritarian management and high-minded austerity, projected as a moral imperative in treatment, by contrast with Swiss and much American practice. Also, it was cheaper all round. The voluntary, lay National Association for the Prevention of Tuberculosis adopted the plan from its foundation in 1898. Nordrach in Wales opened at Pendyffryn in 1900, Nordrach-on-Dee and Nordrach-upon-Mendip soon followed. By 1908 there were at least 90 British sanatoria, 61 'public' and about 30 'private', exclusive of Poor Law infirmaries. Many were enthusiastic imitations of Nordrach, others advertised at least that they employed Nordrach therapies. [16]

The sudden spread of sanatoria around 1900 ended two decades of muddled want of provision for sufferers. Those who could afford it emigrated to the western United States, Australia or the South African Veldt, or settled in Madeira, Mentone or Nice. Others took long sea voyages. Poorer sufferers could try one of the four London specialist hospitals, the two at Bournemouth with a nominal 82 beds, the National Hospital at Ventnor with 100 beds, or the special wards comprising a nominal 44 beds in Liverpool, 50 in Manchester, and five in Newcastle-upon-Tyne. Outside the Poor Law, there was no public hospital special provision for consumptives in Birmingham, Leeds, Bradford or in Scotland outside Edinburgh, or in Ireland. By 1910 the 61 public and 29 private sanatoria in England and Wales offered a nominal 4000 beds but of these only around 2800 were 'efficient' and only about half of these were within the reach of even thrifty workers. General hospitals restricted their admission because they were chronic and infectious. So they drifted about the out-patient wards, visited dispensaries, stayed at home, and found ultimate refuge in the workhouse infirmaries.[17] Meanwhile about 1000 people were dying from tuberculosis every week.

Sanatoria buildings and therapies ranged from the rudimentary to the elaborately comfortable, roughly mirroring the class structure. About two-thirds of all beds were for males, and there were proportionately many more beds for adults than for children. The distribution was also skewed to the south: in 1908 only two private sanatoria existed north of the Trent, although the North and Scotland had relatively higher mortality rates and probably higher incidences of active disease.

Nearly all sanatorium directors published their intention to admit only 'early cases'. For only these could readily benefit from the rest and discipline within the time available for treatment. This view was underpinned by the belief that a salubrious regimen could counteract and defeat the bacilli before extensive cavitation and destruction of tissues had set in. 'Advanced' cases might respond to this therapy but the chances were less good. 'Early' cases, moreover were by definition ambulant and could dress and feed themselves, and hence required less nursing.

The barest, most numerous sanatoria were offshoots from the Poor Law infirmaries. They were established by the local authorities under medical prompting as a way of concentrating phthisics, males at least, and thereby reducing the chances of infection and nursing difficulties in the workhouse. Small unions erected isolation huts in their grounds, following former standard practice during smallpox and typhoid outbreaks. Larger unions occasionally created separate clusters of pavilions and huts on sites outside the town. True to their model, the smaller collections of open air encampments were simple isolation wards with no particular medical attention or therapeutic regime, except fresh air and sunlight. The larger more enterprising unions tried to implement something of the Nordrach ideal. Heswall, in Liverpool, set the pattern early in the new century. The men were admitted through the workhouse. They slept in dormitories in a newly adapted special hospital. Food, heating and bedding were provided according to the strictest economy, partly because not having too much of them was said to advance the curative progress. Heswall was conceived as a preventive institution. It was to admit only early cases, heal them, restore them to employment and so keep them off the rates. Indeed in 1904 beds were kept empty because too few suitable 'young men ... likely to derive some permanent benefit' were available in the workhouses. Most consumptives entered workhouses precisely because their early, ambulant, working stage was passed. Heswall was too expensive to be left empty, and like most Poor Law sanatoria, soon became a staging post for the dying. Of 38 cases transferred from the workhouses during 1903-4, eight had been 'lost' by the end of 1904 and of the remainder, 26 were 'dead' or 'dying', having been discharged, or discharged themselves and ended up again in the workhouse where the company was better; another had died of 'alcoholism'; yet another had died at home; and a single survivor was 'arrested'; leaving a final phthisical pauper silently unaccounted for. Heswall and institutions like it provided a roof and bed for the friendless and homeless and they must have helped considerably in containing infection by incarcerating open cases, but they failed in their pretensions to cure.[18] By 1909 44 per cent of all London male phthisis deaths and 32 per cent of all female phthisis deaths occurred in Poor Law institutions similar to Heswall. In social classes IV and V the proportion of male phthisis deaths in workhouses was over 50 per cent. Overall, they had taken an average of 133 days between their last admission and their death. In Dublin they lasted 70 days.[19] In Scotland in 1921 nearly 37 per cent of admissions had occurred within a month of discharge from a sanatorium or hospital[20] —which gives us a further cause to be cautious about their statistical claims.

Of the 11,000 or so annual admissions to workhouse infirmaries in England and Wales, around 60 per cent, if we extrapolate from the Local Government Board returns for Liverpool, were consumptive and admitted primarily on that ground.[21] I shall return to this point, but this and other figures indicate that tuberculosis was a fundamental cause of pauperisation in the nineteenth and twentieth centuries. Doctors, faced with a stream of terminal and chronic cases arriving without documentation, admitted by receiving officers who did not necessarily consult them, were 'apathetic and uninterested', according to two Ministry of Health inspectors in

1923.[22] Their patients were often edgy, notably ex-servicemen, who were commonly 'grousers' or exposed 'advanced cases' expelled from sanatoria dispensaries or village colonies. At Lewisham they had rebelled against having to appear before the receiving officer. At Woolwich the male inmates wanted to wear their own clothes and rejected the workhouse twill dress because it was 'very stiff and harsh', although the inspectors thought it 'better than their own'.[23] At St James, Lewisham, Wandsworth and Battersea the patients, male and female, also wanted to retain their own clothes. The womens' unbleached linen nightdresses stood 'up by themselves ... emaciated patients [could] not cope with them'. Emaciated patients also suffered from the bed linen which was coarse and unbleached. Private cases subsidised from their pension and by their families, or the local authority at up to three guineas a week at St James, for example, kept their own clothes and enjoyed separate accommodation and a 'special diet'; although this last seems still to have been basicly bread, butter, sugar, tea, potatoes, fresh meat once a week, Irish stew twice a week and beef tea or one pint and a half of milk a day. Kensington was unique in serving all inmates green vegetables on Thursdays. Wandsworth and Battersea were typical in placing consumptives in general wards. They objected, but not on hygienic grounds. St James ex-servicemen demanded a separate ward, like the paying inmates. At St James, Lewisham and Wandsworth consumptives demanded 'separation by social class'. The St James' patients for example, told the inspector they were there because they were 'sick' and not because they were 'destitute'. They were, they said, from a 'good class even ... who would formerly have gone to cheaper nursing homes'.[24] But their savings and in many cases their pensions were gone. Restive J. O'C., aged 55 in 1923, was in St Pancras Infirmary. He told the inspector he had been there three times already. He had also been in a Sussex sanatorium but 'left because it was too cold', and he had spent two years at Colindale sanatorium but then left, apparently suddenly. After a few weeks at St Pancras O'C. was keen to return to Colindale. Bewildered Miss Daisy N., aged 23, was in St George in the East workhouse infirmary. She had been 'in the printing trade'. The inspectors ascertained that she had been 'taken thence, apparently without notice, and certainly without knowing where she was going, to this infirmary by motor ambulance'. She had 'extensive disease', but the inspectors observed that she was 'suffering from nostalgia', perhaps for her printing job. Game T.H., aged eleven, was in Camberwell Infirmary. He had been admitted once before, but was 'sent to Brentwood [sanatorium] from which he ran away and was re-admitted here. Came originally [and apparently friendless] from the Royal Free Hospital; is now nearly all right'. The inspectors thought he might be fit to attend a charity school.[25] In 1931 Dr Letitia Fairfield of the London County Council defended the standard of hospital provision for the consumptive poor at the annual meeting of the National Association for the Prevention of Tuberculosis. Councillor Mrs H. Roberts of Stepney indignantly contradicted her with the assertion that people did not 'want to die in old Poor Law hospitals' and that 'the hospitals [were] not fit for people to live or die in'. This indecorous intervention by a lay person was received in silence.[26]

Heswall, like other public sanatoria, benefited from the provision in the 1911 National Insurance Act which permitted the Local Government Board to make grants to cover three-fifths of the capital costs for establishment or extension of sanatoria, to a limit of £90 per bed. Pavilion camps of about a dozen inmates frequently doubled in capacity after 1911 to become full 'sanatoria'. Ninety pounds per head was around the limit for a basic wood and sheet iron construction to house 20 to 40 inmates in a heated, central pavilion with lavatories, kitchen and administrative offices.[27] It eventuated that this central block could be built even more solidly, because the medically approved wood and canvas shelters for ambulant cases cost only £6 - £8 per couch.[28] The pressure within local authorities for basic hut accommodation was strengthened by the complicated formula by which the central government paid its share. The initial total sanatorium outlay had to be carried by the municipal authority or charitable body, which then recouped the three-fifths subsidy from the Local Government Board. This mechanism effectively blocked building by poor or mean local bodies or charities, but big authorities like Liverpool did well out of it. We do not have the local studies to tell us what the redistributed results were. I suspect that they were very uneven through the country and were small overall, but on the face of it the consumptive poor of great and medium-sized towns probably had more beds available to them in extremis than they would otherwise have had. This central taxation provision was ended in 1921 when all sanatorium benefit under the Insurance Act ceased and county councils were compelled to assume responsibility, just when the flow of 35,000 tuberculous ex-servicemen, about half of whom were in public sanatoria, was crushing the system. Their sanatorium treatment costs (but not capital works) were underwritten by the Ministry of Pensions, but that support was stopped in December 1924.[29]

Easby sanatorium near Skipton opened in November 1903. It was built by the Bradford guardians for patients a little less down the scale than Heswall's: in addition to paupers it was to admit working men who could benefit from the free treatment. They were to be early cases able 'to take exercise and who [did] not require any great amount of nursing', so that only a 'small staff' was required. Easby invoked Nordrach austerity by accommodating its patients in 'temporary' wooden pavilions divided into wards: four singles, four triples, in four and two six bed units. The Bradford guardians seem not to have availed themselves - or perhaps they were rebuffed - of central government help, to 1914, at least. Like most rural 'temporary' sanatoria before the 1920s, Easby had no piped sewage system. Inmates were required daily to excavate and cover 'earth closets'. Sore throats and stomach upsets were endemic.[30]

The Hull and East Riding sanatorium for poor people was similarly justified by the Nordrach system. It too was conceived as a similarly preventive institution, built by the local authority and partly maintained by subscribers. These, mostly employers, could nominate a patient by paying £13 admission fee. This sum permitted a stay of almost three months, too short, in the doctors' experience, to assure longterm improvement, but the limit of the possible. Few patients could hope to have their job reserved for them longer than three months and many discharged themselves early to return to work because their family's resources had run out. Of the 183 discharged through 1902-5 only 23 had maintained their 'improvement' by 1907, whilst the rest were 'worse', 'dead' or 'unaccounted for'.[31] As Dr David Lawson of Banchory, a similar institution, lamented in 1904, these places were grim failures, 'understaffed, and sadly deficient in their scientific adjuncts to the treatment which alone wealth can supply'.[32]

Some of these adjuncts were available free to the patients at Maiden Lane sanatorium in Manchester. Maiden Lane was also unusual among local government institutions at this period in having two of its five pavilions reserved for women and children. It had previously been a 'temporary' smallpox isolation hospital. The buildings were made of corrugated iron lined with wood. They were 'not in any sense heated' and were dimly lighted by gas. Sewage was emptied into 'local streams' and was still blocking them in 1926. As with many other old isolation hospitals the 'temporary' and the 'simple' had become permanent virtues thanks to Nordrach. Nevertheless, tuberculin was administered and inhalation of antiseptics was prescribed for 'suitable cases'. All 'able' patients were required to work their passage by cleaning, cooking and gardening. The children received lessons and 'musical societies ... kindly assisted by giving concerts'.[33]

Kelling in Norfolk and Barrasford near Newcastle-upon-Tyne were typical sanatoria created by private charity for poorer patients. The first was supported by the London Charity Organization Society, the second by the National Association for the Prevention of Tuberculosis. Kelling had 53 inmates in 1905, 16 of whom were women. They were deserving early cases selected by the London committee. The declared aim of the London Society was to 'intercept' tuberculous cases on the way to pauperdom. They would not support 'advanced' cases whose treatment meant waste of money. Kelling patients had their fare to the sanatorium and their outlay on dressing gowns, slippers and toiletries defrayed by the Society. They shared two-bedded cubicles clustered in pavilions built of uninsulated 'mack' slabs and concrete. Between the walls and ceiling there was a three inch wide unblockable gap. When or if the case gained strength he or she had to spend each day in board and canvas shelters where they lay exposed to the sun, turning the shelter every hour or so to enable the open side to catch the sunlight. Patients used to the traditional fug of home kitchens, workrooms and the sick room, with a fire in the grate, the keyhold plugged, paper stuffed against the gaps in the doors and windows, and to short ventures outside the house, well-wrapped up, when the sun came out, found themselves in a new world in which they had to be very brave. The initial capital outlay on facilities for patients had been a careful £1300; the medical superintendent's house had cost an extra £650. The administrative offices and medical officer's suite comprised two other substantial double-storied buildings.

Barrasford's pavilions were also 'temporary'. They were made of wood and corrugated iron, surfaced with 'ceralite' to make them washable. Each case was estimated to cost the National Association two guineas a week.

According to the Kelling superintendent, Dr H.W. McConnell, his institution had been the first in the kingdom to introduce real work for the patients, in 1902. His justification for compelling the inmates to work became the standard one. Poorer patients had to be worked in order to cure them quicker. A daily routine was consonant with their former life, while their systems needed activation. Their average length of stay until the 1930s was about three months, set by the £18 which was the maximum the Society allocated for each case. Wealthier patients might take their exercise in slower gradations. Upon discharge each had to try to return to employment, assisted by the Society's after care committee. But some had lost their jobs before they entered the sanatorium; indeed, their sanatorium sojourn had really been a way of putting off having to go on the rates. In this situation, McConnell declared, sanatoria produced loafers. Patients unused to the good life were made to rest and 'were fed on beef', and rendered dissatisfied with the life whence they had come and the life to which they had to return, albeit under handicap. McConnell was determined to make them look forward to a life of usefulness. He and the after care philanthropists refused to recognise that employers, especially in small factories or shops, would not take back an employee once his sanatorium background became known, whether the employee was cleared of the disease or not. His or her fellow workers resented the lighter routine and shorter hours given the returned consumptive and feared contamination. They usually forced a not unwilling employer to sack the nuisance. Moreover, after two and a half years after discharge, only 60 per cent of former Kelling inmates were able to do even light work if they could get it.

At Kelling the medical officer issued general orders to the overseer, who then directed the patients to cleaning brasses and windows, hoeing and weeding, digging, screening and carting. Women patients picked flowers for sale. Efficient workers stayed on. It seems that Kelling began the system which soon sustained most sanatoria and finally flowered in the village settlements, of retaining skilled people whether they were cured or not. By 1909 Kelling had eight men and two women who worked for their board and lodging and pocket money of up to 5s a week, according to their usefulness. McConnell at this time was receiving about £250 a year, with free housing and domestic help, and the right to private practice. The stayers worked set hours. The women did housework and supervised the work of other patients in the women's wing. The men included a carpenter, a plumber and painter, the driver of the doctor's 'motor', a milk carter, a stableman, a house servant, a poultry keeper who also played the chapel organ, and a man who maintained the gravel on the roads.[34]

The underpaid, unsuperannuated labour of the inmates sustained the sanatoria. In 1934 there were 5400 - a probable majority of whom were ex-patients - employees in sanatoria in England and Wales. Their annual cost to the institutions totalled £560,000 or about £103 a head, most of which must have been subsumed in board and lodging.[35] Settlers in the consumption villages were paid at nearer the going rate, and their wages were about 300 per cent higher, even so, had they been paid at going rates for skill the total expenditure would have risen about fourfold.[36] The need for a cheap substratum became even greater as sanatoria developed surgical and radiological specialties in the late 1920s and capital costs and medical salaries increased by about one-third between pre-World War I and 1932, and expenditure per adult patient jumped from 39s per week in 1935 to 54s in 1937.[37] The increase in medical overheads probably increased the disparities within sanatoria. The first and so far as I could discover, only Ministry of Health investigation of sanatorium costs in 1923-4 revealed that some institutions had up to 6.5 staff for every ten beds while others had 2.3, and that the average expenditure on provisions ranged between 28s and 10s a head, with extremes in total costs per patient of 78s for Halifax to 26s for a children's institution in Somerset.[38]

The Devon and Cornwall sanatorium at Didworthy near Totnes had been created by subscribers in 1903 for necessitous early cases. A subscriber's ticket cost £70 a year. By 1913 Didworthy had beds for 67 patients, 39 men and 28 women. They had won admission, usually for a three months' stay, by accumulating seventeen tickets if they were residents of Devon or Cornwall, or twenty if they lived outside. The process must have taken months of sending begging letters in stamped, self-addressed envelopes. Aspirants made the effort because the Didworthy board admitted 'hopeless cases' at the behest of subscribers, over the opposition of the medical staff who thought it 'inefficient'. Even so, neither board nor doctors liked to report deaths in their institution, so terminal cases were usually discharged to expire at home or in the workhouse. As Dr Latham observed in 1910, these unfortunates had 'died twice', once in finally achieving admission to a subscribers' sanatorium like Didworthy and once in being arbitrarily discharged when their three months was up or their death loomed close.[39] Lanfine Home near Glasgow worked on a similar basis. Unusually among sanatoria, its staff took acknowledged advanced cases, usually as private fee-paying inmates. Their contributions subsidised the subscribers' nominees.[40]

The delays and humiliations inherent in these Poor Law, charitable systems might lead us to expect that respectable lower middle class and working-class people would invent their own self-help schemes. But consumption was a hidden, shameful ailment among families with a job or small business to protect. Only one self-help project ever achieved permanent institutionalised form. This was Benenden. It was directly inspired by German insured workers' sanatoria after an investigation in Germany in 1903 by Dr Alfred Hillier and Mr W.G. Brenn as representatives of British friendly societies. Their visit had been instigated by the annual conference of the Post Office Workers' Union. When Benenden opened in March 1907 its stated purpose was educative rather than avowedly curative: German experience confirmed recent British sceptical observations that sanatoria did not produce full cures. Benenden, a long open U-shaped building open to the south, provided 'accommodation of the simplest efficient kind capable of being imitated in all essentials in the average home of the industrial classes'. By 1913 200 beds were available for men. Their provision cost £100 each. The capital had come from the Hospital Saturday Fund. The Post Office founding fathers expected the National Union of Teachers and the railway servants to join them, together with the Hearts of Oak friendly society, but all three dropped out when the time came to pay. By 1910 40,000 post office employees had sought coverage at one halfpenny per week (2s a year) deducted at headquarters from their wages. Each contributor, should he be declared consumptive, was entitled to six months at the sanatorium on full pay, together with travel and establishment expenses. The founders hoped that wives and children might also be included but that never eventuated.

Benenden did well, not least because post office men, who were picked employees, had relatively low tuberculosis rates—1.8 per 1000 in 1910, with only 153 admissions between 1903 and 1910. Benenden was distinctive in never having a waiting list. Patients stayed twenty weeks on average and the medical staff reported an 'arrest' or 'improvement' rate of over 80 per cent of admissions. The surplus beds were taken up by local authorities who were permitted to nominate cases, paupers excluded, at 30s a week. The sanatorium made a profit. The average bed cost was 26s a week. There was money for a full-time resident medical officer and the food was ample. Patients did graduated work around the grounds, attended lectures on hygiene, and took self-improvement courses. Benenden was a brilliant exception in the dingy, financially starved world of sanatoria for the poorer classes.[41]

Its success made it a crucial element in the evolution of National Health Insurance policies in the United Kingdom. Its medical promoters, Drs Latham, Garland and T.D. Lister broadcast Benenden's successes, especially while Lloyd George and his officials at the Local Government Board were constructing the National Insurance Act. Benenden is not mentioned in the standard histories of this important step towards the welfare state but its German precedents, proven method of contributory self-help and corporate reciprocity with local authorities and a central government body provided a key inspiration for the Act.[42]

In practice, the Benenden model had limited application. Post office workers, as employees of central government, were uniquely privileged. They could obtain six months' leave for treatment and count upon returning to a job at the same level after their improvement was certified. Teachers employed by local boards did not have that security. Nor did privately employed members of friendly societies, railway servants, insurance clerks and others, who avoided taking extended sick leave in case they lost their job status or indeed the job itself. Dr Lister pleaded publicly with Lloyd George in 1911 to extend the Insurance bill to cover regularly employed workers in a manner similar to the post office men, but his arguments went unheard.

Lloyd George dared not arouse more opposition than he faced already.[43] Nonetheless, an opportunity was lost. The introduction in 1911 of an industry-based coverage would have made subsequent national health schemes more decentralised, probably more responsive to preventive aims, and possibly more accessible to the bulk of the working classes, if not to the old and unemployed. Benenden was opened to members of the Civil Service Sanatorium Society in 1933 and apparently continued until the advent of chemotherapy. It had sheltered hundreds of patients and maintained an 80 per cent rate of men 'returned fit for duty'; although, as usual, we have no figures for subsequent relapses.[44] Uniquely among working class institutions its clients could confidently seek treatment at the earliest signs of disease.

Frimley sanatorium was established in 1905 as an outdoor extension of Brompton Hospital. Working-class patients referred from the Hospital were treated without fee, while private patients, at about 25s a week before the First World War, were admitted direct. It too professed to take only 'early' cases but in practice a long waiting list often meant delays while 'early' cases became something else.

Like most sanatoria, Frimley was undercapitalised. Its first medical superintendent, Marcus Paterson, made his therapeutic beliefs yield dividends by compelling inmates to build and maintain the place. The model was Nordrach. Paterson convinced himself and persuaded many of his colleagues and patients that graduated exercise activated the fever to a measurable, controllable extent which in turn activated antibodies in the bloodstream. This process of 'auto-inoculation' developed resistence to the bacilli. This theory was mostly nonsense, as a few of Paterson's medical contemporaries remarked privately, but it gave patients the illusion that they were working to cure themselves and it had a palpable outcome in the institution's sweep of buildings and ornate grounds. The inmates' exercises depended upon 'absolute obedience to orders regulating the amount of work to be done'.[45] Walks were distributed to the yard, up to ten miles a mile a day: patients carried stones in their pockets to count the rounds. Men and women were strictly segregated and took their exercises separately.[46] Two-thirds of the patients were male, on the assumption that breadwinners needed the cure more than wives and were more single-minded in striving for it.

Moreover, fewer women applied to enter public sanatoria. Married women were reluctant to leave their children and husbands and they were notoriously more likely to leave suddenly, regardless of their health, if they learnt of trouble at home or if they became upset in the sanatorium. Doctors noticed that they feared sanatorium life more than men, partly perhaps because they were less used to mingling with outsiders.[47]

The men worked outdoors, graduating from short walks to longer ones, from breaking stones with light hammers to wielding heavy ones, from hoeing with light hoes to digging with large spades, from carrying little bundles of sticks to manhandling logs. The women managed the flower gardens and did graduated amounts of sewing and cleaning. Each grade of exercise lasted a week. Then, depending upon whether Paterson deemed the increase of fever acceptable, the patient moved to the next stage for a fortnight, succeeding grades took three weeks each, until the five or six months stay came to an end. The final grades required exertions more severe than the patient might afterwards encounter while earning his or her living, or so Paterson intended.

When you've walked around the field a dozen times or more,
And the rather bumpy pathways made your feet feel very sore.
Or, when you've been turf-lifting, and the sun is very hot,
And suddenly you do espy a lovely shady spot,
If you yield to strong temptation, and lie down in the shade,
And think, well this, at any rates a very 'cushy' grade,
Don't you wish that Doctor took a nap 'twixt three o'clock and four...
Or, when you're feeling rotten, and your food you cannot eat
And Doctor sends you down enormous quantities of meat.
Because you cannot eat it - to the office you must go.

Irene Jones[48]

Patients built a reservoir ten feet deep, they supplied the places of four nurses, four gardeners, a window cleaner, a general repairs man, a firewood supplier and a poultry keeper. During six years to 1920 they saved the Brompton governors over £10,000 in wages and between 1908 and 1911 they had constructed capital works worth over £3000. Apparently there was little grumbling.[49] Paterson was a charismatic doctor and the patients were justifiably proud of their achievements. The snag was that it was not curing them.

The regime was absolutist. Cases who rebelled were sent direct to the superintendent's office where they waited 'in fear and trembling, outside his office door', awaiting instant dismissal. Smoking was only permitted outdoors. A nurse caught a man smoking in the laundry and ordered him to the superintendent, to whom he readily admitted the act. He was a new arrival and had not received the usual introduction to the rules. Paterson rang a bell and said, 'Prepare to leave'. The man departed. Paterson held to his decision despite a remonstrance from the employer of the smoker's wife, who had arranged his entry to Frimley without going through Brompton.[50]

Paterson and his board were resolved to prevent the growth in Frimley of the notorious sanatorium habit of 'work-shirking', with its concomitant 'moral deterioration'. Patients might only leave the sanatorium with a signed pass stating the times of leaving and return:

> I beg to ask permission to be allowed to go for a walk outside the Sanatorium grounds on Sunday ... from 2.30 to 5 o'clock. If granted this privilege I promise to carefully observe all the rules and directions of the medical staff. I also promise not to enter a public house ... I understand that in the event of my breaking this rule, I shall be dismissed at once from the Sanatorium.[51]

Frimley, like all sanatoria for the lower classes, was dry. The authorities had also to curb the wanderings of their patients. People in villages near sanatoria feared 'lungers' and avoided them. They particularly disapproved 'lungers' who frequented their pub and left infection in the air and in the glasses.[52] They also disliked 'lungers' on the buses. Most sanatoria were cut off from public transport. Patients found it expensive and wearing to get to them and visitors were dismayed by the costs of time and money.[53] Matters improved in the 1930s when town-based surgeons found a need to have the patients nearer to them.

Within Frimley each patient was allocated his or her numbered eating utensils and ordered to use these alone. Each was responsible for washing them after every meal, wiping them with his or her numbered tea towel, replacing them in their numbered places on the rack, where they were checked. Washing up was possibly a less onerous chore than at some other sanatoria because the meals were spartan. The board saved £500 a year by giving 'no milk at all ... to many of the patients'. Handkerchiefs were also allotted individually and numbered.[54] Surprisingly, Frimley, in common with other sanatoria, did not impose any standard dress. Patients continued in the one good serge suit or worsted dress, pyjamas and nightgowns they brought with them. As at all sanatoria where the outdoor life was mandatory, the patients looked frowsy, their clothes always damp and muddy, the women's hair straggly from being blown about and wet. The men's trousers became frayed with walking and digging, the women's cardigans and skirts were soon shapeless from working and sitting about in them. Sanatoria which held to pure Nordrach doctrine, as reinforced by the fashionable heliotherapy at Leysin in Switzerland, issued cotton loin cloths to men and shifts to women to wear when taking the sun, but these were usually the appurtenances of private, middle-class establishments. Middle-class patients, doctors agreed, were readier than working-class inmates to expose their bodies.[55] The patients, bored, easily tired, despondent, strictly non-responsible for themselves, felt 'TB' - 'totally bitched'. Their breath stank, their bodies were slimy from night sweats, febrile patients who had difficulty eating used cocaine sprays on their larynx, with copious doses of heroin to ease the pain while they sucked up liquid food, and tried to swallow their prescribed egg, which they hated. Difficult febrile cases or those who coughed blood were ordered 'complete immobilization' in places, like Frimley, which could supply the nursing. The immobilisation was intended to reduce the 'activity' of the lungs. Patients lay on their side, forbidden to move, forbidden to read, wash themselves, cut up their food, go to the lavatory, talk, indulge 'unnecessary coughs', or receive visitors who only evoked 'talk and laughing'. 'Complete immobilization' was supposed to last one week and then be eased in stages, but patients with persistent irregular pyrexia might be directed to it for the whole of their six months stay. The regime was still being ordered in British sanatoria in the late 1940s. Doctors and nurses eased the aching hours with morphia, especially after 'useful' but painful inter-muscular injections of calcium chloride or galvanic cautery of the larynx.[56]

The early results Paterson claimed for Frimley look impressive. Of the 297 patients admitted from Brompton to the end of 1908, 197 had been 'discharged in full working capacity', 43 were 'improved' or 'stationary' on discharge, 2 had died, and 55 'left early', some of them after 'insubordination'. But three years later only 146 of the 297 were 'well' and able to work, 19 were 'at home' and 31 were dead. A count of the patients discharged through a later five-year period, 1912-17, revealed much the same proportions: 38 per cent were 'well and at work', 14 per cent were 'alive' and the remaining 46 per cent were dead. All these cases had been 'carefully chosen' for their promise of recovery and easy adjustment to Frimley. They were of 'the better working class type' from the London area and had 'clean and careful' homes to support their return to health and employment. We do not know exactly how the Frimley authorities determined when a patient was 'well' or 'improved'. Presumably they relied upon the patient's report of how he or she felt and whether he or she had gained weight and looked better, together with a reduction of the temperature range and the disappearance of bacilli in the sputum.[57] But remarks about individual cases suggest that these rules were not uniformly observed. It is also difficult to recapture the stress many patients must have suffered when they returned to homes, however 'careful', that were crowded, yet avoided by the neighbours, ominous with marital strain, short of money and taut with anxieties about a relapse. Their sanatorium stay had nurtured an obsession with their illness. They had enjoyed for the first time in their lives, quiet rest, clean living quarters, regular meals and middle class standards of sober order. In many families the break in behaviour patterns was never repaired. Yet the fact remains that about half of the discharged patients survived and were able to find some work for up to five years after their return home. Their life chances would not, in the mass, have been much different had they never entered Brompton and Frimley but I have no evidence that they realised that.

By the 1920s and 1930s the main construction and planting work at Frimley was done. It became especially difficult to make work for the women. They still did the flower gardens, and inside they made their beds, cleaned their cubicles, washed their cutlery and dishes. Otherwise, they read women's magazines, chatted, knitted and passed the time with the new craze of jigsaw puzzles - yet another transplant from German sanatoria. Auto-inoculation quietly vanished as a cure. It was replaced, as at other sanatoria, by new therapies involving X-ray machines and thoracic surgery. A new corps of tuberculosis specialists was coming into their own.

Men and women patients were still segregated, but 'Mixing Days' were permitted on Bank Holidays and other special occasions. They lined up on each side of the hall and when the bell sounded, began to mix. After an hour or so of tea, sedate conversation and games, a bell ended the festivities. Women also got a chance to speak to men at church services and during choir practice on Friday evenings. In between, they wrote illicit notes and hid them at secret spots around the grounds. They received less outside leave than men and the messages often contained shopping lists and money. The men would buy the items and leave them at the hiding places on their walks.[58] At sanatoria less closely managed than Frimley there was said to be considerable mingling in the bushy parts of the grounds. When we recall that about two-thirds of patients in most sanatoria were in their early twenties and about the same proportion unmarried or away from their special friends and spouses, it is not surprising that the women were reported in the 1930s and 1940s to talk mostly about the men and TB and the men, even at Frimley, were said in 1939 to talk of nothing but sex and TB.[59]

Frimley's results to 1931 were reviewed again in 1935. There had by then been 10,000 admissions, 8766 of whom, 5800 men, 2900 women, had stayed more than 28 days. They had continued to be 'responsible' workers from the lower rank of the insured classes of the London area. Again the survival rates over any five-year period from admission were about 40 per cent, setting apart the 8 per cent who had vanished. The rates were roughly equal between males and females at all ages, and remained constant under various theraputic regimes. Beyond this it is impossible to go: the presentation of the figures might mildly be described as sloppy. If the 30 per cent figure is about right it again is not dissimilar from the 1920s life expectancy for consumptives who from the diagnosis of their illness never entered a sanatorium. Moreover, this latter, enormously larger group would have included a much higher proportion of 'hopeless' advanced cases.[60]

Pinewood sanatorium at Wokingham in Berkshire was established for a better class of person than entered Benenden. The rates for private patients were three guineas a week in 1908. Its opulent facade expressed its endowment by Wernher, Beit and Co. in 1904. Pinewood was intended for male clerks in banks and mercantile houses. By 1913 it contained 64 rooms heated by radiators, an unusual feature in sanatoria before 1939. These, as in other well-funded establishments, were installed to encourage patients to keep to their cubicles and not congregate around coal fires. There was some token graduated labour, but Pinewood could exist without it and its patients' manual skills were limited. Most exercise came from walking. It housed two resident physicians and boasted an X-ray appliance before the Great War. The X-rays were used to determine desirable early cases, rather than register a patient's progress. Even so, in 1932, 50 per cent of its discharged patients were dead within five years and another 25 per cent were unfit for employment.[61]

Crossley, at Frodsham in Cheshire, was a less wealthy cousin to Pinewood. It was endowed by Sir William Crossley, the Manchester engineering magnate, in 1905. Much of the founder's money went on the main building which was 100 yards long, three stories high and embellished with an imposing facade. Ten of the 100 beds were for poorer patients, subsidised by Manchester Corporation. The other 90 were allocated equally between male and female private patients at two to three guineas a week. Men occupied the main building. Women lived in unheated chalets and revolving shelters dotted about the grounds. Crossley's specialty was hydro-therapy - cold douches, baths, wet blankets, water drinking. According to the medical superintendant it promoted 'a healthy action of the skin and [elimination of] ... effete material'. Visitors were permitted on the last Saturday of each month, the usual allowance for sanatoria, until at least the 1930s. But private patients could obtain permission to receive visitors more frequently. Subsidised patients were confined to the grounds; private patients could take prescribed walks outside.[62]

Crossley's advertisements emphasised that their floors were covered with linoleum. This polishable impervious covering was a guard against the dust and fluff in the joins of the floorboards and awkward corners which enfolded the dangerous dried sputum and thereby preserved the bacillus against sunlight and against the variations in temperature which might otherwise kill it. The linoleum served as a constant, cold reminder to patients of what they had to instal when they returned home. The great linoleum boom of the 1920s and 1930s was at hand. Beliefs about the patterns of tuberculous infectivity, as expressed in sanatoria, dispensary and public health educational campaigns and exhibitions, were a fundamental force for change in domestic design. The hiding places of the dust enemy had to be eliminated. More than a decade before the Bauhaus designers became influential, sanatoria doctors in Germany and Britain were working with architects to produce the new spaces, shapes and textures that were to become the essence of the modern movement. Room corners were rounded, ceilings were cleared of mouldings, picture rails, pelmets, window ledges, head-pieces of wardrobes were abolished. Wallpaper which 'collected organisms and dirt', was replaced with renewable body colour or washable paint, usually of pale neutral colour which would immediately expose the presence of dirt. Plush curtains were displaced by wipeable venetian blinds which could be adjusted to admit more sunlight. The Victorian and Edwardian clutter of objets d'art and pictures on walls, tabletops and mantlepieces, and the jumble of dust collecting, hard to move clumps of furniture with carved or moulded surfaces, draped by velvet or lace covers, were swept off to the newly burgeoning 'antique' dealers. Doctors instructed tuberculous men to shave off their beards, a revolutionary order, because beards in Victorian times had been grown to 'guard the chest' and make 'it easier to draw breath' and trim their moustaches to a thin clean line in order to avoid catching phelgm from their coughs; consumptive women bobbed their hair, adopted lighter dress materials, and set their hems above ankle level to avoid gathering dust and make washing easier. Health visitors, dispensary nurses and tuberculosis medical officers also preached the new fashions in order to smarten up consumptives, whose physical weakness, straitened means and low morale tempted them to slovenliness. Those who could afford it took up their carpets in favour of bare boards, parquet or linoleum. Health visitors warned their working class clients against the custom of using bits of old paper to wrap stored food or to cleanse things and then drop the paper on the floor. The authorities, medical and municipal, joined forces to combat, with much success by the 1930s, the old habit of spitting in public. Working people who indulged in the old hearty cough or sneeze were rebuked into coughing only behind their hand or into a handkerchief. The lesson was a hard one and doctors were severe with male defaulters who, following their home habits, unthinkingly coughed in their faces. Women were more likely to try to stifle their cough and swallow their sputum. Doctors found this equally reprehensible and ordered that women carry sputum flasks in their handbags. This was no easy matter because the sputum had a peculiarly foul, penetrating smell. Male consumptives used powerfully scented brilliantine, females took to strong perfumes. Asian incense came into fashion for burning at home. Health officers recommended paper towels, but they themselves rarely were seen to use them and the habit did not catch on before the Second World War. In sanatoria and dispensaries patients were instructed not to lick envelopes or stamps, kiss on the lips, or moisten baby's comforter or teething ring with their mouth, or to shake hands. There seems to have been widespread reluctance to adopt these prohibitions because the authorities continued to warn against them throughout the 1920s and 1930s. Linoleum and clear floor space became symbiotic with the brush and pan, automatic sweeper and cigarette ash-tray. Simplicity and fresh air became the ideals. Trellised porches and 'airy sleep-outs' proliferated through the 1920s, as did country walking and camping. Careful middle class people took to 'wholemeal' bread, 'farm' eggs, 'farm' butter, and breakfasts with the new natural cereals. Medical directives to drink more milk led to an enormous increase in consumption of cocoa and malted powders to make the milk palatable and build strength and fend off that 'night starvation' which impaired the body's resistance to insidious ailments.[63]

The passage to the modern had many impulses, and the rejection of the muddle and carnage of the War was doubtless a more potent accelerant than fear of tuberculosis; but, coincident with the earliest modernist ventures over a decade before the War tuberculosis as represented by health authorities helped accustom people, indeed render imperative, the shapes and some of the behaviour that constituted the modern style.

Fear of the terrible personal and national costs of tuberculosis set it in the vanguard of those forces which created the twentieth-century obsession with personal well-being. The French began tuberculosis congresses in 1888, the first to be directed to a single malady.[64] There followed Koch's international triumph with his announcement of tuberculin in 1890. The French countered with the putatively international *Ligue contre la tuberculose* in 1892 and two further congresses. The Germans staged the first major international congress in Berlin in 1898. The second followed in London in 1901, with a takeover from the French and the founding of the International Central Committee to Combat Tuberculosis in 1902.[65] There were further international conferences in Copenhagen in 1905, Paris in 1906, Budapest in 1909, and Rome, sponsored by Mussolini, in 1929. There were British Empire conferences in 1923 and 1937.[66] The French meanwhile had recaptured the international tuberculosis round with the founding after the War of the International Union Against Tuberculosis, with its headquarters in Paris and the Germans and Russians ignored.[67]

Delegates to the European conferences wore full decorations. They met in palaces, were received by kings and presidents, enjoyed lavish meals with more wine than they could drink, supplied free by producers who used the fact in their advertising. At each Congress opening luncheon was followed by the 'Roll Call of Nations'; as each delegation leader stepped forward, the orchestra played the appropriate national anthem and the other delegates from that nation formed in a group.[68] Kings and delegates talked much of international goodwill in a good cause, but the undisguised competition, particularly between the French, Germans and British, was intense. There were comparatively few papers - perhaps two daily for about ten days. They were mostly on abstruse pathology, platitudes about sanatorium regimes and outcomes, or boastful accounts of local campaigns against the disease. These were then published in lavish commemorative volumes which remained unread, to judge from their pristine state in libraries, and rarely cited in the literature.[69] The expensive festivals of which they are the only palpable legacy achieved little of their ostensible object and did worse than nothing for the patients by diverting money which could have been better spent.

The real advances came from the laity. The first anti-tuberculosis charity postage stamps were issued in New South Wales in 1897. It was a post office official who established the Cross of Lorraine as the anti-tuberculosis symbol in 1903 and postal officials who forwarded the buying of special anti-tuberculosis stamps as Christmas seals. Britain adopted the practice belatedly in 1932.[70] The National Association, encouraged by its success in staging the 1901 Congress, went on to produce leaflets promoting ventilation and drinking milk, and show cards denouncing spitting. In 1908 they created a Tuberculosis Exhibition, showing part of a ward at the Royal Victoria Hospital in Edinburgh, revealing patients sleeping with open windows in all weathers, spit bottle at hand, and a model of an open air school. Appropriately it was unveiled at the Whitechapel Art Gallery, as the centre piece of another conference. The pilgrimage Exhibition 'travelled all over Great Britain'; over 70,000 people had visited it before it closed in 1914. 'Tuberculosis caravans' began in 1911, carrying exhibits for display in village halls and to support street corner lectures against spitting and kissing.[71] By 1921 the National Association was commissioning educational films warning against the disease. 'The Story of John McNeil' typically conveyed sanitary lessons for a family with a consumptive member. But cinema proprietors fought shy of them: patrons disliked them. The Council for Health Education in 1937 found it difficult to get a screening for 'Health of a Nation'. Anti-tuberculosis talks on radio did not succeed either, except when they were done by members of the Royal Family. 'Health Weeks' in the 1930s proved unexpectedly popular, in terms of attendances at exhibitions, although nobody, it seems, tried to discover what made them popular.[72] The International congresses, did, however, refine nomenclature among the specialists. In 1891 the *British Medical Journal* formally announced that it was dropping 'phthisis' for 'tubercle of the lung', - a term it later rarely used. The *Lancet* ceased to use 'consumption' in its index in 1894, but the term continued in general use.[73]

King Edward VII had been induced to take an interest in consumption in 1898 and it became an item for fashionable philanthropy. His question, 'If preventable, why not prevented', became a catchcry for the advocates of the new sanatoria and the gospel of sunlight and fresh air. The phrase was cribbed from the great William Withering but journalists were glad to attribute such pithy wisdom to His Majesty.[74] The endowment of a sanatorium accessible enough to London for the King to open it was a safe outlay for eminence. Aristocrats headed boards of trustees, Beits, Cassels, Crossleys and Wernhers built lavish sanatoria under royal patronage. Cure through disciplined self-help and a quick return to work was instated as a national good and a good investment.

Simple, disciplined living as a way to health pervaded the regime at one of the leading showpiece sanatoria, the King Edward VII at Midhurst in Kent. It was founded with a gift of £200,000 from Sir Ernest Cassel and opened by the King in 1906, for officers of the army and navy, clergy, civil servants and teachers, ladies and gentlemen in the early stages of disease, whose 'means do not permit of their becoming inmates of one of the private sanatoria' and 'who cannot conveniently make use of' public sanatoria. The fee was two guineas a week. Applicants who had been in domestic service or who obviously were working class were excluded, together with hopeless cases. There were 104 beds. Some of these were initially reserved for other educated private patients at 4 and a half guineas a week. But few applied. Consumptives with that much money could go to a fully private sanatorium or try Switzerland or Mentone.

Midhurst was a cross between Nordrach and a minor public school. The key to cure was discipline. The building itself had no 'unnecessary decoration'. There were no window ledges, mantlepieces or pelmets. The chapel consisted of open arcades, and had no mouldings. The heating circulated under the floor.[75] The daily routine, as outlined by its superintendent, Dr Noel Bardswell, was a slightly more regimented version of the round at most large sanatoria:

7.30 a.m.	gong. patients rise, take temperatures per rectum enter hydro-therapy baths.
8.15	gong. breakfast warning.
8.30	gong. breakfast. compulsory, as are all meals, unless medically directed otherwise.
9.00-9.30	leisure. library open for borrowing. ['exciting' and technical books on tuberculosis were not stocked; they were similarly excluded from most sanatoria: they made difficult patients more difficult, males especially. The sanatorium, like sanatoria everywhere, had strict rules about taking of medicines not prescribed by the doctors - the rule was widely flouted.]
9.30	gong. all patients proceed directly to their rooms, or to that section of the balcony immediately outside their rooms. There they are to lie motionless on their beds or chairs

	until each is inspected by the medical officer or nurse.
10-12.00	rest or exercise as prescribed. Once each week each patient presents him or herself as rostered at the consulting room for possible Xray, sputum tests or further examinations and special therapies.
12.00	gong. All patients proceed direct to their rooms or balconies.
12-1.00 p.m.	rest. Talking forbidden
1.00	gong. Luncheon warning. Patients take temperatures.
1.15	gong. Luncheon 'Patients coughing at table are requested to turn from the table at once'.
2-2.30	leisure. Weaving of raffia bags and coverlets. [Sanatoria officers bear a prime responsibility for making this messy, rubbishy material popular]. Tray making with a fret saw; basket weaving, jig-saw puzzles, crossword puzzles, knitting, crochet work for coat hangers, doilies and men's ties, hand painting of shoe-trees.
2.30-4.30	rest or exercise as prescribed.
4.30-5.00	tea in entrance hall.
5-6.00	recreation. Patients might listen to the gramophone; read; play games, including card games, but not for money. [However, fairly open gambling apparently was rife in sanatoria among male patients. There was no bar. King George VII, like all but the wealthiest private sanatoria, was dry. The men hid smuggled liquor around the grounds, which they drank during the graduated walks and labour exercises.]
6.00	gong. All patients go to their rooms.
6-7.00	rest.
7.00	gong. Dinner warning. Patients take temperatures.
7.15	gong. Dinner.
8-9.30	recreation.
9.30	all patients go to their rooms.
10.00	lights out.[76]

By 1917 the higher professional patients had ceased to apply and the managers admitted an increasing proportion of clerks, shop assistants, commercial travellers and civil servants. The average stay shortened from over six to four or five months, and with it the chances of longterm remissions.[77] Dr Bardswell, was less sanguine of the results than most of his sanatoria colleagues. He calculated in 1917 that those discharged in the first stage of the disease had one-sixth of the life expectancy of a healthy person at the same age, and one-twentieth the life expectancy if they were discharged in the second stage. Bardswell was among the first doctors to admit that the real comparison should lie with the consumptives who had never entered sanatoria, but he noted that no one wanted to collect the figures. In 1932 the Chief Medical Officer of the London County Council, which sent patients to the King Edward VII, estimated that the usual outcome prevailed there too, despite the relative wealth of the institution, its good class of inmates and close supervision: 50 per cent died within five years of discharge and a further 25 per cent were unfit to work.[78] The final irony is that since the 1950s physicians have amassed strong evidence that bed rest is unimportant in the healing of pulmonary tuberculosis.[79]

Middle class consumptives, women particularly, secreted themselves in the hundreds of small private nursing homes scattered through the southern and home counties. Now they have vanished almost without trace: many are now old people's retreats or small hotels.

Rizwan Nursing Home was on the outskirts of Broadstone in Dorset. It existed from the 1920s to the 1940s. We know of it only because it chanced to become the subject of two Ministry of Health inspections. Moreover, the inspectors regarded Rizwan as a wholly typical small private establishment. It comprised a large three-storied brick house, facing south, set in its own grounds, sheltered from the winds. It began with five beds in 1923 and was registered with the Dorset County Council in 1928 by its then proprietor, Mrs Grace Challis. She was a consumptive who had had ten years' experience as a sanatorium nurse but, partly because of her ill-health, she had not completed her training and was not certificated. Most people did not know this. She called herself 'matron'. The Ministry inspector described her as 'efficient and kind'. By the

1930s Rizwan catered for twenty adult patients, mostly women, ten of whom slept in the house and ten in wooden huts in the grounds. Private patients paid three to five guineas a week, and a few beds at £3 a week were reserved for patients subsidised by the London County Council. The fees included X-rays and medicines but not laundry. Matron Challis also accepted cases sent by the Civil Service Sanatorium Society at a fixed charge of £2 16s 0d a week. She estimated that each inmate cost her £2 15s 0d, so her rates were not exorbitant, although they were beyond working class sufferers. Rizwan was genteel, but hardly select.

Most of the patients were in various advanced stages of consumption. Matron Challis made no pretence at limiting admission to 'early' cases, and she did not pretend to cure them. But equally she would not take desperately ill cases who could not get about to wash and feed themselves. By a verbal agreement with the Bournemouth Sanatorium authorities she took difficult neurotic cases off their hands. Private patients had a room to themselves. Public patients apparently began in the huts and graduated to a shared room, as a bed became available. There were no firm rules about therapy, medicines or diet. Most patients spent most of each day in bed and got up for a few hours when they felt like it. Sir Kay Le Fleming, a local physician, had a contract with Matron Challis. He visited twice a week and arranged for X-rays, if necessary, at Wimborne Cottage Hospital. Cases needing elaborate care, such as those with an artificial pneumothorax with their regular need for X-rays and refills, were not admitted. Such cases, whose surgical procedures had failed and had been discharged from the big sanatoria through the 1930s, or who needed refills or sputum tests and had no established medical contact, found it difficult to get readmitted anywhere. Private patients paid Le Fleming by separate account; payments for public patients were arranged by the Matron. In general, private patients stayed nine or twelve months until they felt better or their money or patience ran out and then they moved to another nursing home or back to relatives. Public patients were limited to three months. Then they usually returned home. Over the 25 years or so of its existence as a consumptives' refuge Rizwan must have had 1100-1200 patients pass through it.

Matron Challis' staff comprised two assistant nurses and two probationers, a daily cleaner and a daily cook. The resident nurses lived on the third floor. There was no night nurse, but patients could ring a bell in their house bedrooms which rang in the Matron's bedroom. The hall, dining room and some of the single bedrooms were centrally heated, but no bedroom had running water. There was no day room, no organised occupational therapy, no laundry. Patients made up their personal laundry, including handkerchiefs, into bundles which were taken to the village for washing. Laundry day must have been the liveliest time of the week. Each patient had her own mug for cocoa and her own set of china, and was responsible for emptying her sputum flask into the outside W.C. and rinsing it with Dettol. At intervals the staff boiled the sputum flasks. Each patient received one and a half pints of milk daily and was served four 'plentiful' meals.

The ill-assorted sick, disappointed people mostly in their twenties and thirties who filled outposts like Rizwan, incarcerated with the neurotics from Bournemouth, hidden among the shrubbery and unable even to glimpse the traffic on the road, must have lived a slow nightmare of encroaching debility, boredom and hissed rows about trivia. The inspectors' visit had been provoked by complaints from the Civil Service Society that their patients had complained repeatedly that the place was dusty and that other patients' sputum flasks were not properly washed. The inspectors rather dismissed the complaints: middle class consumptives were a querulous lot and their uneasy part dependence on the Ministry of Pensions caused the Ministry a disproportionate amount of trouble. Rizwan, the inspectors agreed, was a good example of the 'kindly makeshift kind of sanatorium for patients needing rest and nutrition and no vigorous exercise'. Finally in 1947 they ordered Matron Challis to ensure that damp tea leaves were used when the floors were swept and that the sputum flasks were boiled daily.[80]

The one sanatorium in England for wealthy people who did not want to travel or were advised against going abroad was Mundesley in north Norfolk. It began in 1899 as a wholly private venture by a consortium of medical practitioners. In 1913 the minimum weekly rate for the 36 guests was five guineas a week. Although the staff 'insisted upon ... a strict *regime*', 'the comforts of life and cheerfulness are not forgotten' and exercise was restricted to short graduated walks. Mundesley early acquired an X-ray machine to help determine each patient's condition and was quickly into chest surgery in the

1920s. But the main sources of recuperation lay elsewhere: the menu was varied and 'the table in general form[ed] the subject of constant and personal attention'. Mundesley was adjacent to a golf course which patients could use. By the early 1930s it was netting its three proprietors over £8000 a year.[81]

Sanatoria loomed large in the public perception of tuberculosis care. *The Magic Mountain* has fixed the association in the minds of succeeding generations. They absorbed lots of private and public money but their contribution to the solution of the tuberculosis problem was minimal, even in terms of educating their clients and their families. In 1911 during their heyday the 80 or so recognised sanatoria in England, the four in Wales, 21 in Scotland and seven in Ireland housed about 2 per cent of the estimated 300,000 to 350,000 cases in Great Britain, with a notification rate of 60,000 new cases a year. At an average stay of four months the 4000-5000 beds in the system could have coped with around 14,000 cases a year, but the real bed-use rate was lower because some beds were always empty because of shortages of nurses. Moreover, sanatoria admitted mostly only the ambulant, 'early' cases. By 1935 the proportion of known cases in residential institutions was 11 per cent.[82] Advanced cases entered the private nursing homes, the occasional charitable hospice for the incapable such as Friedenheim in South Hampstead with 48 beds for 'patients of refined thought, who have known better days',[83] while thousands of others ended up in the Poor Law infirmaries, but the great majority shuffled out their lives at home. They would have been mostly the warmer for it, and thereby had their lives prolonged. They would have done even better had they been able to use for food and rent subsidies more of the estimated £800,000 a year devoted to sanatoria staff and patients in 1911, or the £1.3 million spent on sanatoria and tuberculosis services in 1922, or the annual outlay of around £3.7 million in the late 1930s, which jumped to about £12 million in 1947. More food, comfort and domestic security might have enhanced the recovery rate and thereby reduced the cost to the community from years of work-time lost, calculated at two and a half years per adult male consumptive in 1901, amounting to £10 million annually in England and Wales.[84]

NOTES

[1]George Bodington, *An Essay on the Treatment and Cure of Pulmonary Consumption, on principles natural, rational and successful,* 1840, (reprinted ed. 1901). The reprint includes a note from the *BMJ,* 11 Mar. 1882, recounting the reception of Bodington's work. He had also advised against bleeding and dosing with calomel against cholera in 1831. Bodington died insane.

[2]J.G. Sinclair Coghill, 'The Prevention of Consumption', *Nineteenth Century,* Feb. 1899, pp.305-6.

[3]Dettweiler in *Lancet,* 16 Jan. 1886, p.124; Herman Weber, *Lancet,* 12 May 1888, p.924.

[4]James Arthur Gibson, *The Nordrach Treatment,* 1901, pp.9-11.

[5]C.T. Williams, *Lancet,* 9 Aug. 1879, 16 Aug. 1879, pp.191,234; J.A. Symonds' vivid account of Davos, first published in the *Pall Mall Gazette,* is partly reprinted in the *BMJ,* 1 July 1882, p.9. Arosa is described in *The Child,* vol.iv, Oct. 1913, p.65.

[6]'A Special Correspondent', (Dr Lindsay), *Lancet,* 8 Jan. 1887, 12 Mar. 1887, pp.93-4, 543; Allbutt in *Lancet,* 3 Nov. 1888, p.873.

[7]Dr William Ewart, 'Arosa as an alpine health resort', *Lancet,* 5 Oct. 1889, pp.688-90.

[8]*Lancet,* 15 Sept. 1888, pp.513-4.

[9]*Lancet,* 20 Oct. 1888, p.792.

[10]Beatrice Harraden, *Ships that Pass in the Night,* 1893. Her picture is confirmed by Agnes Hunt, *Reminiscences,* Shrewsbury 1935, pp.80-96.

[11]Bernard Hudson (physician to Queen Alexandra Hospital, Davos), *St. Bartholomew's Hospital Journal,* Nov. 1913, pp.20-1.

[12]*Tuberculosis Year Book 1913-1914,* pp.371-2; Derek Lindsay, (student inmate), *Transactions of NAPT,1949,* p.241.

[13]Sir Martin Conway in *BMJ,* 11 Feb. 1922, p.248; D. Vesey and William Ewart, *BMJ,* 18 Feb. 1922, p.292.

[14]Felix Savy, *BMJ,* 4 Mar. 1922, p.374; John Bain, *BMJ,* 22 Apr. 1922, p.666.

[15]Derek Lindsay, *Transactions of NAPT,* 1949, p.241.

[16]Claude Chidell in *BMJ,* 7 Nov. 1936, p.950; *Tuberculosis Year Book 1913-1914,* pp.57-60.

[17]Latham and Garland, *Conquest,* pp.50-4.

[18]Bulstrode, *Report,* pp.295-313; Newsholme, 'Public Health Authorities', *Journal of Hygiene,* vol.iii, 1903, pp.382, 462.

[19]*Report of Medical Officer of Health for London County Council, 1909,* p.60.

[20]E. Watt, (Medical Officer, Scottish Board of Health), *Transactions of NAPT, 1923,* p.43.

[21]John Burns, *Lancet,* 29 July 1911, p.312.

[22]Drs E.P. Manby and F.R. Seymour, Report on the Poor Law Infirmaries and Tuberculosis to the Ministry of Health, Mar. 1923. PRO MH55/145.

[23]Ibid.

[24]Dr W.B. Knobel, Report on Poor Law Infirmaries and Tuberculosis to Ministry of Health, 2 Nov. 1922, PRO MH55/145.

[25]Manby and Seymour, Report, Mar. 1923, PRO MH55/145.

[26]*Transactions of NAPT, 1931*, p.37.

[27]A. Salusbury McNalty in *Lancet*, 26 Jan. 1924, p.166.

[28]*Tuberculosis*, vol.iv, 1906, pp.130-5.

[29]The changes of 1921 had their origin in a memorandum by Sir Robert Morant, completed probably on Christmas Eve, 1919. He noted a jump in Sanatorium benefit payments for England and Wales from £550,000 in 1918 to £700,000 in 1919, with an extra £30,000 for Scotland. Dr Addison, the Minister for Health, decided in July 1920 to legislate to compel local authorities to provide sanatorium treatment and take part of the cost on to the rates. PRO MH55/174; Kayne, *Control of Tuberculosis*, pp.93-6.

[30]*Tuberculosis Year Book 1913-1914*, p.286.

[31]Bulstrode, *Report*, p.177.

[32]*Lancet*, 21 May 1904, p.1421.

[33]*Tuberculosis Year Book 1913-1914*, p.214; R.G. Hetherington (Ministry of Health Engineer) Report, 26 Oct. 1920, Manchester Health Committee, Report,Jan. 1926. PRO MH52/343, 344.

[34]H.W. McConnell at *National Association for the Prevention of Consumption ... Conference, ... 1909*, pp.42-5; Bulstrode, *Report*, pp.431, 447.

[35]J.F.H. Coutts, Report on Welsh National Memorial Association, 16 Oct. 1932, PRO MH75/14; J.B. McDougall, *Transactions of NAPT, 1934*, pp.98-100.

[36]Report of response to Joint Tuberculosis Council Questionnaire, *BMJ*, 28 June 1930, p.1183.

[37]Dr Powell, of Talgarth Sanatorium, as reported by J.F.H. Coutts to Ministry of Health, 21 June 1932. PRO MH75/14; Report on costs in Welsh National Memorial Scheme (1932?) with annotations dated 1935 and 1937. PRO MH96/1116.

[38]William Davies (Secretary of Benenden Sanatorium) *Transactions of NAPT, 1934*, p.114; Memorandum, Ministry of Health, 1923, PRO MH96/1114; *Lancet*, 2 Feb. 1924, p.253.

[39]*Tuberculosis Year Book 1913-1914*, p.210; Latham and Garland, *Conquest of Tuberculosis*, pp.59-66.

[40]*Tuberculosis Year Book 1913-1914*, p.366.

[41]*Tuberculosis Year Book 1913-1914*, p.227; Bulstrode, *Report*, pp.395-6; Latham and Garland, *Conquest of Tuberculosis*, pp.76-7, 92; Dr T.D. Lister (Benenden), *Lancet*, 18 Mar. 1911, p.738; A.F. Fountain (Civil Service - formerly Post Office - Sanatorium Society), *Transactions of NAPT, 1943*, p.63.

[42]The scheme was outlined by Arthur Latham, in mid 1909, *Transactions of NAPT, 1909*, pp.36-7; according to Dr Francis Fremantle (Chief Medical Officer for Hertfordshire) Benenden was the basis of the £1.5 million calculation for sanatoriums in the Act. *Transactions of NAPT, 1912*, p.229. David Lloyd George quoted Benenden cure rates, without mentioning it by name, when advocating his Bill in the House of Commons. *Parl. Debs*, 12 July 1911, vol.xxviii, col.421. But the fact remains that I could not find any specific mention of Benenden in the papers of W.J. Braithwaite, who helped prepare the legislation, (W.J. Braithwaite Collection, British Library of Political and Economic Science), or in his memoir of his work at this time in *Lloyd George's Ambulance Wagon*, 1957, nor in the Lloyd George Papers in the House of Lords Record Office.

[43]T.D. Lister, *Transactions of NAPT, 1911*, p.143. Lloyd George, memorandum, 30 Mar. 1911, and memorandum on Lloyd George evading deputation from British Medical Association seeking provision for longer stays in sanatoria, Oct. 1911. W.J. Braithwaite Collection, British Library of Political and Economic Science, vol.ii, 48, 98.

[44]*Tubercle*, vol.xxix, 1948, p.141; Fountain, *Transactions of NAPT, 1943*, p.63.

[45]Paterson, *Auto-Inoculation*, pp.12-15.

[46]J.R. Bignall, *Frimley: The Biography of a Sanatorium*, 1979, p.133.

[47]Paterson, *Auto-Inoculation*, p.182.

[48]Bulstrode, *Report*, p.167. Irene Jones's poem is quoted in Marcus Paterson, *The Shibboleths of Tuberculosis*, 1920, p.119.

[49]Paterson, *Auto-Inoculation*, pp.219, 235.

[50]The 'fear and trembling' comes from Irene Jones's poem as quoted by Paterson, *Shibboleths*, p.119. The dismissed smoker's case is outlined in a letter to Paterson, 30 Jan. 1909, quoted by Bishop, 'Paterson Collection, *Tubercle*, vol.xlviii, 1967, p.73.

[51]AAH (a clergyman) to Paterson, 24 July 1906, and the leave pass, quoted in Bishop, 'Paterson Collection', *Tubercle*, vol.xlviii, pp.70, 73.

[52]Bignall, *Frimley*, pp.43-4.

[53]Bignall, *Frimley*, pp.68-9.

[54]Paterson, *Auto-Inoculation*, p.201; Latham, *Transactions of NAPT, 1909*, p.35.

[55]A. Rollier, (Leysin Sanatorium, Switzerland), *BMJ*, 21 Oct. 1922, pp.742-5; Cf.Paul Jennings, *Transactions of NAPT, 1955*, pp.285-6.

[56]Brian Bulman (a Frimley patient in the late 1930s), *The House Of Quiet People*, 1939, pp.95-100; Paterson, *Auto-Inoculation*, pp.37-9; F.B.Walker to Tuberculosis Society, *BMJ*, 29 Apr. 1922, p.683; Interview with Mrs Sally T., Canberra, inmate of Frimley in late 1940s, June 1985.

[57]Paterson, *Auto-Inoculation*, pp.221-2; Dr W.O. Meek (Medical Superindent from 1912), *Lancet*, 17 Nov. 1917, p.751; for a summary of the ineffectiveness of sanatorium treatment, see Heaf, 'Accommodation for the Tuberculous', quoting Tattersall (1947), *Tubercle*, vol.xxix, 1948, p.3.

[58]Bignall, *Frimley*, pp.133-4.

[59]There are analyses of the age structure of various sanatoria in August 1942 in PRO MH 52/472, 1279. These figures confirm the impression given by novelists such as Bulman. See also Wittkower, *A Psychiatrist*, p.73, on 'fratting', p.73, Bulman, *House*, p.107.

[60]P.H-S. Hartley et al., 'The Expectation of Survival In Pulmonary Tuberculosis', *Brompton Hospital Reports*, vol.iv, 1935, pp.2-53.

[61]*Tuberculosis Year Book 1913-1914*, p.201; *Transactions of the International Conference Against Tuberculosis*, pp.197-8; James Watt (Chief Medical Officer, London County Council), *Lancet*, 20 Feb. 1932, p.428.

[62]*Tuberculosis Year Book 1913-1914*, p.203, Bulstrode, *Report*, pp.348-51.

[63]J.M. Macintosh, *Trends of Opinion about the Public Health 1901-51*, 1953, pp.108, 126; J.G. Sinclair Coghill, 'The Prevention of Consumption', *Nineteenth Century*, Feb. 1899, p.313, denounces bed curtains and valences. E. Ashworth Underwood, *A Manual Of Tuberculosis for nurses* , Edinburgh 1931, p.81, denounces wall paper and dirt collecting corners, and calls for radiators; Guy, *Tuberculosis*, (1923) on moustaches and not fondling babies, p.286; Francis Marion Pottenger, *The Fight Against Tuberculosis*, New York 1952, p.225, on trailing skirts as tubercular dust collectors; cf. George Orwell's *Road to Wigan Pier* diary, 21 Feb. 1936. Penguin edition, *Collected Essays*, vol.i, p.209, 1970; on spitting. Albert Goodwin, writing of his grandfather at about the 1850s, discusses beards as protectors of the chest, in John Burnett, (ed.) *Destiny Obscure*, 1984, p.282; W.E. Snell, 'Changing Aspects of Tuberculosis', *Tubercle*, vol.xxxvii, 1956, p.3 on smelly sputum and eating difficulties.

[64]*Lancet*, 4 Aug. 1888, p.234.

[65]Pottenger, *Fight*, p.112.

[66]The public reports of the 1923-24 meetings can be found in the *Lancet* and *BMJ* for December 1923 and April 1924. The fierce behind the scenes lobbying, especially between Australian and New Zealand support for the charlatan, Henri Spahlinger, and British scepticism about him, can be followed in PRO MH55/53 and PM Dept. E501/16/14 in the Australian Archives, Canberra; *Medical Press* and *Circular*, 27 Jan. 1937, p.70; The Rome Congress is reported in *BMJ*, 21 Sept. 1929, p.550.

[67]*Transactions of the International Conference Against Tuberculosis 1921*, p.186; *Tubercle*, vol.xxxvii, 1956, p.283.

[68]Pottenger, *Fight*, p.235.

[69]see for example, Hilario de Gouveâ, (ed.) *A Conferencia International de Copenhague sobre a tuberculose*, Paris 1905.

[70]Harley Williams, *Requiem for a Great Killer*, 1973, p.41.

[71]*Transactions of the International Conference ... 1921*, pp.186-91; *Transactions of NAPT, 1911*, p.217; Williams, *Requiem*, p.39.

[72]Dr Veronica Dawkins, *Transactions of NAPT, 1937*, pp.21-30.

[73]*BMJ*, 31 Oct. 1891, p.930; *Lancet*, 29 Dec. 1894.

[74]Williams, *Requiem*, pp.11-14.

[75]John Bessner Huber, *Consumption: Its Relation to Man and his Civilization*, Philadelphia 1906, p.284; *Tuberculosis Year Book 1913-1914*, pp.264-7.

[76]Noel Dean Bardswell, *Advice to Consumptives*, 1910, p.66; Duncan Forbes, 'The Sanatorium as an Educational Agency', *Transactions of NAPT, 1909*, p.52.

[77]Bardswell in *Lancet*, 17 Nov. 1917, pp.750-1.

[78]*Lancet*, 24 Nov. 1917, p.795; Dr James Watt in *Lancet*, 20 Feb. 1932, p.428. He was soon to become superintendent of the sanatorium.

[79]Kissen, *Emotional Factors*, quotes studies by Stradling (1955) and Forgacs (1955), which tally with Kissen's own results, p.205; A.L. Cochrane and V. Springett, 'Pulmonary Tuberculosis', in P. D'Arcy Hart, 'Treatment with Rest', *Tubercle*, vol.xli, 1960, p.397; Lord Cohen of Birkenhead, et.al., *Screening in Medical Care*, 1968, p.118.

[80]Report by Dr C.H. Boucher, 6 July 1943; Grace Challis to Ministry of Health, 23 Mar. 1947. PRO MH52/472. The file entitled 'Nursing Homes Registration Act 1927 - reports', PRO MH51/570, is closed until 1987.

[81]*Tuberculosis Year Book 1913-1914*, p.241. Dr Clive Fitts to his mother, 28 Apr. [1930?], Fitts Collection, University of Melbourne Archives.

[82]Garland in *Transactions of NAPT, 1911*, p.132; T.D. Lister gives figures for 1917, in *Lancet*, 17 Nov. 1917, p.739. The 1935 figures are in PEP, *Health*, 1937, p.197.

[83]*Tuberculosis Year Book 1913-1914*, pp.365-6.

[84]G.F. Hardy and F.B. Wyatt, 'Actuaries' Report on Proposed Insurance Scheme', 21 Mar. 1910, Braithwaite Collection, II 4, British Library of Political and Economic Science; *BMJ*, 26 Aug. 1922, p.340; Waldorf Astor, 'The Economic Cost to the Community of Tuberculosis, *Transactions of NAPT, 1911*, pp.202-3; W. Camac Wilkinson in *BMJ* , 8 Sept. 1928, p.444; PEP, *Report* , (June 1937), p.84; S. Mervyn Herbert, *Britain's Health*, 1939, p.163. R.R. Traill, *Practitioner* , vol.clix, 1947, p.296.

5 REMEDIES

Advances in surgery during the First World War, coupled with doubts about the outcomes of sanatoria regimes, led during the 1920s to widespread subjection of sanatoria and general hospital patients to radical surgery.

The surgeons had first begun to find their way, with children, in the late 1880s as antisepsis brought scrofulous necks and the abscesses of various spines and joints within the scope of relatively safe operations. Hitherto these sores could only be washed, poulticed, cauterised, or injected with iodine or other putative germicides, with slow, unsure results. Now biddable youngsters afflicted with what was to be called 'surgical TB' [in the 1920s], could be taken to have the scrofulous gland 'erased', or 'excised' by cutting or scooping.

The procedure rested on the assumption that the infection was localised and that the unsoftened neighbouring gland could confidently be diagnosed as healthy. The operation was commonly accompanied by the removal of 'all sources of irritation', tonsils, decayed teeth and adenoids. One of the 'gland-thirsty' surgeons to the Royal National Hospital for Scrofula at Margate claimed in 1889 to have performed the operation 'for years' and 'never lost a case', although he did not add that he stopped the scrofula.[1] In 1925 Dr J. Lewis' experience with the operation showed 'an almost complete want of success, there being ... a more speedy breakdown of neighbouring glands, accompanied by some pain and lessened chance of a good ultimate result'.[2] There were also 'aesthetic reasons' for abandoning the procedure. Happily, it became unfashionable as the incidence of scrofula itself was rapidly diminishing. During the War Dowling and Charpy independently discovered that vitamin D cleared up lupus,[3] thereby ending, in Britain at least, centuries of horrible disfigurement and horrible ineffectual treatments.

The opening, draining and treatment with germicide of spinal and joint abscesses were more controversial. The healing process took eight or nine months. By 1888 Watson Cheyne claimed to have done 56 cases, 73 per cent of whom he described as 'cured', with 12.5 per cent dead and the remaining 15 per cent missing from his report. The procedure remained popular until the 1920s, when it was first queried. Sir Robert Jones reported that it led 'to mixed infection' and that 70 per cent of abscesses were absorbed if left alone. Scooping out the sac with a surgical spoon was 'indefensible'. In 1901 in four London hospitals 218 joint, bone and gland cases averaging five years of age underwent 415 operations. One child had eighteen, another twelve. Thirty-one per cent, the surgeon, Mr A.H. Tubby explained, 'could be said to be "cured" and 58 per cent "relieved"'. Nine had died in hospital. The hospitals had not publicised the results; nor did the Departmental Committee on Tuberculosis which elicited the figures.[4]

Unresponsive severe cases might be subjected to a laminectomy, the removal of the arches of one or more vertebrae to expose the spinal cord to drain it or remove a lesion, or what surgeons called a costo-transvectomy, in which it appears that one or more ribs were re-sectioned to allow an approach to a lesion on the front of the vertebrae. Sometimes even, as in the United States, deft surgeons fixed the spinous processes of the vertebrae across the lesion by inserting a graft from the patient's tibia. But by 1915 evidence was accumulating that this feat had 'disappointing' outcomes with 'unfortunate complications'. The French and the Americans were more cavalier than the British in their surgery and these kinds of operation seem to have been more frequent there. Sir Henry Gauvain referred to French estimates of a mortality of 75 per cent. Death usually followed sepsis, provoked by a failure to identify the seat of the infection or to contain it during the operation. Gauvain remarked that radical procedures seemed to disseminate tuberculosis.[5]

The relegation of these treatments during the mid 1920s coincided with a general conversion to orthopaedic inventions designed to 'rest' the affected part, by analogy with immobile sanatorium rest for the lungs. Gauvain was notably inventive. For patients with hunchback and side spinal curvature he created a 'spinal board'. This was made 18 inches longer than the patient and 8 inches wider, with sides 4 inches high, except at the foot where 16 inch sides held the bed clothes off the feet. The patient was placed in a 'jean jacket' and laid upon a mattress on the board. The jacket was fastened to the sides of the 'board', and the mattress was pushed up into a lump against the deformity. Then he or she was wheeled outside to cure in the fresh air and dosed to keep his or her bowels open. Gauvain designed a night-shirt with a split down the back, in order that a bed pan could be administered while the patient remained sideways on the board. If the lesion was cervical or in the upper dorsal region Gauvain recommended that the head be immobilised in a box, tied in with elastic. Patients with lumbar spinal deformity were set in plaster of Paris jackets. These, Gauvain taught, were best applied while the patient was suspended vertically; the procedure required a fortnight's training of the patient so that 'giddiness and syncope' did not intervene, 'so distressing to the patient and disconcerting to the surgeon'. The plaster was applied from the base at the pubes to well above the lesion. The patient was forbidden milk or vegetables before the event; plastering tended to induce vomiting. The object of the plaster case was less to support the patient, Gauvain explained, than to 'maintain the spine at rest in the correct position'. Lesions in the cervical region required especially long cases with moulded supports for the chin and forehead. The procedure was expensive and the case had to last three to six months, sufficient time, also, for an arrest of the infection, so Gauvain thought. Then the patient might be transferred into a celluloid removable jacket, moulded from a cast of the trunk. This had to be worn for two to three years. If properly made, it was 'so comfortable that its use is tolerated ... by the patient'.

Children with Pott's disease, paralysis of the legs through tuberculous damage to the spine, were immobilised in a wheelbarrow; with their legs in splints, or sometimes the surgeon might decide to suspend the rigidly splinted patient horizontally. Much individual ingenuity went into these arrangements: surgeons increased their fame with the Phelps Box, the Thomas Hip Splint, the Bradford Frame and many others. 'Once the muscular spasms' induced by immobilisation ceased, that is, the muscles began to atrophy, the patients could be put into a plaster jacket which might allow them to be 'relaxed from continuous recumbency'. By 1915 Gauvain had applied such procedures to 1000 cases at Treloar Cripples' Home. He was cagey about the results: 'under the best conditions, with properly conducted conservative treatment, the mortality should not exceed two per cent; and might even be reduced, if patients who had not been previously operated upon could be excluded. If radical treatment is undertaken the mortality at once rises enormously and seems to vary with various surgeons ... to as much as 50 per cent or even higher'. Hip cases, Gauvain considered, had better chances than spinal ones, without explaining why.[6]   British surgeons continued to claim good results, with 'no shortening in at least 50 per cent' of cases. They disregarded Smith and Watkins' report from the United States in 1929 of only two 'improvements' after five years from 208 operations and immobilisations similar to those performed in Britain.[7] I could not find any systematic follow-up in Britain of this orthopaedic work. The complacency continued to 1945, when Harbert and Williams remarked that 'up to 75 per cent of children ... now do well', without explaining where the estimate came from, or, the same thing, what it meant.[8]

'In Sanatoria [treating London County Council patients]', *The Times* alleged in 1920, '... 54 per cent were dead at the end of four years ... and ... of those not dead it is merely stated that they were alive ... We are neither preventing nor curing, and yet vast sums are being spent each year on the effort'.[9] Sanatorium officers responded to such criticism with obfuscation, while they quickly adopted major chest surgery as a sign that they were deploying new authority and skills. Artificial pneumothorax depended upon the theory that the diseased lung needed rest in order to heal or render the disease quiescent. As post mortems and X-rays revealed, collapse of a diseased lung occasionally happened spontaneously and healing ensued. The artificial induction of collapse had first been tried in 1821 but was little used before the late 1880s. It came into fashion in Britain in the early 1920s. The collapse was effected by introducing sterile air, oxygen or nitrogen into the pleura, measured to normal atmospheric pressure, and subject to controlling changes in mediastinal pressure. In theory, the elasticity of the lung allowed its tissue at the site of the cavity to contract, thereby reducing the gap and, over three or four years, promoting fibrosis and healing. With full collapse the lung became a small solid mass against the spine, with the heart and mediastinum carried over towards the opposite side.

The patient was given morphia and calomel (subchloride of mercury - a powerful purgative) the evening before the 'gassing', as patients called it. The chest was pierced frontally by a hollow needle, after a local anaesthetic, usually novocaine. There was no agreement about the best site for the injection, but finally one seventh or fifth intercostal space in the mid-axillary line became popular. Surgeons said the procedure was painless. Betty Macdonald, the author, who had an artificial pneumothorax in the 1940s, said the job felt as if the doctor was trying to push her over, then there was a 'crunchy feeling and a stab of pain'. Once the surgeon had assured himself that the needle was fully into the pleural cavity, he began to allow gas to be drawn into the cavity under atmospheric pressure. Strychnine and pituitrin were kept ready in syringes in case of 'pleural shock'. The simplest and commonly used apparatus consisted of two bottles connected by a siphoning tube. As fluid was siphoned from one bottle into the other, air was displaced from the second bottle, through a rubber tube and the hollow pneumothorax needle, into the pleural cavity. The second bottle was calibrated in cubic centimetres, and the amount of air displaced was measured by the rise of fluid in the bottle. About 300 cubic centimetres of gas were introduced at the first operation, with a refill of 400 cubic centimetres the following day. Betty Macdonald felt no sensation when the needle was withdrawn, but a few hours later she and other patients suffered 'knifelike pains in the chest' which 'continued for three days and nights'. The first refill was commonly delivered in the midst of this pain, with a second three or four days later. Collapse, if it occurred, was complete in about a fortnight, after five or six injections. Thereafter the collapse had to be maintained by refills every fortnight and every six weeks in subsequent years up to three or four years.[10]

The main danger, its advocates allowed in the 1920s, was gas embolism. This might ensue if the needle pumped gas into the bloodstream or tissue because it was not fully penetrated into the pleura but lodged instead in a vein or pleural wall, particularly if adhesions had grown between the lung and the chest wall. A second danger was pleural shock, with faintness, collapse and 'occasional death'. Sometimes, indeed often, statistics show the needle perforated the lung. This could lead to infection. Fifty per cent of operations were followed by pleurisy.[11] Still, the risk was worth it, according to Dr Clive Riviere, Physician to the City of London Hospital for Diseases of the Heart and Lungs. The 'healthy' lung was protected by the inactivation of a source of auto-infection. After fibrosis at the end of four years, the lung might be permitted to reinflate, 'unless it [was] bound down by a thickened pleura resulting from pleural attacks during treatment'.[12]

Artificial pneumothorax, Dr Neville Cox told the Tuberculosis Society in 1922, was 'the greatest advance in the treatment of tuberculosis in the past 50 years'. The only cases for which it was contraindicated were those with active disease in both lungs, or with a poor physique and low blood pressure, or patients suffering, as consumptives commonly did, from diabetes or asthma. 'There was scope', Cox continued, 'for a great deal of judgement in the selection of the cases ... Careful technique' was everything. Dr Jane Walker agreed that it should be offered to all patients who had been in a sanatorium uncured for more than six months; although she had known some 'disappointments', and she forecast that refills might have to continue for a lifetime. Cox agreed that it 'was ... difficult ... to tabulate statistics'.[13] In fact a Medical Research Council investigation of that year had found 50 per cent dead within two and three-quarter years of the operation. The investigation concluded that the only value of the procedure was that it usually rendered sputum positive patients sputum negative. Moreover it only worked for patients 'of good social position who [could] maintain the treatment'.[14] They were also likely to survive longer to continue it.

By 1924 some conservative authorities were issuing warnings about the high incidence of pleural effusions, 'nearly 50 per cent', the indeterminate length of the treatment and its doubtful results. Dr F.G. Chandler of the City of London Hospital for Diseases of the Heart and Lungs declared that if he were an early case he would not permit an artificial pneumothorax on himself. He added 'reluctance, undue timidity, lack of patience or of confidence on the part of the patient' to the list of contraindicators.[15] H. Batty Shaw of Brompton and University College Hospitals remarked that the procedure had not fulfilled the claims made for it and there was no proof that it prolonged life expectancy.

Yet Batty Shaw conceded that artificial pneumothorax had come to stay.[16] Gung ho sanatorium practitioners found a new cause - professional pride. J.D. Macfie of Winsley Sanatorium, near Bath, after a tour of north America as a member of a British Medical Association Tuberculosis Study Group, told final year medical students in 1931 that 75 per cent of patients in the United States had radical surgery and that the same percentage obtained in continental Europe. Britain, with about 25 per cent, was lagging. There were new opportunities for

'specialists' and 'real' rather than 'pseudo' sanatoria.   The
general practitioner and 'omnibus expert' had no place in
modern tuberculosis work.[17] Macfie and his colleagues ignored
the verdict by E. Rist, a populariser of artificial pneumothorax
in France, and chastened by 1926, that 71 per cent were dead in
ten years.[18]

The specialists continued to operate without producing any
conclusive evidence that the results justified the risks. It was
difficult to establish a control group or a reasonable definition of
'cure': that term varied between meaning 'fit for work' after
non-standardised time spans, but usually five years, and
'survived' for five years, mainly because follow-ups usually
failed after that. In 1936 Dr F.J. Bentley reported to the Medical
Research Council that of 677 in the London County Council
scheme between 1921 and 1930, only 50 per cent were alive after
five years. Sixty per cent of them had never achieved full
collapse of the lung. But that still left the remaining 340 or so
'20 per cent better off', than a group 'treated conservatively
without artificial pneumothorax', whose death-rate at five years
presumably was 70 per cent. Bentley did not canvass the
possibility that the conservatively treated group probably
included a small group of cases considered too 'early' for the
procedure, and a much larger group considered too far gone in
both lungs, or with complications, to be operated upon.[19] A
survey of collapse therapy among second stage patients at Clare
Hall Sanatorium between 1938 and 1948 argued a distinct
improvement in life expectancy. The inmates were 'blackcoated
workers' and they had become progressively younger through
the decade. Despite the authors' claims the results remain
ambiguous. Survival after discharge for three years, with a base
of 100, ran as follows:

	Males	Females
1938	79	104
1940	97	92
1942	110	110

But survival after five years showed:

	Males	Females
1938	84	123
1940	103	96

The variations over two years suggest that the time span,
quite apart from the exigencies of 1940 and 1942 was too short to

yield any convincing results. The authors also insisted that Frimley's 'selected' patients and Midhurst's 'unselected' cases showed 'similar results'. Yet Clare Hall claimed an average 72 per cent survival after five years for its cases, while London County Council patients in Frimley and Midhurst had, according to the authors' figures, reported an average of only 47 per cent, and those on 'conservative' regimens, 29 per cent.[20] Not surprisingly, F.R.G. Heaf summed up his observation of pneumothorax in 1949 with the remark that there were 'still no good statistics', and that no one knew the extent to which it had extended life expectancy or conferred permanent benefit.[21] Patients continued to be afraid of it and continued to demand it. Desperate cases sought it as an extra chance, while bored, ignored 'rest' cases found that it made hospital staff, initially at least, more interested in them. Artificial pneumothorax challenged the 'general futility and aimlessness of sanatorium life'.[22] The patients and surgeons were probably wrong. Dr G.M. Mayberry, of Dagenham, wondered aloud in 1935 'how many cases of pleural effusion and empyema [infection of the pleural membrane, producing pus, and rise in temperature] normally treated by further, urgent surgery can to-day be attributed to the ... bacilli and how many to modern treatment'.[23] Dr Holmes Sellors was reported to have remarked that 15 per cent of his patients selected for surgery did not need it when their turn arrived after a waiting period of eighteenth months, while Dr Lasar Dunner recalled in 1955 that he had known patients who were 'seemingly healed, who were operated on with fatal results'.[24] Exponents of artificial pneumothorax were still performing them, but the procedure was gradually being abandoned because of the belated acknowledgement of high relapse and complication rates and the advance of chemotherapy.[25]

About 1926 the specialists realised, 'after two or three years of intense artificial pneumothorax surgery, that lung adhesions to the chest wall and other difficulties obstructed complete collapses in a majority of cases'. The new object was to open the chest wall, in order to trace the adhesions, which could not be determined by X-ray, cut and cauterise them. H. Morriston Davies, of the Vale of Clwyd Sanatorium, who had introduced these procedures from Germany and Denmark before the War, asserted that complete collapses stopped haemoptysis, reduced fever and lengthened the intervals between refills.[26] The operation was done with a local anaesthetic, accompanied by nitrous oxide, ethylene and oxygen. The ribs were cut through with an incision running down the back over their angles, starting at the lower part. Three centimetres was removed from the first rib, rising to twelve to fifteen centimetres from the eighth, down to the eleventh. The total length of rib removed in one operation was about four feet. When done, the ribs were supposed to 'fall like the handle of a bucket'. Pneumonia and shock were the immediate danger, but enthusiasts like Clive Riviere referred vaguely to 'large statistics' which showed '36.8 per cent of advanced disease are cured, and 24.4 per cent are improved ... no small success when the class of material is considered'.[27]

While the operation was proceeding, adventurous surgeons like Davies, or William Anderson of Aberdeen would administer a further novocaine injection and 'tear out the phrenic nerve which was close to hand'. This nerve controls the movement of the diaphragm. Its removal usually caused the diaphragm to rise and so further contract the lung cavity and enable the diseased lung to rest. As Anderson described it, thoracoplasty was a 'mutilating operation, with much tearing of tissue, bleeding which difficult to control' and a high chance of shock.[28] Removing the phrenic nerve hardly added to the disturbance and made the operation more thorough.

The results claimed for these operations varied enormously, as did their distribution through the country. The authorities at Aberdeen, the Cheshire Joint Sanatorium, The King George V Sanatorium at Godalming, Brompton and Papworth all appear to have been enthusiastic operators. The Cheshire doctors reported in 1938 that between 1924 and 1932 'of the patients selected for artificial pneumothorax ... in whom phrenic evulsion was also carried out 83 per cent were alive four years later when the collapse was complete; 60 per cent when it was partial, and 46 per cent when it failed.' Similar groups 'without phrenic evulsion scored 62 per cent, 22 per cent and 25 per cent respectively'. It is hard to know what these superficially precise percentages mean. It appears that they cover only 260 patients who stayed at least six months. But 331 patients apparently began the course and nearly all, it appears, underwent some surgery: 121, or about 37 per cent, were missing from the report. One can only wonder what their results were and why they were discharged or departed early.[29] Papworth claimed much less. Between 1936 and 1938 their surgical unit performed 34 thoracoplasties on cases with extensive lesions but less than one-third of the lung affected. Artificial pneumothorax had already failed in each. By early 1939 25 were still alive: thirteen of these were 'apparently arrested', with half of them at full work at the village: the remaining twelve had 'active tuberculosis'. Three had died during the operation and a further five had died soon after from 'progressive tuberculosis'.[30] Brompton reported very similar results between 1922 and 1936 over a much larger sample of 437 thoracoplasties. Again the figures are opaque. Fifteen per cent were said to have been 'clinically cured', while operative mortality averaged 14 per cent, with 'subsequent mortality', 12 per cent. Four per cent were untraced, leaving 66 per cent said to be 'alive', although this seems to mean that they lived for at least three years after the operation.[31]

At Winsley and elsewhere superintendents who took up surgery proudly declared that they had changed the sanatoria from 'convalescent homes' to 'hospitals'. Money was diverted into building operating theatres, X-ray rooms, sterilizing rooms, 'filling stations' equipped with expensive new pumps like the Potain, which could gas two patients simultaneously. The superintendents and boards also sought to recruit trained theatre nurses, who themselves had to be paid higher wages than ordinary staff. Formerly, about 20 per cent of patients were confined to bed, while the rest largely nursed themselves; now 50 per cent were bed cases, and for nine months' treatment rather than six. One nurse to six beds became the norm, replacing the old one to eight. Costs per bed per year rose from £150 to £700. Sanatoria which could move nearer town did so, or established surgical units, so that they were more 'accessible to consultants'.[32] Under the Local Government Act of 1929 which gave block grants to local authorities and made them responsible for hospital accommodation and which permitted them - only half had done so by 1938 - to take over Poor Law infirmaries, additional beds and buildings suddenly became available.[33] 'Our sanatoria are true "chest hospitals"', Dr P. Heffernan, Tuberculosis Officer for Derbyshire boasted in 1934, '... the days of the shack-sanatorium are over'.[34]

Emerging chest hospitals installed glossy X-ray apparatus. In the mid 1920s skiagrams became a necessary prelude to surgery, apart from their use in diagnosis. Theoretically, the skiagram accurately delineated the extent of the lesion and might reveal chest wall adhesions. Subsequent skiagrams traced the progress of the artificial pneumothorax and the closure of cavities.[35] By 1931, 129 out of 140 tuberculosis authorities had X-ray 'arrangements', to service sanatoria, hospitals and dispensaries. Lancashire made an X-ray 'routine' for every visit for treatment.[36] By the early 1930s specialist radiologists challenged physicians for the dominant role in interpreting skiagrams, but were rebuffed. Ambitious young physicians became interested in tuberculosis, for the first time in a generation. Physicians argued that X-rays missed shadows and tiny lesions which 'clinical judgement' would discover both in the skiagram and by auscultation of the patient.[37] Progressive employers, like the Philips Radio Factory at Mitcham, began compulsory X-rays of all employees in 1934.[38] There must have been considerable make-believe. The 'woolly mottling' of active disease was difficult to distinguish from 'the characteristic appearance' of quiescent or healed tissue. X-ray pictures distorted at any range closer than five feet. They were 'very hard to read', one experienced user confessed, especially in the upper pleura and in thickened pleura.[39] Little wonder so many needles ended in the wrong place and artificial pneumothoraces failed.

'The surgeon's relation to his patient is usually more impersonal', Mr F.G. Chandler of Charing Cross Hospital explained in 1928. 'The mental and physical strain imposed by operation and the possibility of post-operative complications are sometimes belittled'. Emotionally, surgeons were poorly rewarded. After the operation, whether the patient did well or badly, it was the physician who drew the gratitude or the blame. Consideration for the physician compelled the surgeon to 'hesitate in desperate cases'. Moreover the surgeon had 'his own credit to consider ... His mortality figures cannot fail to be regarded as a reflection on his skill'.[40]

As surgeons became more proficient, ligaturing pulmonary vessels and the pulmonary artery, performing even more adventurous pneumothoraces, they tended to leave refills to juniors, general practitioners or nurses. The accepted number of refills increased during the early 1930s to three or more a week within the first month and they became an intrusion on valuable time. 'Few doctors visit their clinics that often', Dr Peter Edwards of the Cheshire Joint Sanatorium remarked in 1939. Nor would specialists provide night clinics for employed patients who could not otherwise get time off. On the other hand, each specialist held to 'his' patients: they refused to release 'their' X-ray photographs to another practitioner or dispensary and never managed to arrange rotas to cover their absences on holidays, while forbidding their nurses to act when not under their 'supervision'.[41]

Possibly they did prolong the existence of some decaying cases by immobilising badly affected lungs and promoting fibrosis. But the evidence is unclear. After all, only patients with presumptively one affected lung, and one healthy one, were selected, and their chances of survival, with or without surgery, were fair. When the fashion turned against radical surgery in the early 1950s as chemotherapy began to prove its worth, critics noticed that Holland, which had one of the lowest European tuberculosis mortality rates, had also one of the lowest rates of surgery, at under 25 per cent of patients. Other advocates of old-fashioned rest allied to the new drugs, declared openly to their colleagues for the first time that 'much excision of isolated lesions' had been 'unnecessary'.[42] Dr William C. Fowler ironically summed up three decades of tuberculosis surgery in 1956: 'Let us be grateful to all those human guinea-pigs by whose sufferings and fortitude hope was kept alive which enabled our surgeons and biochemists to step up a ladder runged with blood and sweat and tears ... bereft of many ribs, of phrenic nerves and transverse processes, padding out their vests to hide their scoliotic figures'.[43]

The specialists' impulse to be seen to be doing something led them in the mid 1920s, in addition to tinkering with Finsen lamps and other heat-ray devices, to employ massive exposure to X-rays, and to put patients on courses of injection of gold salts. Some doctors had tried salvarsan, but they had found that it had 'no specific value', adding euphemistically that it 'was not devoid of risk'. Intratracheal injections of menthol, olive oil, guiacol [Beechwood Creosote - an antiseptic - it can cause profuse perspiration], pig spleen extract, all gave 'good results'. Silica and colloidal preparations of silver, copper, brass, aluminium and antimony had each their devotees: the first issue of *Tubercle* in 1919 reported 'striking results with a preparation of brass digested in oil', but none produced any measureable benefit in the long run. The X-ray therapy gave ambiguous results. Patients lost their hair, but Dr R.A. Young of Brompton descried 'some benefit' in 1924, especially when the rays were 'directed to the spleen'.   There was no experimental proof that the bacillus was sensitive to X-rays: Young surmised that the unspecified 'good results' derived from 'tissue reaction'.[44]

Gold salts, partly because they were so exotic and expensive, enjoyed a longer vogue. They had been administered in France since at least the 1830s, and became very popular in the 1860s. Koch had observed in 1890 that gold salts, especially cyanides, inhibited the growth of tuberculous bacilli in vitro. After a succession of German scientists had produced variants and made great claims for them, Holger Moellgaard of Copenhagen announced sanocrysin in 1925. It was, he said, a thiosulphide of gold, which penetrated the lipoid envelope of the tubercle to kill the bacillus, combined with an antiserum which neutralised the tuberculous toxin liberated from the attacked bacillus. Sanocrysin then conferred passive immunity. The Danes had established a factory to mass produce it.

Moellgaard's recommended dosage was a massive half to one gramme in shots of 20-40 cubic centimetres of antiserum, injected intramuscularly every three or four days. The injections provoked fever and albuminuria, loss of weight, and skin eruptions - Moellgaard's experimental animals regularly died of shock. One wonders how he proved his trial experiments.   Of the 42 trial patients, nine died of shock or prostration, and 19 out of 21 'severe' cases showed no improvement, while the remaining twelve slight cases were discharged 'symptom free', presumably when their fever and albuminuria abated.   Moellgaard and his Danish backers represented this episode as a triumph. Sanocrysin 'worked with both early ... and chronic cases', even though the treatment was 'not agreeable'.[45]

Varrier-Jones tried it on Papworth patients in 1926, but reported that it had no effect on the disease.[46] Dr Mary Nannetti, however, claimed 'highly satisfactory' results in 'suitable cases', defined as 'exudative-type with nodular caseous pneumonic force breaking down with cavity formation', that is, late stage I or early stage II patients. As usual, she defended the procedure by asserting that Moellgaard's recommended dose was too big. She injected one fifth of a gramme every one to two weeks, rising to half a gramme, accompanied by injections

of caffeine or digitalis preparation, for a six weeks course. Dr
Nannetti said that the patients' general condition was
improved, their temperature took a more regular curve, they
lost their tiredness, and the bacilli vanished, despite their still
suffering shock, loss of weight and skin eruptions.[47] Drs
William Stobie and Sheila Hunter at the Radcliffe Infirmary
also tried sanocrysin on sputum positive patients. They
claimed 'definite improvement' in 25 out of 45 cases during two
years of presumably six week courses. Of the remainder, the
treatment was abandoned in ten cases because of
'complications', seven more showed 'no improvement', and
three patients left before their course ended. At the end of their
table, Stobie and Hunter mention a further ten 'abandoned'
patients. It is a sad indication of patients' desperation that half
the group endured to the end the pain of injections, vomiting,
diarrhoea, anorexia and fever that sanocrysin induced. The
course cost £4 5s 0d in gold salts alone. The price precluded it,
fortunately, from mass application through the dispensaries or
out-patient wards. Patients were restricted and needed 'close
observation': altogether, Stobie and Hunter warned dabbling
general practitioners that it was a job for specialists.[48]

As happened with strict immobilisation, sanocrysin
enthusiasts evaded patient resistance by concentrating on
children. Dr H.T. Ashby of Liverpool administered specially
small doses to pulmonary cases only - he never publicly explained why - over courses of ten to twelve injections in 1930-1.
He announced the usual 'encouraging results', without giving
the totals involved, details of the patients or the periods of the
trials.[49]

Sanocrysin continued in use until at least the Second World
War. Some doctors combined it with collapse therapy.[50] Its
advocates ignored the continuing want of proof of its
effectiveness. They also ignored Dr Gregory Kayne's warning in
1935 that Moellgaard had fudged his results. His first laboratory
success had been obtained by infecting guinea pigs with highly
attenuated bacilli, and his co-workers had never been able to
repeat his experiments, although they kept that bad news to
themselves. Suggestions to the Danes that they mount
controlled tests had been disregarded. Medical authorities in
Sweden and Norway had stopped its use.[51] The next year an
American researcher, Frank Terrill, declared it impossible to
demonstrate Koch's or Moellgaard's claims that gold acted on

tubercle.[52] Certainly, sanocrysin failed to help John Osborne's tubercular father in 1938. By 1947 it had 'almost completely disappeared', and Dr. R.R. Traill told readers of the *Practitioner* that it had had 'disastrous results in skin and kidney complications'. Its demise, Traill implied, marked an advance.[53]

Registered practitioners sharply distinguished themselves from unregistered ones, whom they dismissed as charlatans, yet the line between them, particularly in their treatments and dealings with patients, was often indistinct.[54] Commonly quacks mimicked orthodox treatments but occasionally, as with inhalation procedures, the orthodox seem to have copied from the quacks.[55] After the Medical Act of 1858 unregistered practitioners were unable to sue for fees for their medicines or treatments, but they could charge for time spent on the case and the prohibitions seem rarely to have prevented them from getting their money. During this century they have been cumulatively barred from signing death certificates, working in public hospitals, administering vaccines, practising surgery, pretending to recognised qualifications which they do not possess, amongst other curbs, but otherwise they are free to trade and make what they can.

From the 1880s quacks began to tap the rising disposable incomes of lower middle class and working class people through mass advertising and direct mailing. Holloway and Beecham were challenged on the hoardings, in the newspapers and in the corner shops by innumerable new competitors, often working on commission from small firms with 'sucker lists', who provided the product, packaging and advertising.

Forbidden surgery, quacks were confined to selling diagnosis and medicaments. They counterfeited the regulars by parading qualifications, sometimes degrees or diplomas from obscure foreign colleges, more often strings of meaningless letters after their names, and by adverting to enviable posts they had held or cures of notables they had effected. They drew upon medical textbooks and language, and invoked the pharmacopoeia, often with a dash of traditional herbalism or homeopathy, and divination from birthdates or examination of faeces. Strong traditional beliefs in mechanistic theories of the body and illness, faith in decisive, particular interventions and the regular occurrence of apparent 'cures' all served desperate patients and plausible quacks.

George Thomas Congreve's guide to confirmatory self diagnosis and collection of puffs entitled *On Consumption of the Lungs or Decline; and its Successful Treatment: showing that formidable disease to be curable in all its stages ...* (new edition, London c.1887) price, one shilling, is one among dozens published between the 1880s and 1920s. It is neatly printed and bound and resembles a devotional work. Like its fellows, it contains two sections. The first provides a simple, minatory account of phthisis and its symptoms and directs the reader to diagnose it in him or herself. This part is intimate and furtive - many of the guides, like Congreve's, have no title on the spine. The second, larger portion, presents dozens of seemingly independent puffs in the third person for Congreve's Balsamic Elixir from evangelical Protestant and suburban newspapers, and individual grateful clients. All of it echoes material in similar books and the authors probably pillaged one another. We do know that two other irregulars, Edwin Alabone and Henry Morton, wrote many of the puffs themselves and solicited 'unsolicited' letters from patients.[56] Cases mishandled by regulars and rival quacks reported themselves saved - just in time - by providentially turning to Congreve. They answered advertisements through the post, purchased his book, or applied direct to him at Coombe Lodge, Rye Lane, Peckham. He confirmed their descriptions of their symptoms - I have been unable to discover whether he issued a tendentious questionnaire, but many of his brethren did - and sold them Balsamic Elixir by direct mailing in a range of bottle sizes, 22s, 11s [family size], 4s 6d for four fluid ounces, 2s 9d, 1s 1^{1}/$_{2}$^{d}, , or cheaper if need be, over a prolonged course of medication. The course included a strongly inculcated, mostly helpful, self-controlled regimen covering 'proper diet' - red meat and fowl, - 'fish ... affords little nourishment ... lobsters, crabs ... are improper', as were tea, coffee and alcoholic drinks. Congreve prescribed cocoa. It was better advice than that of regulars who imposed starvation diets or over-feeding. Working class patients might have felt better at forgoing the lobster they could rarely afford, while middle class clients with their 22s bottles could congratulate themselves on renouncing foods that only provoked dyspepsia. Congreve, like many irregulars, conducted a 'personal' correspondence with his clients, inviting trust from otherwise friendless secretive sufferers. In Alabone's and Morton's cases, the letters were written to formulae by ill-paid junior clerks.

Congreve's bright red Balsamic Elixir, was he claimed, 'exclusively herbal'. Some of it might have been, because his medicines like those of other quacks, varied in their composition,   but one batch at least contained aromatic sulphuric acid - (it reduced night sweats). Samples also contained traces of balsam of Tolu and Peru balsam, both stimulants and antiseptics, the latter normally applied only externally - (it can cause renal failure), - Virginia prune, a sedative, much sugar and cochineal, and over 28 per cent by volume of alcohol. Adults, following the directions to take a teaspoonful three or four times a day, would have found it relaxing, and children eight to fifteen years, on two-thirds of a teaspoonful, perhaps even more so. They might also have found it addictive. On my calculations, an adult would consume a 4s bottleful in about ten days. Congreve's recipe was not markedly different to those prescribed by many regulars, and might readily have been plagiarised from one of them.[57]

Dr Derk P. Yonkerman Co. Ltd, was an American firm with agencies in London and Australia. It flourished from between the 1880s and the Great War. Yonkerman had begun as a horse doctor in southern Michigan, the burnt-over heartland of perfectibilist healing cults: besides Yonkerman, it nurtured the Kellogg brothers and Ellen Gould White, a founder of Seventh Day Adventism.

The Yonkerman book, *Consumption and How it May be Quickly Cured*, [British ed. (1907?)] was issued free to inquirers who answered the firm's   imperious advertisements in newspapers, featuring the doctor, a twin to Cecil Rhodes, fixing the reader with a glittering eye and arm and forefinger outstretched,   prefiguring Lord Kitchener, declaring: 'Consumption Can Be Cured'. The means was self-control and 'Tuberculozyne', 'a wonderful specific ... discovered ... after twenty years of almost ceaseless research and experiment in his laboratory'.   Enquirers received two half ounce bottles of 'Tuberculozyne' by mail together with a bill for £2 10s 0d and directions that the medicine be taken absolutely as prescribed, given the applicant's weakened state, 30 drops from each bottle in strict sequence and never mixed, in milk three times a day immediately after meals.

Tuberculozyne had what self-obsessed, worried patients and desperate, wasting sufferers needed, 'almost miraculous curative power.... Its healing virtues have been demonstrated in not only the early stages of consumption but in far advanced and seemingly hopeless cases as well ... The consumption germ ... cannot live in the presence of copper, and as the Tuberculozyne introduces copper into the blood, the consumption germ cannot live'. Yonkerman confirmed his clients' disillusionment with orthodox therapies: 'intra-venous injection ... proved absolutely ineffective...'; 'inoculation with tuberculin ... frequently hastened ... death.... antimony, prussic acid, emetics, blisters, mercury, iron, digitalis, clover ... all ... useless...; creosote was ... wrong'. Tuberculin, moreover, had been foisted on the British public by Koch, a foreigner. The nostrums peddled by other advertisers were equally wrong and quackish: they did not contain copper.

By comparison with the orthodox therapeutics Yonkerman listed, 'Tuberculozyne' was benign. Bottle number one contained a bright red liquid consisting of about 85 per cent alcohol, with glycerine and potassium bromide, and traces of cassia oil, tincture of capsicum, caustic soda, with cochineal. Bottle number two held a brown liquid of varying brightness and viscosity. It was 82 per cent water, much burnt sugar, 18 per cent glycerine with a trace of almond oil - a purgative. The estimated costs of the ingredients of both bottles was $2^{1}/2^{d}$. There was no copper. After the opening bid of £2 10s 0d, the Company dropped to 40s in its fourth follow up letter, down to 10s 'to be paid later', with a special voucher for discounted further supplies, when patients proved recalcitrant. 'Just at this time, when the patient has been taking our treatment for some weeks and it is beginning to permeate her system through and through, courage is needed, for great improvement may not yet be apparent though her cure is assured'. The copper had disappeared, if it had ever been included, analysts surmised, because it was precipitated on the sides of the iron drums in which Tuberculozyne was concocted and stored.[58]

The use of the feminine pronoun adds to what little we know about consumers of other patent medicines, that women comprised an important section of the market.[59] Many tuberculosis, scrofula and cancer cures, like Scott, Henderson and Company's 'Liquorzone', - mostly soap, 1.7 per cent sulphuric acid and a lot of powerful laxative - included

'Women's diseases' among the maladies they listed for cure. It seems to have been intended as an abortifacient; however ineffective, women might have bought it   primarily for that purpose[60] I have no firm evidence, but it seems plausible to imagine that consumers included many house-bound women, especially domestic servants, who were otherwise precluded by duty and the need for secrecy from seeking advice or continuing with general practitioners or dispensaries. They would not have wanted calls from health visitors. Moreover, the names appended to the puffs in the advertising volumes are exclusively male.

There were dozens of other remedies. 'Crimson Cross Fever and Influenza Powder for the Cure of Consumption' was a purplish powder made up in boxes of about 100 grains. The instructions directed adults to add one tablespoonful to a pint of water and take one tablespoonful of the mixture three times a day. It was 99 per cent ammonium chloride - an expectorant and diuretic. The ingredients cost about a half farthing.[61] 'Lung Germine', at £1 per two ounce bottle, was 9 per cent sulphuric acid, with traces of iron, magnesium and manganese, possible entering from the container in which it was mixed. The wrapper warned, reassuringly, that 'when these germs are being torn from their lodgements and discharged, together with impurities and secretions, it often weakens the patient considerably'. But that was the 'turning point'. Thereafter, continued doses accelerated recovery. 'Lung Germine', Paster Felke's Honey Cod Liver Oil - 0.05 per cent of it in raspberry syrup - and 'Bacillentod', a 'family tea' consisting of 'dog nettle' - were distributed by a group of evanescent companies variously registered as the Sovereign Remedy Company, the Drouet Company and Weidhaas Hygienic Institute whose proprietors, rival quacks alleged, were German and Polish Jews. Certainly, they drew heavily on traditional German *Naturheilfunde* in their propaganda. They also extended their sales by paying pharmacists to send them the names of consumptive customers and by promising their own clients a discount on further medicines when they supplied confidentially the names of fellow sufferers. Another alien, Dr H.H. Crippen, also from southern Michigan, was associated with at least the first two firms.[62]

Despite demands from the medical profession, successive governments, encouraged by newspaper barons, refused to legislate against misleading claims and the sale of non-scheduled drugs in patent medicines. The patents on the secret recipes yielded a huge, easily collected income to government and the Post Office. Over 46,000,000 patent items were sold in the United Kingdom in 1904-5, representing a net outlay of over £3,000,000. The state tax receipt was one-eighth of the full retail price of each item.

Major C.H. Stevens, proprietor of 'Stevens Consumption Cure', was by contrast with his rivals, a true Briton. He was born in 1880 in Birmingham. In 1897 he was by his own account, informed by his doctor that he had a lung weakness: 'my boy: you are for it'. The doctor advised Stevens to try the veldt. In Bloemfontein, Stevens recalled, a Dutchman introduced him to a Kaffir witch doctor dressed in a leopard skin. The witch doctor produced some crushed root and proceeded to boil it in water. Then he gave the decoction to Stevens to drink. He did. He vomited. But he took the remainder of the root, boiled some and drank it every morning and evening for two months. After that he 'felt as well as he ever did'. He then returned to England, bringing a supply of the root. It baffled the analysts. Stevens gave decoctions gratis to 22 consumptives. They all 'got well'.[63]

When the Boer War began in 1899 Stevens returned to South Africa. He served, he said, first with the Scottish Yeomanry and then joined the Cape Mounted Police. In one of these forces he attained the rank of major. At the war's end Stevens set up as the New Hudson Cycle and Motor Agency in Cape Town. The Agency was, he claimed later, 'very successful'; but in the next year the business was destroyed by fire and Stevens was uninsured. It emerged long afterwards that he was an undischarged bankrupt from about this period. He returned to distributing the root and began to charge for doses. He now first learned the Kaffir word for it, so he said later - *umkaloabo*. Meanwhile, the Cape medical fraternity ignored his repeated offers to demonstrate the root's miraculous powers. Oddly, although he now knew the original name, Stevens was marketing the remedy as 'Sacco'. Between about 1903 and 1907 he said he received £6,000 a year from it, £5,000 of which he gave, he declared later, bursting into tears, to the poor of Cape Town. His gifts had been anonymous, apparently, because there was no record of them. The 'Sacco' business suddenly collapsed. It emerged later that a rival had sued him successfully for infringement of patent. Stevens moved to Johannesburg and began to sell 'Lung-Sava'. It was based on an improved recipe, 'in consequence of certain tests', and was guaranteed to stop haemorrhages. The improved recipe contained a lot of alcohol. Registered practitioners twice successfully prosecuted Stevens for purveying alcohol to a native and once for pretending to be medically qualified. After a third conviction, whatever it was, Stevens abruptly left Johannesburg.

During 1907 he turned up at 204 Worple Road, Wimbledon, the headquarters of the C.H. Stevens Consumption Cure Co. Within a year he was employing, he said, 50 people to make, pack, and post *umkaloabo*, and to handle advertising, direct mailing, his personal letters to sufferers, and the company accounts. His Wimbledon enterprise, which was to continue for over 30 years, inspired H.G. Wells's Tono-Bungay Company of 1909, which also had its headquarters in Wimblehurst, although the Ponderevos sold their product at only 1s 3^{1}/2^{d}, and 2s 9d. Engaging Uncle Teddy Ponderevo is a recognisable sibling to the engaging, emotional, fantastical and deceitful Major Stevens.

The C.H. Stevens Consumption Cure Co. soon advertised a new remedy, *chitytse*, which reinforced the impact of the *umkaloabo* when taken in conjunction with it. *Chitytse* too had originated with a Kaffir witch doctor. 'The African herbs which my cure is prepared from have never been used by any white Doctor or chemist before I introduced same to civilization ... These herbs have defied our cleverest analysts'.

The Major wrote the English of the board school model letter. It was a language which his audience must have found both familiar and authoritative; and excitingly promising, if they remembered Rider Haggard's popular African mystical erotic adventure stories, such as *Allan Quartermain* or *Ayesha*. It seems that they responded in their thousands to Stevens's advertisements and 'personal' letters. He encouraged patients to tell him the name of their regular, failed, practitioner, to enable him to send the beleaguered doctor some free samples of *umkaloabo-chitytse* to try on himself or use experimentally on his patients, who must be declining under the doctor's ordinary, old-fashioned therapies. Indeed, a few regulars reported good results with his remedy. Stevens quoted their findings in his newssheet and obliged them by spontaneously upgrading the qualifications after their names.

His dosage instructions were typically exact and exacting and, typically, diverged slightly from those of his rivals. One teaspoonsful from bottle number one had to be taken in a wineglass of hot water one hour before breakfast, and one teaspoonful from the second bottle two hours after the last meal of the evening, 'unless the patient be in the habit of waking between 12 midnight and 3 a.m., [many consumptives were] in which case an extra dose may be taken then'.[64] Each bottle contained two and a half ounces of clear red fluid and after the introductory three month course costing £2 12s 6d for the pair, further bottles were 5s each. (Comparable provincial prices were Payne's gents' footwear, 8s 11d, 10s 6d, 12s 6d; stout, 3s per dozen; World's Stores Butter 1s per pound; lamb forequarter, 6½d per pound; Lux soap, 1d per packet; double mattress, 22s 6d; Gladstone bags 16s 6d to 22s 6d. *Southampton Times, Manchester Daily Mail, Oxford Journal* 1907.) Stevens's follow-up letters adjusted the price to the client's preparedness to pay. He reminded waverers and hypochondriacal subscribers ready to transfer to another nostrum that *umkaloabo* cured not only consumption but that it was 'also ... a vegetable germicide, strong tonic, blood purifier, stomach cleaner and nerve stimulant'.

Stevens's speciality, used also by some other quacks, was the guarantee bond. This device circumvented the law forbidding unregistered practitioners charging directly for medicines. His 'No.1 Bond' provided in ornately serifed large type, with much small print, that after a three months course pursued as directed, at £2 12s 6d pre-paid, the patient's improvement would be certified by the patient's own registered doctor, and the payment remain with Stevens for his time and interest. Otherwise, Stevens promised to refund the pre-payment. The 'No.2 Bond' provided that at 'a later period', after an unspecified number of further courses, there would be a total disappearance of the tubercle and a 'complete cure', again to be certified by the patient's own doctor. Upon this consummation the full payment would revert to Stevens; in the extraordinary event of a non-cure the money would be returned. It was a mechanism exquisitely framed to infuriate the regulars and to destroy what remained of their relationship with patients already given to distrusting them. The small print contained saving clauses, including the ominous one providing that when the patient died within six months of the issue of the first bond the guarantee was void. I know of only one person who got her money back: a widow from Basingstoke who sued for it. A few regulars certified improvements and cures.[65]

From the outset Stevens was banking his £6000 a year in numerous small accounts under various names in banks around Wimbledon. The onslaught on quackery in the populist *Truth* in 1906-7 impelled the British Medical Association to proceed with its own investigation in 1908-9. A Select Committee investigated the trade in 1914, after a Royal Commission scarified it in Australia in 1912. The analysts found no *umkaloabo* or *chitytse* in bottles one or two. Indeed, they did not know what to test for because the substances were unknown to the South African or British *Pharmacopoeias*. The analysts reported Steven's remedies to contain about 20 per cent proof spirit, 15 per cent glycerol, mixed with water and a trace of alkali, possible Krameria root, a powerful astringent which might have helped stop haemorrhages.

Faced with this kind of exposure, most quacks quietly continued to trade, sometimes under a new set of names, secure in the hope that their clientele were unlikely to believe the medical profession's self-interested allegations. But the Major ostentatiously challenged the British Medical Association to inoculate him at Brompton Hospital with the fiercest tuberculosis germs they could find in the Hospital and then to watch him cure himself with *umkaloabo* and *chitytse*. They rejected his offer as unethical.[66] His challenge made him famous. He then went further on the offensive, drew on his bank reserves, and sued the British Medical Association for libel. The case dragged on between 1912 and1914. Stevens lost the first trial and brought a second action. His witnesses included Captain J.H. Bailey from South Africa, a journalist, who swore that he had seen *umkaloabo* used by natives in South Africa in the manner described by Stevens. The root was 'something like a small Spanish onion'. Dr Jameson, of West Ham, and Dr E.F. Grün, a tuberculosis specialist, but currently a Poor Law medical officer, swore that they had given the plaintiff's medicine to a number of patients with beneficial results. Another elderly registered practioner, Dr A.H. Bennett swore that he had seen *umkaloabo* used by natives in Liberia and elsewhere in Africa and that it cured consumption and bronchitis. An analyst formerly employed by Stevens swore that his analysis proved that the remedy contained *umkaloabo*, but the defence exposed him as an alcoholic ex-analyst. A Church of England clergyman, a male cashier in a cotton mill, a male pharmacist given only three years to live, railway clerks, nurses, and lady typists swore that they had been cured of consumption or tuberculous hips by the Major's advice and *umkaloabo*. Stevens's case faltered, however, when William Smith, a senior railway servant, told the court that he had gone to 204 Worple Road with two of his juniors who were consumptive, and had been examined by Stevens with a stethoscope, pronounced consumptive, given an injection of *umkaloabo*, advised immediately to buy a course and 'call again'. Smith swore that he had always been completely healthy and had never exhibited any of the symptoms of tuberculosis. Meanwhile, analysts and doctors gave evidence for the defence that *umkaloabo* was not to be found in Stevens's bottles, and that he had a history of fraud and bankruptcy. Stevens lost this trial, too, with costs of £2000.[67]

He continued to advertise and sell *umkaloabo*, undaunted by the revelation that he had stolen the patent - Krameria root or whatever it was - from one Myers, a tailor in South Africa who sold patent medicines as a sideline. Myers was the rival who had prosecuted Stevens in Cape Town and forced him to flee to Johannesburg and change 'Sacco' to 'Lung-Sava'.

In the early 1930s two long accounts of Stevens's life, litigations and healing triumphs appeared, written by 'An English Physician' and 'G.P.'. Both books also reported the claims of Dr. Adrien Séchehaye, who had since 1920 used *umkaloabo* with great success in his Swiss sanatorium. Séchehaye's main report, *Traitement de la tuberculose par l'umckaloabo*, appeared in English translation in 1930 and 1938, published in the same linguistic style, in the same format, by the same otherwise unknown publisher, B. Fraser and Co., as the 'English Physician's' *Tuberculosis and its treatment and cure with the help of umkaloabo* (Sp. Stevens), of 1931 [?] and its sister book, largely a report by 'G.P.', in 1933[?]. The linguistic style moreover, is consistent with Stevens's advertisements and 'personal' letters. Séchehaye was a graduate of Basel but is otherwise unknown to Swiss medicine. Yet the Swiss doctor's scientific-sounding report that *umkaloabo* 'neutralizes or destroys the tuberculinic toxins' and 'disarms the bacillus' made an impression, not least on the Social Credit journalist and disciple of Gurdjieff, A.R. Orage, who quoted it in his *New Age* in 1930.[68]

Stevens' boasts were now more extravagant than ever. He revived an old claim that *umkaloabo* healed lung cavities without scarring, thereby attracting prospective white collar applicants for life assurance or superannuation who faced X-ray examinations.[69] Still, many of his other commands were helpful, like those of other charlatans. Patients had to 'stay off alcohol' for the duration of his treatment. They were, after all, getting it in the '*umkaloabo* cure'. They were to take regular rest, keep warm and generally look after themselves. Clients who had emerged uncured from sanatoria or who had relapses after being discharged must have taken courage from his congratulations upon having escaped from these 'landslides to the grave'. Politicians with a populist, technocractic, conspiratorial view of the world took up his cause. In 1931 Sir Waldron Smithers, Conservative member for Chislehurst, became upset when the Minister for Health, Arthur Greenwood, refused to agree to an official test of *umkaloabo*. Smithers suspected that the Minister was in the grip of secret medical advisers leagued against non-medical benefactors of mankind:[70] a view that was not entirely unfounded. Smithers was later to find fame by harassing Lindemann, Lord Cherwell, Churchill's wartime scientific adviser as a German spy. Edward Williams, a Labour miners' MP from Glamorganshire, demanded in 1932 that the Minister examine the evidence, presumably from the eminent Dr Séchehaye, of certified cases 'speedily cured by the Stevens treatment'. The Minister, a Conservative on this occasion, said 'No', whereupon the right-wing Tory Sir Cooper Rawson, MP for Brighton, asked the same question and received the same answer. Herbert Williams, the Conservative engineering entrepreneur, asked during an exchange in 1933, 'Does the Minister of Health take the view of the medical profession that anything which has not been invented by the medical profession is no good?' The Minister did not reply.[71]

This range of support shows that Stevens's constituency was not drawn exclusively from the lower middle class or respectable working classes. Rich families also had their consumptives who did not respond to orthodox therapies.[72] Yet the tone of his advertising and the addresses on alleged clients' letters suggest that the lower ranks provided his staunchest supporters and probably most of his patients. Consumption loomed as a special catastrophe to members of these classes at the margins of economic security and gentility. They were too proud to frequent out-patient wards, too private and too constrained by working hours to become regulars at dispensaries, too poor to pay for specialists, too fearful of losing their jobs and of the neighbours' alienation if they were notified, and too short of savings to enter sanatoria as longterm patients. To them, as indeed to patients in sanatoria who secretly subscribed, direct mail sellers of patent medicines were a godsend. The patient could obtain, alone, remedies that were affordable in the short run, which promised an alleviation or cure that the sufferer dearly wanted to believe in, which certainly induced soothing numbness and a pleasant addiction, and which came in plain wrappers.

They were a godsend, moreover, in what appears to have been a peculiarly Protestant world. Congreve's and Stevens's collections of testimonials, and several others that I have read, are notably lacking in addresses from southern Ireland, Irish names or encomiums from Catholic priests, by comparison with those from evangelical Anglican and Nonconformist clergy. Mountebanks seem never to have advertised in Catholic papers. They offered salvation through new private rituals: self-cleansing through purgatives and sober living, purification of the blood through careful eating - some quacks enjoined vegetarianism - moral and physical strengthening through tonics, malt, cod liver oil and fresh air, consummated by the quack's particular germicide which fought the bacillus, the sin within the body. Thus the justice of Providence was restored in a world otherwise bereft of miracles and the intercession of therapeutic saints, and liberated from threatening intermediaries, doctors, health visitors and High Church busybodies. The culminating point for this kind of self-salvation, of the triumph of the will over the body, realised in the spirit refined in the body perfect, was Christian Science.

Despite their parasitic theft and clinically worthless nostrums, quacks did little real harm. They did not kill patients or cause pointless pain and shock, as did registered practitioners toying with Moellgaard's sanocrysin or hit or miss surgery. The quacks' sugared water, diluted chloroform, morphine and alcohol were, by comparison, gentle blessings. Quacks were avaricious but their 'cures' were no more expensive than the charges levied by the regulars for their generally inefficacious procedures. Anxious sufferers found in quackery a modicum of 'personal' attention and rituals of private self-control that must have been helpful in the short run. Quacks told lies, but their lies gave comfort. It was a contemporary of Major Stevens and Sir Henry Gauvain, an American expatriate like Dr Crippen, a physically weak man with an ailing estranged wife, who remarked, 'human kind Cannot bear very much reality'.

NOTES

[1]W. Knight Treves (Surgeon to the Royal National Hospital for Scrofula, Margate), *Lancet*, 14, 28 Sept., 5 Oct. 1889, pp.544, 634, 687. The jovial reference to '"gland-thirsty" surgeons', was made by one of their colleagues, Bertram Thornton, Physician to the Bathing Infirmary, Margate, *Lancet*, 31 Aug. 1889, p.456.

[2]J. Lewis Thomas, 'Ten Years' Welsh Tuberculosis Dispensary Work', *Practitioner*, vol.cxiv, 1925, p.149.

[3]F.B. Airey, *Transactions of NAPT,1952*, p.267.

[4]Watson Cheyne, *Lancet*, 12 May 1888, p.926; Sir Robert Jones 'Cripples', *Practitioner*, vol.cxii, 1924, pp.9-10; A.H. Tubby to Departmental Committee on Tuberculosis, n.d. (1912?), Astor Papers, Reading University Library, MS1066/1/1042.

[5]Sir Henry Gauvain, 'Tuberculous Cripples', in Kelynack, (ed.) *Defective Children*, pp.120-2.

[6]Ibid., pp.121-41.

[7]*BMJ*, 21 Sept. 1929, p.546.

[8]Williams and Harbert, *Social Work*, p.14.

[9]*The Times*, 21 Feb. 1920, quoted in Bolton Tomson, *Prevention of Tuberculosis*, p.vi.

[10]R.A. Young, (Brompton) Lettsomian Lecture, gives a clear, detailed account, *BMJ*, 22 Apr. 1924, p.533, Betty Macdonald, *The Plague And I*, 1949, pp.129-34; H.S. Souttar (London Hospital), 'Recent Advances in the Surgery of the Chest', *BMJ*, 5 June 1926, p.935.

[11]Young, *BMJ*, 22 Apr. 1924, p.533.

[12]*BMJ*, 1 May 1926, p.775.

[13]*BMJ*, 29 Apr. 1922, p.683.

[14]L.S.T. Burrell and A. Salusbury McNalty, *Report on Artificial Pneumothorax*, 1922, pp.56, 83.

[15]F.G. Chandler, *BMJ*, 4 Oct. 1924, pp.617-8.

[16]H. Batty Shaw, 'The Treatment of Consumption by Artificial Pneumothorax', *Practitioner*, vol.cxii, 1924, pp.99-103.

[17]*BMJ*, 28 Nov. 1931, p.1011.

[18]*BMJ*, 30 Jan. 1926, p.216.

[19]F.J. Bentley, *BMJ*, 19 Dec. 1936, p.1267.

[20]F.A.H. Simmonds and W.J. Martin, 'The Results of Sanatorium Treatment and Collapse Therapy', *American Review of Tuberculosis*, vol.lviii, 1948, pp.539-48.

[21]*Proc. Roy. Soc. Med.* vol. xliii, 1949, p.248.

[22]L.E. Houghton (Consultant to Middlesex Tuberculosis Service), *Tubercle*, vol.xxviii, 1947, pp.179-80.

[23]BMJ, 15 June 1935, p.1239.

[24]Lasar Dunner in *Tubercle*, vol.xxxvi, 1955, p.393.

[25]A.T.M. Roberts (Chest Clinic, Bristol), *Tubercle*, vol.xxxvii, 1956, p.294.

[26]H. Morriston Davies, *BMJ*, 20 Dec. 1924, p.1148; there is a brief history of the operation by Edward W. Archibald in Lawrason Brown, *The Story of Clinical Pulmonary Tuberculosis*, Baltimore 1941, p.299.

[27]Souttar, *BMJ*, 5 June 1926, p.935; Riviere, *BMJ*, 1 May 1926, p.774.

[28]Anderson, *BMJ*, 23 Apr. 1932, p.755; Davies, *BMJ*, 20 Dec. 1924, p.1145.

[29]Peter W. Edwards, *Report ... 1936*, quoted *BMJ*, 12 Feb. 1938, p.345.

[30]*Papworth Research Bulletin*, vol.1, 1936-1939, pp.7-12.

[31]Anon., 'Fourteen Years' Experience of ... Thoracoplasty', *Brompton Hospital Reports*, vol.v, 1936, pp.103-6.

[32]James Watt (Medical Superintendent, King George V Sanatorium, Godalming), *BMJ*, 23 June 1934, p.1137.

[33]Wilson, *Health Services*, pp.106-12.

[34]*BMJ*, 14 Apr. 1934, p.690.

[35]J.H. Mather (Radiologist, Royal Southern Hospital, Liverpool), *BMJ*, 4 Oct. 1924, p.615.

[36]*BMJ*, 27 Dec. 1930, pp.1107-8, quoting Dr S. Hastings and Arthur Greenwood, Minister of Health, *Parl. Deb.* vol.246, cols 24-8 (9 Dec. 1930). *BMJ*. 7 Nov. 1925, p.862.

[37]W. Stobie (Physician to Radcliffe Infirmary, Oxford), and W. Burton Wood (Physician to City of London Hospital for Diseases of Heart and Lungs), *BMJ*, 25 Mar. 1933, p.509. Drs J. Yule and Southwood, *Transactions of NAPT, 1934*, pp.120-2.

[38]Dr Banszky, *Transactions of NAPT, 1939*, pp.123-4.

[39]Dr Hilary Roche, 'Tomography', *British Journal of Tuberculosis*, Oct. 1938, pp.1-5.

[40]*BMJ*, 6 Oct. 1928, p.605.

[41]Peter Edwards, *Transactions of NAPT,1939*, pp.44-8; Dr Robert Monod, *BMJ*, 15 Aug. 1936, p.341; Councillor Mrs R. Sandford (Camberwell) on doctors failure to arrange rotas, *Transactions of NAPT, 1939*, p.66.

[42]Felix Savy, *Tubercle*, vol.xxxiv, 1953, p.60; Lasar Dunner and M. Sanger Hicks, 'A Plea for Conservative Treatment in Pulmonary Tuberculosis', *Tubercle*, vol.xxxiii, 1952, p.311.

[43]*Tubercle*, vol.xxxvii, 1956, p.66.

[44]*BMJ*, 15 Mar. 1924, p.478; *Tubercle*, vol.xxxvii, 1956, p.144.

[45]*BMJ*, 24 Jan. 1925, p.176; 7 Feb. 1925, p.273; 28 Mar. 1925, p.609; 1 May 1926, p.774.

[46]*BMJ*, 3 July 1926, p.21.

[47]*BMJ*, 5 June 1926, p.945.

[48]*BMJ*, 2 Feb. 1929, p.194.

[49]*BMJ*, 18 Apr. 1931, pp.668-9.

[50]Hilary Roche (Montana), *Lancet*, 2 Jan. 1932, p.57.

[51]*BMJ*, 8 June 1935, p.1190.

[52]Frank I. Terrill, 'Results of the Sanocrysin Treatment of Tuberculosis', *American Review of Tuberculosis*, vol.xxiv, 1938, p.156.

[53]Osborne, *Better Class of Person* , p.90; Traill, 'Advances in the Treatment of Tuberculosis', *Practitioner*, vol.clix, 1947, p.293.

[54]I have treated this subject in more detail in Barry Smith, 'Gullible's Travails: Tuberculosis and Quackery, 1890-1930', *Journal of Contemporary History*, vol.20, no.4, Oct. 1985, pp.733-56.

[55]Ibid, pp.734-5.

[56]Ibid, p.736.

[57]Congreve, *On Consumption*, pp.16, 68-9, British Medical Association, *Secret Remedies*, 1909, pp.26-7; *Royal Commission on Secret Drugs*, Commonwealth of Australia, *Parliamentary Papers*, 1907, vol.iv, p.189; 1912, vol.3, p.26.

[58]*Secret Remedies*, pp.21, 32-5; Commonwealth of Australia, *Parliamentary Papers*, vol.iii, 1912, pp.32-3; 'Report of Select Committee on Patent Medicines', recounted in *Lancet*, 12 Sept. 1914, p.704; Yonkerman's first publication was *How to Buy a Horse ... Also, the Symptoms for Glanders*, Cleveland 1879.

[59]F.B. Smith, *The People's Health 1830-1910*, 1979, p,77, 345.

[60]Commonwealth of Australia, *Parliamentary Papers*, 1907, vol.iv, pp.127-8.

[61]Ibid, 1912, vol.iii, pp.179-81.

[62]'Lung Germine', Paster Felke and Bacillentod, ibid, 1907, vol.iv, p.155; 1912, vol.iii, p.22; *Secret Remedies*, p.36.

[63]Stevens's career can be traced in 'GP' [CH Stevens], *Tuberculosis and the Umkaloabo Treatment*, [1933?], and in his evidence in a libel case, *The Times*, 22 July, 28 Oct., 1912.

[64]*Secret Remedies*, p.31.

[65]Ibid, pp.30-1; *Truth*, 3 Aug., 14 Sept. 1905; 27 July 1910.

[66]Australia, *Parliamentary Papers*, 1912, vol.3, p.30. *Lancet*, 12 Sept. 1917, p.705.

[67]These cases can be followed in *The Times*, 22, 23 July, 23-30 Oct., 1 Nov. 1912; 17-24 July 1914.

[68]'G.P.', *Tuberculosis and the Umkaloabo Treatment*, [1933?], pp.15-16, 23, quoting *New Age*, 1 May 1930.

[69]*The Times*, 31 Oct. 1912; 'GP', *Tuberculosis*, p.4.

[70]*Parl. Deb.* 1930-1, vol.255, cols.756-7, 2442 (16, 30 July 1931).

[71]Ibid, 1931-2, vol.268, cols.102, 908, 979 (11 July, 29 Oct. 1932); vol.274, cols.344-5, (9 Feb. 1933); vol.286, col.2024 (8 Mar. 1934).

[72]For a similar range of support for Henri Spahlinger, see Smith, 'Gullible's Travails', *Journal of Contemporary History*, vol.20, no.4, Oct. 1985, pp.748-51. The official files dealing with Stevens and *umkaloabo* (PRO MH55/1170, 1171) are closed for 75 years from 1958.

6 ENVIRONMENTAL ETIOLOGIES

The sanatorium movement was concerned with therapeutics rather than prevention. When critics began in the 1920s to argue that the sanatoria were failing even their professed immediate object, to cure, the attack soon spread to cover the movement's neglect of wider environmental etiologies of the disease.

In 1921 Dr Ernest Ward, Tuberculosis Officer for South Devon, published a damaging survey of sanatorium, home and untreated patients which found that 54 per cent of non-sanatorium stage I cases were 'cured' at four years after diagnosis, compared with 31 per cent of sanatorium patients, while the figures for stage II cases were 10 per cent against 7 per cent. His 270 sanatorium cases were, like his 597 controls, all from the 'poorer classes'. The sanatorium people abused Ward, but none rebutted his figures, which implied that his sanatorium colleagues were wasting patients' time and public money. Ward went on to reject graduated labour as useless and absolute rest as a myth: 'a patient will exert himself more in a simple fit of coughing than by feeding himself at meal times for a whole day'.[1] Ward rattled the sanatorium superintendents. Dr Thompson Campbell of the West Riding Sanatorium at Ilkley declared that if sanatorium regimes were 'not infinitely superior to treatment elsewhere', it would follow that the sanatorium physician 'must be a "mental defective."'[2]

The major attack on sanatoria as healing units came in the study of Northern Ireland by two of Karl Pearson's eugenist disciples, Percy Stocks and Noel Karn. They misused their shaky data to conclude that 'the average ultimate progress was undoubtedly worse in the "sanatorium treated" than "otherwise treated" for patients first seen in the incipient stage'. Their finding held, they said, for young people and adults of both sexes, and progress had no correlation with length of stay in a sanatorium. Many in their sample had stayed only a fortnight, the maximum they could afford in 1926.[3] The *Lancet* editor was shocked, and described the Stocks-Karn report as the 'most serious onslaught yet'.[4] The sanatorium defenders now did their usual huffing and puffing and missing the point. Dr

F.R. Walter, President of the Society of Superintendents of ... Sanatoria, declared that 'sanatorium treatment is not so much a remedy as a way of life', although he did not specify for whom. His solution was to spend more money to enable patients to stay longer.[5] Dr Felix Savy, of the Grampians Sanatorium, wanted 'more "suitable cases"' and 'not mere statistical considerations', despite the mere statistical finding that sanatoria did not favourably serve stage I cases.[6] Dr John Gillespie, Tuberculosis Officer for County Down, took the Stocks-Karn investigation as a personal insult. 'He and his colleague were doing their best'. 'Anyone who ha[d] done ... sanatorium work ... [knew] ... that the Irish are ... the worst patients we meet with'. Nonetheless, Gillespie destroyed Stock's and Karn's apparently solid statistical base. He showed that they had indiscriminately grouped active and passive cases, they had ignored a three month gap between patients first seen at a dispensary and then admitted at a sanatorium, and, worst of all, they had disguised the fact that 29 per cent of their 'sanatorium treated' patients and 51.6 per cent of their 'otherwise treated' cases were 'lost sight of'. Like Pearson's earlier work on heredity and tuberculosis, they were building with hopelessly shoddy information.[7] But Gillespie and his allies did not dispute the order of magnitude in Stocks' and Karn's presentation.

Their report, although it upset the medical-sanatorium world, apparently by-passed the laity. Members of the National Association, aldermen, politicians, patients seeking admission, all combined to believe in sanatoria as the main curative resource. The report's main immediate effect was to extend surgery in the sanatoria in an attempt by superintendents to show that they were doing something. The striking thing is the rarity of such investigations. In 1936 Sir Percival Hartley and his colleagues, after an elaborate but often fatuous survey of Brompton patients between 1905 and 1931, concluded that a patient's 'real chances depend[ed] upon the state of his tuberculosis when entering hospital'. Hartley found that artificial pneumothorax increased the chances of survival, but only when the tuberculosis was restricted to one lung - which was supposed to be the sine qua non of the operation. Their last finding was also sobering: the prognosis of patients unsuitable for pneumothorax had not altered since 1901, that is, before the sanatoria and dispensary movement was underway, although Hartley did not make this conclusion explicit, and the editor of the *British Medical Journal* managed to interpret it to mean that Hartley had provided the 'first evidence that sanatoria treatment really helps'.[8] The Ministry of Health, which one might have expected to be interested in such investigations, apparently limited its curiosity to checking the stages of patients admitted and the proportions who remained six months. Dr H. Timbrell Bulstrode's full scale study of 1908 was never repeated. But even the Ministry's limited surveys cast light on sanatoria proponents' rhetoric about only admitting early cases who could benefit. In the second survey between 1934 and 1936 about 63 per cent of all admissions were stage II and stage III patients, but stage I patients were more likely to be kept for the full six months. This report, like its precursor of 1926-9, was never published.[9]

Critics argued that sanatoria could never handle more than a tiny proportion of the population at risk and that they were irrelevant to coping with tuberculosis and its complications in the aftermath of war and economic depression. Sanatoria regimes, predicated on dubious therapeutics for cases assumed to be lightly affected, had no bearing on the massive incidence of severe infection increasingly documented among the ill-fed, huddled working people and the poor. It followed that tuberculosis could be beaten only by preventive social and economic reforms. The correlations of high morbidity with bad housing and with general poverty had been established after the turn of the century, but the burgeoning sanatorium movement had for two decades obscured them.

The early revelations had been too stark to be faced in terms of redistributive policy. Indeed, Lloyd George's adoption of sanatoria in the National Insurance Act was a brilliantly executed diversion. In 1904 Dr A.K. Chalmers, Medical Officer of Health for Glasgow, had told the Committee on Physical Deterioration that mortality from pulmonary tuberculosis was recorded at 2.4 per 1000 among families occupying a single room, at 1.8 per 1000 - the average for Glasgow - among families with two rooms, and at 0.7 per 1000 for families in larger dwellings. 'After Care', Chalmers remarked some years later, 'in a city where two-thirds of the population lived in houses of two rooms or less ... [was] meaningless'.[10] Dr Shirley Murphy, Head of the Public Health Department of the London County Council, corroborated Chalmers' findings with evidence from London.

About a quarter of all persons in social classes 6 and 7 lived more than two to a room in occupancies of less than five rooms, compared with under 7.5 per cent of persons in social class I. Classes 6 and 7 had a recorded consumption mortality of over 2 per 1000, more than four times that of class I and about two-thirds more than classes 3, 4, 5.[11] Nonetheless, this correlation was not a straightforward indicator of infection chances: Dr Arthur Newsholme and other observers believed that consumptives unable to continue in full employment drifted downwards with their families into more crowded quarters in meaner districts.[12]

Subsequent investigations confirmed the pattern. Between 1918 and 1927 All Saints' ward in Newcastle-upon-Tyne, filled with 'bad housing', reported a tuberculosis death-rate of 2.228 per 1000, whereas Jesmond ward, with 'better housing' recorded 0.71 per 1000.[13] Dr Lilli Stein, surveying Glasgow between 1935 and 1939, found that the gap in mortality and notification rates between the most overcrowded areas and the least overcrowded had narrowed since the 1920s (variously defined but usually meaning three or more inhabitants aged over ten to each room of a dwelling), but still inhabitants of wards with over 50 per cent declared overcrowded suffered a death-rate of 1.15 per 1000 and notification rates of 2 per 1000 compared with 0.45 per 1000 death-rates and 0.78 per 1000 notification rates for people in wards with less than 5 per cent declared overcrowding. The most overcrowded wards had proportionately six times as many people on poor relief as the least overcrowded.[14] The mechanism of these relationships was worked out in the early 1930s by F.C.S. Bradbury, who studied Jarrow and Blaydon in the worst period of unemployment. He concluded that overcrowding was more related to tuberculosis mortality than to the number of children in the family, the unsanitariness of the dwelling or undernourishment. But it was less related than 'general poverty'. Eighty-nine per cent of the families had experienced overcrowding with sickness other than tuberculosis before tuberculosis occurred. The sickness, Bradbury concluded, probably followed the overcrowding, and 'led to tuberculosis'. Jarrow, which contained more poverty than Blaydon, had three times as much insanitary housing - structural defects, dampness, no indoor water supply, no through ventilation - as Blaydon, and nearly five times as much tuberculosis. Moreover, the tuberculous families in both towns were concentrated in the insanitary houses.[15] Overcrowding under insanitary conditions reduced the inhabitants' resistance to sickness, especially respiratory infections, and made them more likely to be repeatedly exposed to bacilli from open cases. Overcrowded consumptives were less likely to sleep by themselves than uncrowded cases. In Cardiff, for example, in the late 1920s only 46 per cent of notified cases did so. A study of Northampton between 1921 and 1948 revealed a 33 per cent greater likelihood of tuberculosis being reported in houses next door to dwellings containing an active case, and a 48 per cent worse chance of its being reported in the same dwelling within a three year period.[16]

The solution was clear. Liverpool Corporation, led by its Medical Officer of Health, Dr E.W. Hope, between about 1907 and 1909 condemned insanitary housing in the old parishes and rebuilt it as municipal housing. They also stopped overcrowding in lodging houses. The phthisis death-rate fell from 4 per 1000 to 1.9 per 1000. The death-rate of the dwellers in municipal housing in 1909, 1.35 per 1000, was lower than that for the city as a whole and much lower than that for the surrounding uncleared districts. Since 1864 the corporation had spent over £900,000 on new housing. Hope asserted unfashionably that it was better spent on that than on sanatoria.[17] Chalmers of Glasgow agreed similarly that the £1.5 million allocated to sanatoria under the National Insurance Act would be more helpfully spent on rent subsidies to enable consumptives to move to less crowded dwellings.[18] Just such a pioneering, under-funded scheme was already operating in Rutherglen.[19] Other critics wanted the £1.5 million devoted to new garden cities, full of model airy, sunlit cottages with 'airspace' around them. Bournville, Port Sunlight and Letchworth were said to have the lowest mortality rates in the kingdom. 'More garden cities', Harold Pearsall declared in 1911, 'will achieve more than sanatoria'.[20]

In 1930 Hull Council wanted to reserve 15 two or three bedroom houses, with rent rebates, for consumptives returning from sanatoria. Technically, the Council had no power to use its grants in this way. Yet the Ministry of Health privately allowed them to proceed.[21] Leeds, Wakefield and Sheffield and later Newcastle, Stockport and South Shields exploited a dubious after care provision in the Public Health (Tuberculosis) Act of 1921 to allocate houses in new estates for tuberculous families with a rental rebate of about £10 a year. The consumptive occupier had to sign a promise to keep a separate bedroom and have all the family attend a dispensary.[22] Their illness was supposed to be secret, but the news soon spread through each estate and the consumptive family was forced to leave. The schemes never became popular. Newcastle gave up. Their reserved houses were dubbed 'consumptives' houses' and were shunned by the tuberculous and the sound alike.[23] Councillor Mrs Roberts of Stepney told the National Association conference in 1931 that her council 'wouldn't dare set aside flats for tuberculous cases ... people ... won't stand for it', and the council auditor, more mindful of the law than his fellows, would not let them subsidise consumptives' housing.[24] However, from 1935 London County Council secretly scattered designated houses through its estates and apparently the recipients managed to keep their secret. But such schemes were never widespread. Only thirteen county boroughs were helping with housing in 1938, and another twelve gave rent assistance. Only Wakefield, with 26 specially designed houses with bedrooms opening on to verandahs, openly tried to provide what were thought to be the most appropriate dwellings.[25]

Poor diet was also believed to be implicated in the development of infection, but again, beyond broad correlations the mechanisms were and are little understood. In the nineteenth century lay and medical belief in the diathesis and individual moral liability rendered malnourishment a concomitant to tubercle rather than a primary cause.[26] Newsholme in 1903 produced a remarkable table showing that the graphs for the fall in the price of wheat in England and phthisis mortality closely followed one another, but this insight seems not to have been followed up until after the Great War.[27]

In the 1919 *Registrar-General's Report* Dr T.H. Stevenson noted that 41 per cent of the total increase among tuberculosis deaths during 1917 had occurred among lunatics. The death-rate among lunatic males had risen 152 per cent in 1913, and 106 per cent among females to 52 per 1000 in 1918. Twelve of the 97 British lunatic asylums had been evacuated to make way for soldiers. The lunatics were crowded worse than ever, tended by a skeleton nursing staff, and less well fed.[28] In the wider mad world, when food became scarce in Germany in 1916, tuberculosis mortality rose for the first time in 25 years, to 162 per 100,000, and during the 1917-18 blockade the death-rate jumped to 230 per 100,000, higher than the 225 per 100,000 of 1900.[29] It had been Newsholme, in 1906, who first publicised the appalling tuberculosis death-rate among incarcerated lunatics - 15.8 per 1000 inmates in 1901 - 1000 per cent higher than the national average and affecting 1/300th of the population of England and Wales. He had observed that 'insane consumptives seldom expectorate',[30] nor did they exhibit fever, or cough much. This limited infection, but some doctors argued that the bacillus was spread through infected excreta and soiled bedclothes. No asylum appears to have segregated active cases. The patients' habit of swallowing sputum led to repeated re-infection; 50 per cent of inmates had intestinal lesions.[31] The only immediate outcomes were denials by lunacy authorities that lunatics caught tuberculosis in their institutions and demands for money for more complete incarceration on the grounds that imbecility clearly impaired resistance to tuberculosis and such 'low grade defectives' endangered   only   themselves by remaining locked up.[32] 'Ventilation' was improved through the 1920s and 1930s. Leavesdon Metropolitan Asylum kept its windows open, although patients disliked the steady 55° F temperature of the halls, as did 'visiting members of committees and ... Commissioners of the Board of Control'.[33] Diets were said also to have improved in the 1930s. In the Royal Eastern Counties Institution, for example, after 'ventilation' came in from 1927 and better diet in 1934, the tuberculosis death-rate dropped from 0.34 per cent of inmates during 1927-34 to 0.18 per cent in 1935.[34] Good food and cleanliness, probably together with better physical health before entering an asylum, did make an enormous difference. West House of the Royal Edinburgh Asylum between about 1909 and the early 1920s had a tuberculosis death-rate four times that for Scotland. West House was overcrowded and was badly ventilated. Craig House of the same institution, contained 'the richer classes'. It was run on sanatorium fresh air lines, apparently with overfeeding, and had a tuberculosis rate below that of the general population, and presumably about 500 per cent less than its neighbouring ward.[35]

Tuberculosis mortality and possibly morbidity in asylums undoubtedly fell sharply during the 1930s, only to jump again in 1940. One unstated reason for the fall was that asylum authorities, anxious about publicity, had begun to discharge active cases. In 1931, the Welsh National Memorial Association even decided formally, but quietly, not to admit them, and instead to 'support them *at home* .' [36]

During the Second World War, mental hospital mortality jumped 40 per cent on the 1937-8 figures; in 1941 the rise was 185 per cent for males and 85 per cent for females. Yet the actual deaths were only a quarter of those for 1914-18. Diet was better, care less austere, but the differential between male and female death-rates suggests a further factor - stress - which contemporaries did not discuss. I shall return to this later.

Nonetheless, diet is clearly an important factor. Marc Daniels noted that during the Second World War, the south of France, which suffered food shortages, recorded a continuous rise in tuberculosis mortality, while Brittany, where food supplies were relatively good, experienced a continuous decline. He also calculated that the worst years of mortality in England and Wales, 1941 and 1943, coincided with the lowest average individual protein intake.[37] Bradbury had already observed that tuberculous households in Jarrow and Blaydon consumed less meat, butter and fresh milk, and more bread than non-tuberculous households. The highest differential occurred with milk: less than half a pint per head per week against a still pitifully low two-thirds of a pint. 'Milk is used ...', Bradbury recorded, 'as a luxury', especially in large families with children. They used condensed milk instead.[38] A recent authority suggests that protein calorie malnutrition can reduce an individual's cell-mediated immunity, particularly when it is associated with intercurrent infections.[39] The trend of rising real wages for a generally widening majority of the working people, which enabled them to consume more meat, fish and grains, coincides with the long term retreat of tuberculosis and it seems reasonable in the light of the scattered evidence to suggest that improving nutrition contributed fundamentally to that retreat.

It is curious that medical practitioners have shown so little interest in the links between nutrition and ill-health. Their own 'low diets' for consumptives, weak tea, diluted milk, toast in water, gruel, sago - no meat or eggs, fruit or vegetables, allied to purging and blistering, could not have helped, while the 'overfeeding' of twentieth- century practice is now known - it was demonstrated in 1920 by McCann and Barry but largely ignored - to exacerbate pulmonary activity and fever and make the patient uncomfortable.

Poor diet, bad housing, tuberculosis itself, were components of poverty. As Dr John McVail remarked in 1911, 'phthisis causes pauperism in one generation and pauperism causes phthisis in the next'. Nearly 50 per cent of cases in families notified in 1909 were found, when investigated, to be below Seebohm Rowntree's York poverty line.[40]   Bradbury's investigation of Jarrow and Blaydon between October 1930 and December 1931 provided the clearest evidence of the association between tuberculosis and poverty. The towns had each about 32,000 inhabitants. They both had large and approximately equal overcrowding according to the 1921 census. Yet Jarrow's tuberculosis death-rate, 2 per 1000, was twice that of Blaydon's. Bradbury's team visited every fifth house in the old centre of Jarrow and found 50 per cent of the families were 'poor', judged at 10s or less a week income from the head of the household. The 'poor' families were more likely to be overcrowded, underfed and house more members, and to have more cases of serious tuberculosis. Families were also overcrowded, underfed and overlarge in Blaydon, but the miners there brought home more money each week and lived rent free in colliery houses.[41] 'Poor' families in Jarrow were twice as likely as 'not poor' families to be sputum positive and contain galloping consumption cases aged 0-15. 'Adult' tuberculosis was more common in Blaydon and four times as likely to be found in a 'not poor' family.[42]   'Poverty', Bradbury said, reversing McVail's dictum, 'causes tuberculosis, rather than tuberculosis leads to poverty'.[43]

Bradbury's formula soon became a dogma. Labour councillors began to make outspoken interventions at formerly highly decorous, deferential meetings of the National Association. In 1931 they virtually captured the meeting from the medical panjandrums and aristocratic ladies who normally ran it. When Dr Harley Williams reported to the meeting on the National Association's round of popular lectures, cinematograph demonstrations and travelling exhibitions, he remarked that he had also tried to reach the poor at open-air meetings, but that he had found it difficult to deal with questioners who asked: 'Is not tuberculosis due to the social organization of this country?' usually with a supplementary attacking sanatoria; 'Is not tuberculosis caused by bad feeding and bad housing?'; 'Is not tuberculosis a disease of the poor?'. This last 'tremendous interrogation', nearly always came up and Williams found it 'very difficult to answer'. 'Certainly when people get together in a crowd their mentality seems to decline very much from the logical and rational'.[44] Williams was not utterly wrong. Poverty might 'predispose' infected persons to active pulmonary tuberculosis, but rich people still developed it, too. Infection through droplets or dust remained the main paths, although the poor were more exposed.[45] Deaths from tuberculosis dropped steadily through the Depression, and the largest fall occurred between 1931 and 1932. Lancashire, with much of the worst unemployment and deprivation, had a tuberculous death-rate from 1926 lower than the national average.[46]

The retreat of infant and child tuberculosis could have been accelerated by preventive methods which were materially available but unacceptable to powerful interest groups.

The first method involved the elimination of tuberculous milk and meat. A link between diseased cows and tabes mesenterica and other tuberculous affections in children had long been assumed by laity and doctors, although the mechanism was unknown.[47] Serious investigations began around 1870, coincidentally with studies of polluted water and milk as sources of typhoid fever. Cohnheim, Gerlach and others in Germany during the late 1870s established the probability that the 'virus' was contained in the tuberculous matter in abscesses on the udder which fell into the pail during milking or was coughed up by the cow into the atmosphere and thence into the milk. When a child drank the milk the 'virus' lodged in the digestive tract. It also seemed probable that the 'virus' could pass through the intestinal walls into the bloodstream and thereby travel to the lungs and joints.[48] Boiling the milk seemed to be a fallible preventive: pigs fed with boiled milk in England still developed tubercles.[49] Anyway, few people boiled milk.[50]

It remained unclear until the 1920s whether the bovine infection was identical with human tuberculosis, but the important point was the probability of transmission of a causative agent: some investigators surmised that the bovine 'virus' or later, the bacillus, developed into a human-type bacillus once it began to cause inflammation, deposit, and cavitation in the human body.[51]

Stopping tuberculosis at its source in the cattle was politically impossible. The near universality of the disease made the dominant rural representation in both political parties unyieldingly opposed to legislative intervention. From the late 1880s medical spokesmen called for the inclusion of tuberculosis in the Contagious Diseases (Animals) Act (which covered only diseases transmitted between animals), but the legislators ignored them when they amended the Act in 1894. The Dairy, Cowsheds and Milkshops Order of 1885 was permissive on local authorities and 'disease' as defined in the Order excluded tuberculosis. The successive Royal Commissions appointed in 1890 and 1894 were not expressly asked to make recommendations for legislative action. As the law stood, local authorities were powerless to inspect and seize affected animals and they could not block the distribution of milk from affected cows. Usually during a bad outbreak of bovine tuberculosis, as at Paisley in 1887, some owners acceded to pleas from the local authority to stop selling milk from diseased animals, but others took the opportunity to capture the newly open parts of the market with milk from cows equally blatantly tuberculous.[52]

The prevention campaign was weakened by disunity in the veterinary ranks. In general, academic veterinarians supported their medical brethren, but field veterinarians, whose livings depended on their fellowship with farmers, opposed compulsory slaughter of diseased beasts and harped on practical difficulties.[53] Any dairy inspection and milk and meat seizure scheme had necessarily to be universal, rather than applied only within the boundaries of local authorities who could afford the expenditure and the farmers' and butchers' wrath. Yet such a scheme was, in the short run, unworkable and politically impossible. Rural parishes neither could nor would support inspection.[54] Meanwhile, tuberculous milk vendors, spitting copiously, continued to sell milk from cows that local authorities were powerless to quarantine or destroy. The milk was carried in open cans and ladled into the customer's container.[55]

Some influential medical men also remained unconvinced. Haughty Dr R.D. Powell of Brompton Hospital informed the

Royal Commission that there was no proof that children acquired tuberculosis from milk - as indeed there was not - that there was no need to boil milk, and that the milk at Brompton was never boiled.[56] Dr J.E. Goodhart of Guys supported him with the boast that his hospital took 'no special precautions ... about tuberculous patients': their milk was not boiled and they were given raw meat.[57] Dr John Tatham of the Registrar-General's office weighed in with the calculation that although male milk sellers in England and Wales had a higher death-rate than general occupied males, notably a 23 per cent higher mortality from alcoholism, they had a 10 per cent lower rate for phthisis.[58] T.H. Elliott of the Board of Agriculture spoke for a wide range of entrenched belief when he told the Royal Commission in 1898 that 'scientific men [were] alarmist about milk' and that the question of strengthening the laws against the sale of tuberculous milk was 'not an agricultural one'.[59]

The rural veterinarians' and farmers' resistance was buoyed by the would-be interventionists' failure, which they never overcame, to produce legally defensible proof that human beings could catch tuberculosis from bacteria conveyed in milk. The slow development of human symptoms precluded rapid epidemiological surveys on the pattern of typhoid fever outbreaks. Some investigators and spokesmen for dairymen asserted that the dilution of milk from tuberculous cows with that from healthy animals rendered the milk innocuous. When experiments in the early 1890s were interpreted as proving that the bacilli sank to the bottom, the legal basis of sampling was upset and the advocates of dilution much reinforced.[60] It also remained uncertain, despite intense microscopical studies, whether bovine forms of the bacillus were distinct from the human one. Some students believed bovine bacilli to be smaller, but others found that bacilli in both bovine and human matrices varied in size by up to 50 per cent. Others held, into the 1920s, that bovine forms were 'juvenile' bacteria which 'matured' into human forms when they entered the human body, and that therefore bovine bacilli were less virulent.[61] Villemin had already demonstrated in the 1860s that lesions in rabbits induced by bovine material were distinctly more virulent than those from human material but his discovery had been ignored. Above all, it remained unclear whether humans could transmit bovine tuberculosis which could excite or develop into the human form of tuberculosis.[62]

The confusion was worsened by a pronouncement by Koch at the London International Medical Congress in 1901. His statement is woolly, but his hearers interpreted him, rightly, as intending to say that human and bovine tuberculosis were distinct and that the former could not be transmitted to cattle. He was evasive about the reverse transmission, but said it was unlikely and rejected the need for precautions. It was the utterance of a great man whose powers had gradually diminished. An eminent deputation pleaded with him to withdraw or at least equivocate, but he would not budge. British tuberculosis experts, appalled, moved the government to appoint a new Royal Commission on the question.[63] Unprecedentedly, it conducted its own research, rather than take evidence from independent witnesses.

The sanitarians' agitation to stop the trade in tuberculous meat similarly was frustrated. A decade before Koch's rebuff, wrangles about veal and beef as possible transmitters of tuberculosis had overtaken the disputes about milk, occasioned by an outbreak of pleuropneumonia, the discovery of its causative organism and the assumption that it was related to the tuberculosis bacillus.[64] Doctors and veterinarians had known since the 1870s that guinea pigs could develop tubercles after being fed tuberculous meat. In England from at least 1881 epidemiologists had been suggesting that human consumption of tuberculous meat increased the danger of inflammation and tubercular deposition.[65] These untested and untestable hypotheses (although some doctors called for the use of criminals to benefit mankind)[66] met the obvious reply from rival doctors, veterinarians, farmers and meat traders that Britons had long been eating meat from animals, 90 per cent of which exhibited tubercules, with, according to Dr Alfred Carpenter, 'no apparent harm'.

Lesions were commonest in the cheapest cuts from viscera, udders and lymphatic glands. Carpenter and his allies reasonably demanded that the connection between tuberculous meat and phthisis and joint tuberculosis be proved before the lower orders were deprived of those portions most accessible to them, particularly when the beast had been otherwise generally sound.[67] The protective effects of cooking were also unclear. Austrian and German authorities usually held that the bacillus could survive in the recesses of the meat left raw by the perfunctory roasting and boiling common in poor households. French spokesmen asserted the opposite by claiming that cooking, French style, rendered the meat innocuous.[68] But their governments dared not antagonise their farmers: the Germans and Austrians sold tuberculous meat with notices attached warning housewives to cook it properly; the French sold carcases with the worst portions excised.[69]

The United Kingdom government wavered. Cooking might destroy the tubercles, but many medical men held that it could not destroy the 'spores'. In 1888 an interdepartmental committee on animal tuberculosis had recommended that the powers of local inspection, seizure, slaughter and compensation applicable to cattle murrain and other diseases scheduled under the Contagious Diseases (Animals) Act be extended to cover tuberculosis, and going beyond the Act, that breeding from condemned cattle be prohibited.[70]

Their recommendation was ignored. The trade in 'mincers' and 'wasters' continued. These animals were commonly slaughtered outside the boundaries of those towns which inspected abattoirs under local acts and the Health Act of 1875. The most offensive bits were sent for pig feed and the rest brought to market in cheap cuts and sausage mince. Inspection itself was often perfunctory, outside London and Liverpool and a few other large towns with wealthy, active corporations. In Glasgow, one of the better regulated places, one man looked over hundreds of beasts in the saleyards in under four hours. Under the Nuisance Act he was empowered to 'inspect' but not to condemn: that was the prerogative of the Medical Officer of Health's man under the Public Health Act of 1885. But this officer could not compensate for seizure and therefore, when he was summoned, settled for butchers excising the worst parts and using the rest for sausages. This accord, similar to many throughout the kingdom, made the inspector's job easier and encouraged the butchers to cooperate. Much depended on the butchers' public-spiritedness because they could not sue the vendor of a beast which, after slaughter, yielded unsaleable meat.[71]

In 1890 after a test case in Glasgow went against the butchers, the Scottish and English Local Government Boards sponsored an investigation at the behest of the meat trades. The doctors wanted a royal commission, but the government outflanked them by appointing a single pathologist, Professor Julius

Dreschfeld, of Manchester. He reported, predictably from his earlier researches, and rightly, although he could not then confidently have known it, that tuberculous meat if well cooked carried no threat of conveying live bacilli. Dreschfeld ingeniously used rabbits, normally resistant to human tuberculosis. His findings enabled the Minister for Agriculture, Henry Chaplin, to reject a medical deputation's plea for a scheme to confiscate and compensate for tuberculous meat. Chaplin told them that there was 'no proof of a connection' between bovine and human tuberculosis and that the 'danger [was] exaggerated'.[72] A month earlier, he had launched a costly plan of controlled slaughter and compensation to eradicate pleuropneumonia, which did not impinge directly on human health.[73]

Enterprising protectors of the public health such as Dr H.D. Littlejohn in Edinburgh used Chaplin's new pleuropneumonia regulations to clean up cowsheds and seize likely tuberculous beasts under the rule that the presence of one pleuropneumonia sufferer in a herd permitted the seizure of the herd, and compensation. Of one batch of 300 animals Littlejohn seized in this way, 120 had tuberculosis with no outward signs.[74]

The problem of securely diagnosing tuberculosis in cattle appeared to be solved in the early 1890s by the application of Koch's tuberculin, and confirmation of its reliability by a royal commission in 1898. Tuberculin raised the temperature of an infected beast more dramatically than a healthy one. The test could be presented in legal contests about seizures; but it still depended upon sanitary officers pretending to a non-existent power to administer the tuberculin and report the results irrespective of the owner's wishes.[75] Moreover, a mass testing programme directed to eradicating tuberculous animals was impracticable. Farmers disliked the test because they thought it a bureaucratic intrusion on their farm which upset the cows. The procedure took one and a half days: during the last 24 hours the temperature of each - by now fractious - cow had to be taken every two or three hours. Veterinarians generally lacked the nerve to face the farmer and the skill to handle the cows. Tuberculin was hard to get. No British laboratory produced it in commercial quantities. The cost of testing an animal, including the veterinarian's fee, was between 2s and 3s in 1898 and most farmers begrudged it. Had the government paid, as some sanitarians proposed, even a minimum of 50,000 tests a year among the 11 million cattle in Great Britain would have cost over £5,600.[76] And if a conservative 20 per cent of the 11 million were reactors, compensation at the pleuropneumonia average rate of £15 a head would have cost nearly £40 million in Great Britain and around another £20 million in Ireland.[77] But Ireland was beyond recall: it had separate ineffective legislation, no tuberculin testing and less seizure of meat or examination of milk - and more tuberculosis.[78]

In the United Kingdom the law presumed that meat was fit for human consumption until it was proved otherwise. The Royal Commission of 1898 settled for this view. It recommended standards for condemning and seizing meat, that is, the visibly affected parts were destroyed and the remainder passed for sale, as in France. This provision evaded the legally tricky problems of whether the bacilli were disseminated, although concealed, through the glands and bloodstream, and the establishment of a primary infection site, together with healed lesions and definitions of recrudescence. Despite representations about the success of compulsory German and Danish farmers' insurance and compensation schemes predicated on the idea that diseased parts made the general carcase unfit for human consumption, the Royal Commission majority report backed off recommending compensation.[79] As Thomas Nuttall, spokesman for the Chamber of Agriculture warned, people would next want compensation for horses sold to them as docile which turned out dangerous. One could never get round the intention to deceive.[80] Thereafter the issue lapsed. Meanwhile the American states led by New York, and Canada, largely eradicated bovine tuberculosis between 1917 and 1937 by tuberculin testing, compulsory slaughter with compensation and state accredited herd schemes with high meat and milk standards.[81]

Interest in the meat question revived in the 1920s and reports of high incidence of tuberculous beasts in slaughterhouses began to circulate again. In 1922 the Ministry of Health issued Memo 62 Foods, which tightened the rules about inspection and seizure. Henceforth an organ or part of a carcase was subject to discretionary seizure when disease was found in it or in the regional lymph-nodes. The whole carcase might be seized if the beast was emaciated, or the lesions were acute and multiple, or when the lungs revealed miliary lesions. Inspection was still conducted by sanitary inspectors, and veterinarians considered that they were over-rigorous. Veterinarians were excluded because they could not agree with the corporations about fees. In 1924, for instance, 28 per cent of cows and 4.4 per cent of bulls of superior quality slaughtered at Aldgate were declared tuberculous.[82] Seventy-four per cent of superficially sound cattle in Newcastle slaughterhouses had tubercle.[83] In the following year the Minister for Agriculture, E.F.L. Wood, later Lord Halifax, finally introduced a compensation scheme. It was to cost £67,500, £50,000 of which was to come from the Treasury, the remainder from local authorities, and none from farmers. The National Farmers' Union lauded the scheme. Butchers were excluded.[84] Within eighteen months farmers had received £90,000.[85] By 1934, after 141,000 cattle had been destroyed during a period of low prices, the farmers had received over £521,000, rising to £572,000 in 1944 alone. The total national annual loss on meat and milk and breeding potentialities in these cattle was estimated at two million pounds.[86]

The butchers' exclusion from the scheme had the unexpected result of making them more choosy. And they were able to choose among better beasts as the scraggy animals were eliminated. Finally, in 1944, Dr Roydhouse Gloyne summed up general medical opinion by remarking that tuberculous meat was not a serious threat. The bacilli did not survive 'usual cooking', and children did not consume much beef or veal.[87] The persisting disputes about the status of meat fell away during the Second World War when centralised abattoirs were instituted, but meat inspection remained patchy until the 1950s.[88]

The milk story was less happy. Despite Koch, tuberculous milk was dangerous to humans, especially children. In May 1904 the Royal Commissioners issued an urgent interim report contradicting him, and calling for the strengthening of protective legislation. The Royal Commission researchers, Louis Cobbett, A. Stanley and Frederick Griffith and Arthur Eastwood constituted a brilliant group of experimentalists. They produced further reports in 1907, 1910, 1913 and 1914 conclusively establishing the links between bovine tuberculosis and milk transmission to humans.

The rural interest in parliament remained unmoved. The trade retained to itself the control of milk standards. Municipal milk depots and private vendors in comfortable suburbs might trade in a small way in certified milk for middle class mothers and children, but the general poor quality of British and Irish milk continued unchecked. In 1910, 20 per cent of British milk supplies and 10 per cent of butter contained 'living tubercle'.[89] No legal minimum germ count or butterfat standard existed. Health reformers' efforts to obtain them failed against the dairy lobby and popular fears of dearer milk. They did, however, win the Public Health Amendment Act of 1907 which empowered inspectors to forbid a notifiable infectious person from distributing milk, and providing for six weeks quarantine. But tuberculosis was still not a notifiable disease. The American states were introducing sealed lids to churns and ice packing, but Britain did not follow suit. The Tuberculosis Order of 1913 was the first national move to compel veterinarians to notify tuberculous cows and to compel dairymen to keep their milk separate: it could still be sold.[90]   Some progressive corporations, notably Manchester and Liverpool, had had by-laws since the mid 1890s giving them powers to ban milk with unsatisfactory bacteria counts.   The number of samples of tuberculous milk in such places had fallen by a third in little over a decade.

Variation in milk quality reflected the class divisions in the nation.   Careful rich people ordered 'certified' [allegedly tuberculosis-free with a higher butterfat content] milk, at up to a penny a pint retail above the price of 'grocer's milk'.   Poorer people bought tiny amounts of the cheapest skimmed milk. But consumers seem to have been passive about milk quality, grumblingly content with the taste they knew.   When Liverpool Corporation secured pure milk regulations in 1894 and strengthened them in 1900 and soon afterwards established municipal pasteurisation depots, Liverpudlians would not buy the dearer stuff with an unfamiliar taste.[91]   Graded, certified milk still amounted to less than one per cent of consumption in 1926.[92]

A Milk and Dairies (Consolidation) Act for Great Britain was carried with little debate in May 1915.   It provided for permissive local authority control over sale of milk at the point of sale, thereby ending the anomaly that bad milk could be imported from outside municipal boundaries; it forbade sale of milk from cows with suppurating udders and permitted prohibitions on selling from open churns, and for stronger inspectorial powers over dairies and byres; and the exclusion of notified consumptives from employment in dairies. The Act was immediately suspended. It was generally postponed again in 1917, when graded milk was recognised but not accorded full legal status. Grade A milk henceforth was distinguished by a higher butterfat content. But sampling was patchy and penalties for false claims were light. Voluntaryism and tenderness to farmers also vitiated the Milk (Special Designations) Order of 1917. It permitted the sale of milk declared to be from tuberculin-tested herds, and created a registration procedure, but by 1936 only 266 such herds had been registered. Many of these had been cleansed, not by the indentification and slaughter of infected beasts but by the quiet sale of reactors to complaisant butchers and small farmers. The reformers' efforts to strengthen the 'milk and water' Act failed.[93]   Lord Astor founded the National Clean Milk Society in 1916 and used his *Observer* to press the Society's demands for the full implementation of the Milk Act, together with pasteurisation under the supervision of the Ministries of Health and Agriculture. Astor pointed out that infant deaths at home during 1914-15 doubled deaths at the front, but his message went unheeded.[94] The Tory farm lobby blocked all attempts at compulsion and central government intervention. In 1930 they defeated a Labour Government move to exclude tuberculous cattle from agricultural shows - a more serious affair than it looks because so many older, pedigreed animals were infected.[95]

This surprising distribution was largely an outcome of the age structure of the cattle population: good cows were retained for breeding and milking. The incidence of tuberculosis among them rose sharply after two years and the first calf and continued to rise thereafter: cows above five years or their fourth calf, when they were giving their greatest quantity of milk, were also at their most infectious. A five year old cow was four times as likely as a yearling to be tuberculin-positive.

The best research on these problems was conducted in Denmark by B. Bang and his colleagues. This brilliant, forceful group had effectively nationalised the Danish dairying industry by 1890. In a nation becoming dependent on its exports they shaped legislation fixing high standards for animal husbandry, tuberculosis-free herds, milk and meat. The Danes eased their compensation burden by sending mildly tuberculous live cattle to Britain.[96]

The exigencies of the War might have led to widespread pasteurisation, if only as a preservative, but in fact the emergency served to help farmers and milk dealers stave off interference. In 1922 Alex MacLennan told the General Meeting of the British Medical Association that 'the present treatment of milk was a disgrace'. When the Milk Act was finally implemented in 1925 it made little difference: in Edinburgh, for instance, in 1927 the traditional average of about 42 per cent of inspected cattle exhibited 'gross lesions'. At this rate, over 750,000 cattle in Britain would have had to be seized annually, but the prospective compensation involved made the Act mostly inoperative.[97]

The majority of dairy farmers, moreover, had herds of under 50 cows and they could not afford to try the proposition that tuberculosis-free cows gave milk more regularly, lived longer and, if they were pedigreed, could be sold abroad. Even in herds of over 50 the threepence a gallon extra for Grade A milk barely covered the £8 a year it cost to test each cow. As long as the responsibility for reporting tuberculosis rested with the farmers and local veterinarians, the farmers saw no point in ridding themselves of reactors. There was more to be gained by keeping the animal until she became emaciated and made compensation worthwhile.[98]

The indictment of tuberculous milk became more compelling in the late 1920s when A. Stanley Griffith began to publish his researches into the provenance of human tuberculosis:

England 1911-27

Variety of tuberculosis	No. of cases	Ages 0-5 human	bovine	Ages 5-15 human	bovine	Ages15+ human	bovine
cervical glands	112	3	16	28	25	31	9
lupus	176	23	36	48	51	15	3
bone and joint	511	60	24	277	65	81	4
pulmonary	202	-	-	10	-	190	2
meningeal	30	2	1	11	7	9	-
post mortem cases	181	72	31	49	8	23	3
totals	1212	160	108	623	156	349	21

[recalculated from the original]

from Savage, *Prevention of Human Tuberculosis of Bovine Origin*, p.11[99]

These alarming results were in fact understatements. Griffith drew his evidence from the region around Cambridge which had a low incidence of bovine tuberculosis. The rural north of England and rural Scotland had rates of both bovine and human tuberculosis 300 per cent higher.[100] Even in 1945-6 attested herds, comprising only 4.2 per cent of English cattle, were concentrated in the Home Counties.[101] Griffith's second set of findings for the early 1930s showed an overall decline, but still terrible outcomes, terrible not least because they were preventable, of bovine originated infection:

Variety of tuberculosis	all ages		ages 0-4		ages 5-14	
	no. of cases	% bovine	no. of cases	% bovine	no. of cases	% bovine
cervical glands	116	45.7	21	85.7	54	48.1
lupus	177	48.6	75	57.3	87	47.1
meningeal	63	30.1	23	34.8	29	31.0
bone and joint	520	18.0	88	27.3	351	18.5
pulmonary	492	0.8	-	-	-	-

Scotland c.1927-32

cervical glands	144	73.6	53	84.9	71	74.6
lupus	13	53.8	3	100	5	60.0
meningeal	15	13.3	12	16.7	3	-
bone and joint	196	42.8	86	60.5	65	38.5
pulmonary	548	3.8	-	-	-	-

An Investigation of 3,000 Cases in England c.1927-32. A. Stanley Griffith, *BMJ*, 18 Nov. 1933, p.905[102]

This table indicates about 2,000 infant deaths in Great Britain annually from bovine infection. From the 1890s the tuberculosis death-rate for children held constant while the rate for adults had fallen steadily. Expenditure on treatment, convalescence and years of after care cost a possible £9 million annually.[103] Through this period about 40 per cent of cows were reactors and up to 5 per cent were highly infectious. The official palliatives of accredited herds and sketchy inspection and compensation schemes had made little difference. The failure to emulate Denmark, Finland, Canada and the United States in eliminating bovine tuberculosis represents a massive waste of national resources, quite apart from the individual misery it caused. The failure is the more prodigal because the cattle surplus of the earlier 1930s and underconsumption of milk invited action.[104]

G.S. Wilson and his colleagues continued Griffith's survey during the war:

General type of tuberculosis	England 1943-5			
	human no. of cases	bovine no. of cases	total	% bovine
meningitis	183	71	254	28.0
surgical	550	190	740	25.7
	Wales 1943-5			
meningitis	62	7	69	10.1
surgical	31	12	43	27.9
	Scotland 1943-4			
meningitis	498	62	560	11.1
surgical	325	166	491	33.8

Graham Selby Wilson et.al., *Non-Pulmonary Tuberculosis ...*, 1952 p.5.[105]

This table contains only cases as reported. It was not based on a full random survey and rests upon insecure diagnosis in perhaps half the Scottish and Welsh cases.

Many veterinarians and some bacteriologists regarded Griffith's and Wilson's tables as slurs on their competence. During the 1920s veterinary and sanatoria spokesmen eagerly adopted speculation emanating from Vienna that ingestion of tuberculosis in childhood immunised the child, by an implicit analogy with smallpox, against the development of pulmonary tuberculosis.[106] This hypothesis was a convenient argument against the introduction of compulsory pasteurisation. Dr R. Stenhouse Williams, Research Professor of Dairy Bacteriology at Reading University, was worried that 'Government Regulation' and pasteurisation would diminish the standing of

veterinarians.[107]   He assumed that pasteurisation was an
ineffective last resort which would abet lazy handlers of dirty
milk.'If you pasteurize on a large scale', a colleague exclaimed,
'you are going to destroy the whole incentive to produce
"healthy milk"'.[108]

But their cause was already lost.   The tuberculosis-free herd
scheme was stalled.   In 1929,   9.1 per cent of London milk
samples contained live bacilli, an apparent increase on the
levels reported for 1908-14, although the testing techniques had
been refined.   The case for pasteurisation became even stronger
in 1933 with the proof that live bacilli could be conveyed in cow
dung.[109]   This was the more important, because small dairy
farms were notoriously mucky: of 346 examined around
Manchester in 1925, only ten were declared 'clean', 147 'fairly
clean' and the remainder were 'dirty'.[110]   Tuberculin testing
was becoming less reliable because farmers could buy it and
administer it to valuable tuberculous cows before the
veterinarian arrived, thereby rendering the animal immune to
the tester's subcutaneous reaction.   Despite this abuse, the
Ministry of Health bowed to farming pressure and excluded
tuberculin from the Therapeutic Substances Act of 1925, which
enlarged the schedule of dangerous or sensitive drugs.[111]
There were no agreed cultural tests for bacilli in milk, even
between Edinburgh, Aberdeen and Glasgow, although Scotland
from the late 1920s had more rigorous inspection procedures
than England, excepting London and a few of the great towns.
Edinburgh, with about 8.5 per cent infected samples, performed
duplicate guinea pig inoculations.   The first guinea pig was
tested and examined at four weeks, the remainder at up to eight
weeks.   Aberdeen, with 5.5 per cent infected samples, made do
with a single guinea pig, which was 'kept if necessary' for eight
weeks; while Glasgow, with 2.6 per cent of samples infected, also
used a sole guinea pig and killed it at three weeks.   Poorer or
meaner towns in Scotland and England employed direct film
examination of the centrifuged deposit.   It yielded only one-
tenth the number of positives yielded by guinea pig inoculation
after eight weeks.   Other places with inept health officers used to
culture the milk, as they did with sputum, but the method was
even more fallible than direct film examination because of
random contamination with other organisms.[112]

Hitherto, the spread of bovine infection to children had been
contained by two habits with little to do with officialdom.   The

first was the tiny amounts of milk consumed. The amounts and their outcomes are illustrated in the following table from the late 1920s:[113]

	Edinburgh per cent	Sheffield per cent
a) Pints of milk distributed per head per day	0.42	0.27
b) Percentages of mixed milk samples found to contain tuberculous bacilli	20.0	7.5
c) Percentages of bovine infection in bone tuberculosis in children under 16	26.3	6.0

When the Depression deepened in the early 1930s, Bradbury found that Tynesiders used 'practically no cow's milk' because they 'simply [could] not afford it'. This observation helps explain why the incidence of surgical tuberculosis fell sharply in the early years of the Depression. The introduction of the school milk scheme in 1934-5, using the cheapest surplus untested milk, might explain why the decline slowed again.

The second preserving habit was the resort to dried milk, especially among middle-class new mothers keen on mothercraft, but also among working-class mothers influenced by clinic sisters. The only available statistics, for 1901-14 and 1934-8 in Great Britain, are rudimentary but they do indicate a dramatic rise in consumption of powdered milk: if we divide the total consumption by the number of likely main consumers, that is, children under four, in 1913 and 1934-8 we obtain a figure that suggests a jump of the order of just over one pound per head per year in 1913 to about 18 pounds per head in 1934-8. The immediate blessing of dried milk, contemporaries said, was the enormous fall in summer diarrhoea, but they also agreed with Dr T.M. Clayton, Medical Officer of Health for Gateshead, in praising dried milk as the 'real cause of the fall in children's bovine tuberculosis'. Powdered milk was relatively cheap, it could be stored, it contained guaranteed nutritive value, it was near sterile and its use encouraged mothers to boil the water in which it was mixed. The improvement in child health might have come earlier and faster had not English infant welfare centres not persisted so long with certified milk and not waited until 1930 to recommend dried formula products.[114]

Boiling the milk was a third prophylactic, but that seems never to have been popular. In 1898 Sir Charles Cameron,

Professor of Hygiene in the Royal College of Surgeons of Ireland, told the Royal Commission that people disliked the taste of boiled milk. 'I myself never drink it; I have a great objection to ... it. I would rather rather run the risk of getting tuberculosis and drink it as it is'. Boiling made 'the albumen very ... indigestable'. Doctors Ralph Vincent and Bernard Myers advised readers of *The Child* in 1911 that boiled milk was positively deleterious, because a healthy infant raised on real milk had 'a healthy alimentary canal' which would 'make short work of the ... tubercle bacilli'. Doctors were still advising nurses and mothers against boiling milk in 1929.[115]

Popular objection to boiled milk helps to explain the slow introduction of pasteurisation, although the opposition of farmers and small milk dealers was more potent and immediate. Stenhouse Williams, for the veterinarians and farmers, promoted inept experiments with rats intended to prove that pasteurisation destroyed the nutritive qualities of milk and impaired the fertility of those who drank it.[116] His work was almost immediately demolished by J.C. Drummond, but William's findings were taken up by dairymen and anti-pasteurisers.[117] C.W.K. Glossop, a farmer's MP, told the House of Commons that pasteurised milk induced tooth decay.[118] Dr Halliday Sutherland, the tuberculosis specialist, joined Sir Arnold Wilson, the soldier, in denouncing pasteurised milk because it threatened 'national fertility and strength'. At the other extreme were natural health faddists who could afford attested milk and who believed in conspiracies against simple food and simple folk. One representative spokesman for this phalanx was Dr Norman Macfadyen of Letchworth Garden City. Tuberculin-tested milk, he declared, was 'purer' and 'more natural' than its pasteurised rival.[119]

Tuberculosis specialists and sanatoria promoters also opposed pasteurisation. Dr Marcus Paterson of Frimley Sanatorium rejected it because it inhibited 'immunizing' doses of tuberculosis in childhood. He added, inconsequentially, that pasteurisation could not protect because butter and cheese carried bacilli.[120] The combined Medical Officers of Health of South Yorkshire blocked pasteurisation in their region in 1929 because, they said, it reduced the nutritional quality of the milk. D.S. Rabagliati, Chief Veterinary Officer for the West Riding, recommended against it in 1931 because it would 'retard the campaign [for] ... clean milk'. It would upset 'the friendly character of the relations between veterinary surgeons and farmers'.[121]   Another veterinarian called pasteurisation 'revolutionary':   it would 'upset the ideas of the last twenty years'.[122] The local doctor in Easington overruled a proposal by the town council to pasteurise milk in 1933.   Doctors were also prominent in the campaign of that year against a move by the Manchester Corporation to gain enabling powers to compel pasteurisation.   Newspaper proprietors, as on other occasions, rejected advertisements explaining pasteurisation, and the ratepayers rejected it because they assumed it to be expensive, harmful to health and, incongruously, because 75 per cent of their milk was pasteurised already.   The remaining 25 per cent was the problem.   It was supplied by struggling small farmers who were fierce in defence of their livelihood.   The city had suffered six epidemics of milk-borne diseases in the three preceding decades.   Raw milk samples showed an average 10.7 per cent containing live bacilli, with nearly 16 per cent in 1931, when children were particularly malnourished and vulnerable. The milk might have appeared cheap, but Manchester's 130 cases of surgical tuberculosis hospitalised annually at the sanatorium at Abergele each cost £20,000.   The sanatorium had cost the Corporation £182,000.[123]

As early as 1908 the indiscreet Dr Camac Wilkinson had noted that if milk fanatics like von Behring were right - he had contradicted Koch and stressed the importance of infection in infancy through milk - doctors would become redundant in controlling the disease.[124] Two decades later S. Lyle Cummins, Professor of Tuberculosis at the Welsh National School of Medicine and Director of the National Memorial anti-tuberculosis campaign, publicly announced that 'milk was not that important'.   Dr David Nabarro, consultant bacteriologist at Great Ormond Street Hospital for Children and famed for his earlier work on sleeping sickness, agreed.   'The boiling of milk killed the bacilli, and even if a few survived they would not do harm' - depending on a change of habit towards boiling milk and repeated ingestion.

Sir Robert Philip, who had built his career on the dispensary and sanatoria movement, dismissed pasteurisation in 1931 as 'not the solution'.   He preferred tuberculin-tested herds.   He was proud of the tested herd maintained at his Edinburgh sanatorium, although whether it was tuberculosis-free is another matter.   Philip and his allies dominated the National

Association for the Prevention of Tuberculosis, which publicly discussed pasteurisation only once, during the lay revolt of 1931, and even then dismissed it, despite protests from local councillors and a plea from the nonconforming Dr Nathan Raw who complained that the Association had done nothing to educate the people to 'realize what a very large part milk ... [played] in the production of tuberculosis in children'. The United States, Canada, New Zealand and South Africa all had compulsory pasteurisation. Surgical tuberculosis in American children had disappeared within ten years of its introduction.[125] The *British Medical Journal* editor remarked of the meeting: 'in the general discussion compulsory pasteurisation made its usual facile appeal'.[126] A speaker at the 1933 meeting of the British Dairy Farmers' Association was more blunt: 'the talk of conveying bovine tuberculosis to human beings by milk was all humbug'.[127] The farmers were the more anxious because the big distributors, Express and United particularly, had been ready to pasteurise milk since the early 1920s, and they were especially keen to do it after dried milk made inroads on their sales. Even by 1935 less than 1 per cent of their milk came from attested herds.[128]

Pasteurisation procedures required a considerable outlay on plant and supervision. There was no legislation governing the process and equipment remained unstandardised. Until the mid 1930s it was usual to heat the milk to between 145° and 150°F for 30 minutes and then cool the milk to under 55°F. The bacilli could be killed in five minutes at this temperature, but the major dairy companies, United, Sterilized Milk Co., and ABC had begun to pasteurise as a way of giving a 24 hour life to bulk mixed milk, and not primarily to eliminate tuberculosis.[129] The results were defective. Two medical speakers at the National Milk Conference in 1925 described British procedures as 'absolutely useless'. Butter made from pasteurised milk in Sunderland in 1926 was found to carry live bacilli.[130]

In the United States, Ontario and New Zealand, where pasteurisation had been introduced before the War and been regulated since the early 1920s, the cheaper, faster and more foolproof 'flash' method of quickly heating the milk to 160°F and then immediately cooling it to 55°F through a continuous system was already in place. The British clung to their 'holder' process, which was made the sole official procedure under Milk

(Special Designation) Orders in 1936 and 1938, thereby perpetuating inferior installations, although careful local corporations, such as those in the four Scottish cities had, already introduced some 'flash' plants.[131]

But pasteurisation remained voluntary and rather slipshod. A Milk Industry Bill in 1938 to enable local authorities to impose pasteurisation was withdrawn at the first reading under violent rural opposition.[132]   In the heart of the Reading University dairy research empire 7 per cent of milk samples sold as 'pasteurised' in the town in 1938 contained live bacilli - as did 74 per cent of raw milk samples - while 2.5 per cent of London pasteurised samples also had live bacilli. Five per cent of the Reading pasteurised milk also harboured *Brucella abortus*, the causative organism of brucellosis - 74 per cent of raw milk samples, some of it from attested herds, also carried it.[133] By 1942, 90 per cent of London milk and up to 70 per cent of town milk sold through the major distributors was pasteurised, mainly to reduce the *Escherichia coli* level and prolong the shelf-life. In Scotland only about 44 per cent of town milk was pasteurised, with, as in England, very little pasteurisation of milk sold in the countryside.[134] Provision for compulsory pasteurisation was finally carried in Parliament in 1948, but its full implementation took several more years.[135]

Pasteurisation saved lives and could have saved them earlier. The major fall in non-pulmonary tuberculosis mortality occurred in the ten years after the advent of the Second World War when pasteurisation spread quickly.[136] It was also helping before then, as the following table illustrates.

Mortality from non-pulmonary tuberculosis in selected
areas, in England and Wales, 1911-37

	0-5 years		% fall	5-15 years		% fall
	1911	1937	fall	1911	1937	fall
a) London county council area, with considerable pasteurisation	231	33	86	46	10	78
b) aggregated county council boroughs	237	52	78	45	15	67
c) aggregated urban boroughs	198	49	75	38	12	68
d) aggregated rural boroughs, with least pasteurisation	136	44	68	29	10	66

Source: Wilson, *Pasteurisation*, p.154.

In 1911 2,700 children under five died in England and Wales from non-pulmonary tuberculosis: in 1937, 143.[137] G.S. Wilson, who did much of the scientific work and who campaigned over twenty years for effective pasteurisation against rancorous opponents, deserves remembrance as a major health-preserver in modern Britain. Still, in 1951 human tuberculosis of bovine origin was proportionately more common in Britain than in any other industrialised country.[138]

The leaders' reaction to another available prophylactic, the vaccine *Bacille Calmette et Guérin*, reveals a similar pattern of professional defence by insularity, ignorance and innuendo. BCG was not widely administered in Great Britain until the late 1950s, after the incidence of active tuberculosis had fallen sharply with the advent of streptomycin and its adjunct drugs. But 30 years earlier, vaccination of infants and children with BCG preparations had been demonstrated to protect up to 80 per cent of the population at risk, and administration to calves had been shown to protect most calves for twelve months, but British doctors dismissed the information and blocked lay attempts to act on it.[139]

The vaccine comprised a suspension of attenuated live bacilli in ox bile. It was developed by Albert Calmette, a bacteriologist at the Pasteur Institute and Camille Guérin, a veterinarian. They had joined the serum discovery race in 1908 and bested their competitors with a safe, effective vaccine by 1923.[140] Calmette held that the common route of human infection was through the digestive tract. He sought and found a vaccine that could confidently be administered orally (he also used injection) to new-born infants before, as he and his colleagues believed, tubercular infection could occur through the highly permeable membranes of the intestines. This same permeability, Calmette asserted, enabled the vaccine to enter the bloodstream. Early vaccination was crucial in his plan because he maintained that most tubercular infection came from human airborne bacilli which spread in the baby via the digestive tract after the infant's weak mesenteric glands had failed to intercept the germs. Vaccination within ten days of birth pre-empted the bacilli and avoided the possibility of a dangerous reaction in a child already infected.[141] Calmette's assertions about the high probability of airborne infection from tuberculous mothers to their babies underpinned the Grancher scheme.

Testing on humans began in 1921 and in 1924 the French government adopted the vaccine.[142] During 1925 the British Ministry of Health which hitherto had ignored BCG, was pressed to try it by New Zealand and Australian politicians attending the Wembley Empire Exhibition and its associated tuberculosis conference.[143] The antipodeans were too timid to proceed without the mother country, yet presumably they were impressed by Calmette's claimed results after three years' administration of his vaccine: nil mortality in mid 1925 from tuberculosis among 2,070 new born babies of tuberculous mothers vaccinated in 1924, compared with a tuberculosis death-rate of one in four among an unstated number of unvaccinated infants of similarly afflicted mothers.[144]

The vaccine, apparently a further attenuated strain of the 1921 batch, was given in ten milligram doses in a teaspoonful of milk to newborn babies on the fourth, sixth and eighth days of life. McNalty, the medical officer at the Ministry, already pressed by the New Zealanders, strongly advised his Minister against BCG. It was a live vaccine and must put its recipients at risk and 'the same [went] for calves', in whom it would activate old lesions and render them tuberculin-positive and thereby upset the attested herds programme.[145] McNalty showed no acquaintance with the literature and no sign that he intended to obtain information. The New Zealand and Australian authorities backed off and, like Britain, did not adopt BCG until after the streptomycin revolution.

Like other pioneers of good things, Bodington and Villemin for example, Calmette was the wrong man to win friends for his discovery. He was a chauvinist Frenchman with a penchant for upsetting Britons. Like Pasteur, he fudged his results and thereby enabled adversaries to produce rational-seeming objections to a procedure they scorned on other grounds. In 1926 Dr T.M. Ling of St Thomas's Hospital proposed, with Calmette's approval, that BCG be prepared in a Ministry of Health laboratory and be administered to infants at risk. Marcus Paterson armed the permanent medical officers with a flat veto on any trial, while Major Greenwood, the sanatorium statistician, warned that Calmette's 'statistics [were] no good'.[146]

Calmette's assertions were slippery. It soon turned out that of his vaunted 2,070 infants saved in 1925, he had only traced 423.[147] The death-rate among his babies could have equalled the one in four among the unvaccinated population or even been worse. After this rebuff, he admitted to a 1.84 per cent tuberculosis mortality among infants vaccinated between 1924 and 1926.[148] And it was not clear that the rate among the unvaccinated was 25 per cent: Z.P. Fernandez of Leeds pointed out that it was near impossible to diagnose tuberculosis in infants under twelve months, particularly as a cause of death, and that the French returns were often guesses.[149] Greenwood soon explained that the absence of compulsory notification in France meant that Calmette's 25 per cent mortality figure 'must be a guess'.[150] Careful Danish figures showed a tuberculosis mortality of only 4.9 per cent in unvaccinated infants of tuberculous mothers. Either Calmette was inflating his case, as L'Oeuvre Grancher was wont to do, or things were really bad in France. Calmette riposted with new statistics. Greenwood destroyed them too. Instead of Calmette's 1877 infants observed from birth to death or to the end of two years, only 679 remained under observation at eight months and only 367 at twelve. The rest had 'disappeared'. These outcomes again suggested that Calmette's BCG babies had no better survival rates than their unprotected contemporaries. He promptly blamed his assistants for the errors and produced fresh figures which nonetheless repeated the discredited orders of magnitude between BCG infants and the rest. Calmette also set about undermining, by misstating, the low mortality rates for unvaccinated infants at risk reported by his German and Danish rivals. Finally a triumphant Greenwood revealed that Calmette's figures did not distinguish deaths before and after vaccination. His publications were not, Greenwood declared, 'a serious contribution to scientific literature'. Irrelevantly, Greenwood added, 'I do not understand how a *living vaccine* - that is, something quantitatively indeterminate - can be a satisfactory means of therapeutics'.[151]

The French, meanwhile, had been promoting BCG at the League of Nations. The League's Health Committee adopted BCG in the autumn of 1928 and called a conference to launch it. The British were in a quandary. Privately the Ministry wanted the United Kingdom to be officially represented, armed with secret experimental and statistical evidence to explode the

French. But the Medical Research Council, completely sceptical of the vaccine, vetoed any experimental work and, moreover, there was insufficient time to do any. Since 'it would not be ... desirable for British scientific credit merely to send an officer who could not participate in the discussion', Sir George Buchanan of the Ministry recommended that '"official engagements" make it quite impossible for anyone or any officer to attend'. None did.[152] This decision confirmed the British in their resolute neglect of Continental work with BCG. When the distinguished Italian, Alberto Ascoli, published seemingly well-founded good results from BCG in early 1929, the *British Medical Journal*, which was close to the Ministry and the sanatorium leaders, remarked that Ascoli's results simply made it 'more difficult ... to prove or disprove' Calmette's claims and recommended that BCG not be tried, except perhaps in desperate cases.[153]

The difficulty was that Calmette's influence was spreading. Ascoli's enthusiastic report was one among many. Even the Scandinavians, Britain's former scientific allies against the French, were known to be conducting trials; only the arrogant Austrians and the benighted Portuguese held aloof. But relief was at hand. Three Canadians reported in March 1929 that 30 per cent of a batch of guinea pigs and 100 per cent of a group of calves developed tuberculous lesions after BCG injections. American researchers weighed in with reports that introduced tuberculosis developed faster in vaccinated calves than in an unprotected control group. Their results reinforced allegations by Petroff in New York, an inveterate and, as it emerged, unscrupulous and inept rival to Calmette, that he had proof that BCG could spontaneously reactivate in virulence. In 1931 the American Veterinary Association officially rejected BCG.[154] From hindsight it seems clear that BCG varied in its preparation and bacterial composition, its methods of storage and its age when administered (Calmette insisted that it had to be administered within ten days of preparation to ensure that the bacilli were living). Thanks to international rivalries, the vaccine was not standardised until the 1950s.[155]

In the spring and summer of 1930 the sceptics were, it seemed, vindicated by the Lübeck disaster. The details remain opaque, but 249 newborn infants in the municipal children's hospital were given BCG, apparently orally, between late February and 25 April 1930. The February babies began to die in mid-April and by the 25th it was established that their deaths resulted from acute - though non-meningeal - tuberculosis. By June, 67 were dead and another 80 or so were gravely ill. There were at least eight more deaths to the end of January 1931 and probably more by November of that year, but after that reports ceased. The cover-up had begun before the end of April 1930, when one of the senior physicians destroyed the hospital's tuberculosis vaccine stores. Case and experimental records later proved missing. Some of the physicians had been surreptitiously experimenting with a virulent strain of human bacilli. The charitable but, in the circumstances, unlikely, explanation is that the BCG vaccines, which were old and poorly kept, were accidentally contaminated in the hospital. Investigations by the Reich Health Council (there were two - the first was a fiasco) and by the municipality, and the subsequent trial of the medical people, were all mismanaged. But the second Health Council investigation cleared BCG, although this important finding went unpublicised, except in France.

The trial of three physicians and a nurse in the autumn of 1931 became a national Expressionist spectacle with anguished parents interjecting from the galleries, witnesses shouting back, mysterious Bulgarians and Hungarians suddenly emerging to allege similar catastrophes in their countries - later to be authoritatively denied. BCG and French science were on trial rather than the defendants. Outside the courtroom the September elections were proceeding: the Nazis won 6,000,000 votes. A distraught Calmette demanded the right to appear, and was rebuffed. The Reich Health Council, despite its second report, advised against BCG. The British continued to misquote the episode until 1980. Altogether the Lübeck tragedy was a fitting backdrop to the death of the Weimar regime and the rise of Hitler.[156]

Lübeck encouraged other anti-BCG forces to declare themselves. The Americans were almost uniformly hostile. The influential Professor Georges Dreher at Oxford reported findings similar to those of the North American researchers and told the Medical Research Council which supported his work that BCG was 'not necessarily safe'. Dreher was trying to develop his own vaccine. He had been sent by the Medical Research Council to study the Lübeck affair and had early reported adversely on the role of BCG. His report was not published, even after, or perhaps because, BCG was exonerated, despite calls for it in the House of Commons. Dreher and his colleague, S.R. Douglas, had spent their time in Germany trying to hold the German investigators to their initial decision to inculpate BCG. Some of the Germans, they found, were 'pro-Calmette'. Dr A.S. McNalty and a medical colleague in the Ministry included a reference to 'some reactivation of the ... bacilli present in BCG' in the Ministry's annual report, 'if only in our own defence'. Their ministers in the parliament, Arthur Greenwood and Susan Lawrence, damned BCG.[157]

The 1931 meeting of the National Association was devoted to rejecting BCG. Earlier that year Calmette had passionately defended it with his usual gimcrack statistics at a special meeting of the Royal Society of Medicine. The medical old guard had been alarmed by the interest he had evoked, and the first reports of the Swedish work, which I shall discuss later, among a few of the younger practitioners. Sanatorium consultants such as Dr L.S.T. Burrell explained that BCG was 'of little value' because it did not build resistance to infection. Sir Robert Philip and his collaborator (and future second wife) Dr Edith McGaw professed to have 'followed the proposals sympathetically and sifted the evidence', but they felt 'constrained to express the view that there remain grounds for hesitancy ... [because] introduction of the vaccine is not always harmless', but, 'before a large audience it was unnecessary to go into detail'. They preferred the 'national communal effort' which, they said, had succeeded over the last 30 years. Sir Henry Gauvain, the orthopaedic surgeon keen on immobilising and leaving his patients in the open air, predicted that 'if a patient were inoculated and ... his resistance was at that time lowered ... there would be great danger of serious infection and great harm might result, ... [but] I will not go into that'. He preferred his own well tried procedures on those who had been unfortunate enough to develop the disease, abetted by 'sunlight ... education ... and ... vitamins'.[158] There was plenty for him to work on. In 1926, the only year, apparently, for which there are returns, over 50,000 elementary school children were registered as crippled from tuberculosis. Children under one year were still being recorded as dying from tuberculosis at the rate of about 1.4 per 1000 live births in 1931.[159] Enterprising doctors, such as Bernard Schlesinger of Great Ormond Street Childrens' Hospital, had to be quietly talked out of trying it.[160] Professor S. Lyle Cummins had already tried BCG in Wales on fifteen infants without 'untoward effects'. The fifteen, luckily for the anti-BCG front, comprised too small a sample to be impressive: other mothers had refused Cummins access to their babies. By 1932 Cummins had half recanted and in 1935 he allowed himself to be quoted in denunciation of the vaccine.[161] As Dr Letitia Fairfield instructed the laity and local tuberculosis officers in 1931, 'the administrative officer must ... step aside and leave the field to the bacteriologists and clinicians'; she admitted that BCG seemed wonderfully successful in France, yet she failed to suggest that they go abroad and study what was being done.[162]

Meanwhile, the British tuberculosis leaders maintained their hostility. Sir Robert Philip attacked BCG at the 1933 meeting of the National Association. Professor W.M. Crofton of University College Dublin declared that it was 'beset with dangers' and alleged that it must cause deaths, although he did not produce any instances. Sir George Buchanan at the Ministry of Health issued a memorandum against it in March 1933. He admitted that it worked with calves, but advised against widening its use without explaining why, and then warned against giving it to infants, 585 of whom had died from tuberculosis in 1930. 'There would be some risk indeed that by so doing we should detract from the efficacy of other measures of control in which we have greater confidence'.[163] Calmette died soon after. He had been broken, it was said later, by the Lübeck affair, by a similar scandal in Chile, and by British contempt.[164]

The first full-scale defence of BCG in Britain appeared in 1934. K. Neville Irvine's book was well-founded in the European literature and personal observation, but it had no effect on British policy. The real result of his book was to introduce English readers to A. Wallgren's work in Göteberg where, by 1933, 355 children, two-thirds of them from high risk tuberculous families, had received the vaccine intravenously and, after seven years, only one had developed active tuberculosis.[165] In France over 423,000 infants had received BCG orally, with probable saving of life among high risk cases, and no ill effects. Older children whose von Pirquet tubercular tests showed them to be tuberculosis positive were being given BCG with good results.[166] Another 600,000 persons, mainly children, had received it with similar outcomes in Romania, Poland and Spain. Petroff's experiments had been discredited.

Irvine pleaded for limited trials in Britain. Westminster Hospital was prepared to become the central preparation laboratory. But Sir Robert Philip, described by a contemporary as 'dominating, actorish, manipulative ... with a huge ego', remained 'doubtful'. He had yet to be convinced that the immunity was 'permanent'.[167] Calmette, Wallgren and Irvine had never claimed that it was. Canada provided a striking test. Tuberculosis-ridden Quebec had adopted BCG in 1926. English-speaking Canada rejected it. By 1934 Canadian BCG children in risk households showed a mortality rate of 1.7 per cent compared with 6.2 per cent for non-BCG children in similar circumstances. Similar figures for morbidity and mortality were reported from Greece, from the mid-1920s. The Canadian Government finally tried it in 1946 on the Indian peoples, among whom tuberculosis was rampant. The results were miraculously good. The contrast with the United States' grudging efforts is horrible. Aronson had demonstrated a differential of over 800 per cent between vaccinated and unvaccinated groups, but his work was never acted on.[168] G. Gregory Kayne remarked in 1937 that it was 'discouraging' that BCG had not been tried in Britain, although he added that it had 'no place in England as a general measure'.[169] Two years later, as collaborator with the eminent Walter Pagel and Laurence O'Shaughnessy in writing the British standard text on tuberculosis, Kayne and his colleagues rejected BCG because its statistical supports contained 'gross errors' and it was not a *virus fixe*. They added that it was used in France, Scandinavia and Romania without including the results claimed for it in those countries. In France, they remarked, exaggerated enthusiasm for it had 'abated'.[170] E. Ashworth Underwood's *Manual of Tuberculosis*, in its new edition of 1945 still harped on the Lübeck disaster.[171] Meanwhile the first official British trials on calves were just getting under way.[172]

BCG finally slipped into Britain about 1947 as 'propaganda' to comfort sanatoria nurses. The sanatoria were near collapse for want of staff. Moreover, many of the nurses were Irish with a higher incidence of latent tuberculosis. Sanatoria had always been short-staffed, but they became even less appealing when the new health legislation created further opportunities for nurses in general and specialist fields. The shortage had been acute during the War and as early as 1943 the National Association and Joint Tuberculosis Council had asked the

Ministry of Health for a trial, but apparently nothing happened until about 1947.[173] The National Association took the revolutionary step in 1949 of inviting Wallgren to describe his successes in Sweden and K.A. Jensen to tell about BCG in Denmark. There was no British speaker on the topic. Jensen said that 30 years experience of BCG showed that it increased natural resistance, but gave no absolute immunity. Wallgren told the meeting that BCG children developed primary tuberculous four to ten times less often and tertiary pulmonary tuberculosis two to three times less often. No BCG child developed meningitis or miliary tuberculosis. It was cheap and effective. 'Why not use it?' Wallgren asked.[174]

The Ministry agreed in 1949 to a 'selective trial', although nothing happened immediately. The delay might be explained by the attitudes of influential specialists such as Dr Alice Macpherson of Brompton Hospital who explained in 1952 that BCG did 'not have a primary place in our scheme of treatment'. It was given to patients who asked for it, but she and her colleagues were 'still learning about it'.[175]

The first Medical Research Council sponsored trial began in 1950 under the direction of Dr P. D'Arcy Hart. After four years' observation of 56,000 fourteen year olds he reported that the unvaccinated showed a pulmonary tuberculosis rate of 1.94 per 1000, consonant with the average for the general population, while the BCG groups showed a rate of 0.37 per 1000. Among the Mantoux test negative class the BCG group had only one-fifth the incidence of later infection of the unvaccinated controls. No BCG subject developed acute or miliary tuberculosis, compared with six of the unvaccinated.[176] In 1954 10,000 tuberculous-positive children were vaccinated in Birmingham, at a cost of £5000. Notifications among the 10,000 were 80 per cent less than the unvaccinated and tuberculous-negative group. The £5000 outlay was much less than the projected cost of treatment among the 10,000 had they developed the disease at the rate of their unprotected counterparts.[177] By the late 1950s it was becoming clear in Britain that BCG protection time was lengthening and had reached about six and a half years, thereby again cutting projected vaccination costs.[178] These reports did not stop Fraser Brockington in his *Short History of Public Health* (1956), explaining that BCG 'was not favoured in Britain' because 'the statistical evidence upon which it was based was not considered adequate'.[179] Walter Pagel and his colleagues in their standard text book also made some odd, grudging switches in their handling of BCG in successive editions from 1948. Their cool, curt reportage of Wallgren's Swedish results and good results in Norway and Denmark was deleted from the fourth edition (1964). They admitted that Scandinavian examples stood, but dismissed 'the French school' and added that 'BCG is not a cheap substitute for a well-organized anti-tuberculous scheme', even though, as they pointed out 'the MRC (1956, 1959, 1963) has demonstrated its reliability' - 30 years after the Swedes and others.[180]

We now know that protection afforded by BCG does vary between nations. Bacteriologists surmise that this is partly because of cross infection and immunity conferred by other types of *Mycobacteria tuberculosis* , partly because the protection of the vaccinated depends on the incidence of tuberculosis among the unvaccinated, and partly because of variation in dosages and methods of administration.[181] But the failure even to study the Swedish work or experiment with BCG in Britain remains one of the signal failures of British medical policy. The editor of *Tubercle* remarked in 1971, reviewing 50 years of BCG, that 'future medical historians will find the story of BCG vaccination a strange mixture of endeavour, inertia and ineptitude'.[182] He was too kind.

NOTES

[1]*Lancet*, 12 Mar. 1921, pp.53-4.

[2]*Lancet*, 19 Mar. 1921, p.612.

[3]*BMJ*, 28 Aug. 1926, p.397.

[4]*BMJ*, 11 Sept. 1926, p.560.

[5]*BMJ*, 30 Oct. 1926, p.809; *Lancet*, 25 Sept. 1926, p.681.

[6]*Lancet*, 9 Oct. 1926, p.779.

[7]*BMJ*, 18 Sept. 1926, p.543; see also B.R. Clarke (Forster Green Hospital, Belfast), *BMJ*, 27 Nov. 1926, p.1021.

[8]*BMJ*, 21 Mar. 1936, p.589. Hartley was consultant physician at Brompton, Daneswood Sanatorium and St Bartholomew's.

[9]J.E. Chapman, 'Tuberculosis Analysis and Progress', Ministry of Health, ND. [1939?] PRO MH55/120.

[10]*BPP*, 1904, vol. xxxii, Qs6020-2, and appendix xi, table c; *Transactions of NAPT, 1912*, p.229.

[11]*BPP*, 1904, vol. xxxii, appendix xiii, table 3, Qs9495-6.

[12]Arthur Newsholme, 'Inquiry into ... the reduction in the death-rate from phthisis ... ', *Journal of Hygiene*, vol. vi, 1906, p.309.

[13]Councillor John Barker, (Newcastle-upon-Tyne), *Transactions of NAPT*, *1929*, p.21, probably quoting the investigations of H.K. Mott.

[14]Lilli Stein, 'Tuberculosis and the "Social Complex" in Glasgow', *British Journal of Social Medicine*, vol. vi, 1952, pp.12-13. Overcrowding was not defined by statute until the Housing Act of 1957 when it became effectively one and a half persons or more aged over ten to a room or dwelling.

[15]F.C.S. Bradbury, *Causal Factors In Tuberculosis*, n.d. [1933], pp.22-6, 43-4.

[16]R. Cameron (Cardiff), *BMJ*, 11 Aug. 1928, p.243; Josephine Webb and Alice Stewart with Ian Sutherland, 'Spread of Tuberculosis from House to House', *British Journal of Social Medicine*, vol.5, 1951, p.26.

[17]*Transactions of NAPT*, *1909*, pp.69-70; *Lancet*, 25 Feb. 1911, p.507.

[18]*Transactions of NAPT*, *1912*, p.228.

[19]*Lancet*, 25 Mar. 1911, p.844.

[20]*Prevention of Destitution*, p.68; Dr Fraser, Medical Officer of Health for Portsmouth, made a similar case at the same conference, p.63.

[21]Hull Council to Minister of Health, 14 Oct. 1930, PRO MH52/300.

[22]Bolton Tomson, *Transactions of NAPT*, *1931*, p.113.

[23]Harold Kerr (Medical Officer of Health Newcastle-Upon-Tyne), *Transactions NAPT*, *1929*, p.26.

[24]*Transactions of NAPT*, *1931*, pp.161-3, Noel Bardswell, *Transactions ...*, *1935*, p.149.

[25]Wilson, *Public Health Services*, pp.101-2.

[26]e.g. editorial, *BMJ*, 20 Mar. 1886, p.553.

[27]'Public Health Authorities', *Journal of Hygiene*, vol.iii, 1903, p.451.

[28]*BPP*, 1919, vol.x, pp.lv-lvi; see also H. Hyslop Thomson (County Medical Officer of Health, Hertfordshire), *BMJ*, 18 July 1936, p.150.

[29]Arnold R. Rich, *The Pathogenesis of Tuberculosis*, second ed., Oxford 1951, p.619.

[30]Newsholme, 'An Inquiry', *Journal of Hygiene*, vol.vi, 1906, p.372.

[31]Hyslop Thomson, *International Conference Against Tuberculosis*, 1921, p.87;

[32]H. Hyslop Thomson, *Tuberculosis And Public Health*, 1920, p.25.

[33]R.M. Stewart, *BMJ*, 25 July 1936, p.197.

[34]E.J. Fitzgerald, *BMJ*, 11 July 1936, p.100.

[35]Halliday Sutherland, *BMJ*, 4 July 1936, p.46.

[36]F.J.H. Coutts 'Report on Welsh National Memorial Association', 16 Dec. 1930, PRO MH75/12; 'Report on meeting of Welsh NMA', 1 July 1931, PRO MH75/13.

[37]'Tuberculosis and Nutrition', *Tubercle,* vol.xxix, 1948, pp.20-1.

[38]*BMJ,* 10 June 1933, p.1018; *Causal Factors,* pp.40-1. For similar evidence from Stockton-on-Tees, see D.M. Dunlop, *BMJ,* 24 Dec. 1938, p.1299.

[39]J.L.Turk, 'Leprosy and tuberculosis', in P.J. Lachmann and D.K. Peters (eds), *Clinical Aspects of Immunology,* vol.ii, Oxford 1982, p.1417.

[40]*Transactions of NAPT, 1911,* p.139; James Niven, quoting G.H. Lock 'of the Tuberculosis Office', *Prevention of Destitution,* p.49.

[41]F.C.S. Bradbury (Tuberculosis Officer, Lancashire County Council), *BMJ,* 10 June 1933, p.1018.

[42]Bradbury, *Causal Factors,* pp.82-4.

[43]quoted by Councillor G.A. Griffith (West Riding Council), *Transactions of NAPT, 1933,* p.81.

[44]*Transactions of NAPT, 1931,* p.79.

[45]Dr W. Bruce Fay, *BMJ,* 24 June 1933, p.1127.

[46]*BMJ,* 3 Nov. 1928, p.815; *Lancet,* 23 Sept. 1933, p.719.

[47]for a representative account, see Jacob Hare, *Lancet,* 29 Oct. 1842, p.160.

[48]Sheridan Delépine, *Transactions of Aberdeen Congress 1900 of Royal Institute of Public Health,* Aberdeen 1901, p.221; 'Tuberculosis as a Contagious Disease', *BMJ,* 8 May 1880, p.705.

[49]editorial, *Lancet,* 22 May 1880, p.813.

[50]*Lancet,* 22 May 1886, p.983.

[51]Charles Creighton, *Bovine Tuberculosis in Man; An Account of the Pathology of Suspected Cases,* 1881. See the debate between leading veterinarians in *BMJ,* 25 Feb. 1888, p.419, and William G. Savage, *The Prevention of Human Tuberculosis of Bovine Origin,* 1929, pp.8-9. From the late 1920s it was clear that bovine tuberculosis grew much better than human bacilli in glycerine culture. Bovine bacilli also killed rabbits, while human bacilli only did so in massive doses, and pigs could only be infected with human tuberculosis. Gloyne, *Social Aspects,* p.24.

[52]*BMJ,* 16 July 1887, p.157; Arthur Ransome in *BMJ,* 22 Mar. 1890, p.648.

[53]George Fleming (Principal Veterinary Surgeon to the Army), *Lancet,* 7 Apr. 1888, p.698; Victor Horsley to Royal Commission on Tuberculosis, *BPP,* 1896, vol.xlvi, Q.1683.

[54]Medico-Chirurgical Society of Edinburgh, Memorial to Privy Council, *BMJ,* 7 Apr. 1888, p.750.

[55]R.S. Marsden (Medical Officer of Health for Birkenhead) to Royal Commission, *BPP,* 1898, vol.xlix, Q.2388.

[56]Royal Commission, *BPP,* 1896, vol.xlvi, Qs.1137-45.

[57]Ibid, Qs.1405-10.

[58]*Supplement to 55th Registrar-General's Report, BPP,* 1897, vol.xxv, p.xlv.

[59]Royal Commission, *BPP,* 1898, vol.xlix, Qs.213-4.

[60]Dr James Niven to Society of Medical Officers of Health, *BMJ*, 1 Apr. 1893, p.699, G.F. McCleary (Medical Officer of Health for Battersea), 'The Infants' Milk Depot: Its History and Function', *Journal of Hygiene*, vol.iv, 1904, p.363.

[61]G. Sims Woodhead, *Lancet*, 14 July 1888, p.53; Royal Commission, *BPP*, 1896, vol.xlvi, Qs.165 (Dreschfeld), 219-30 (Woodhead), 538-40 (Klein).

[62]John Francis, *Bovine Tuberculosis, including a contrast with Human Tuberculosis*, 1947, p.128.

[63]S. Lyle Cummins, *Tuberculosis in History* , 1949, pp.189-90; Pottenger, *Fight Against Tuberculosis*, pp.231-2.

[64]Arthur Ransome, *BMJ*, 22 Mar. 1890, p.648.

[65]Charles Creighton, *BMJ*, 15 Oct. 1881, p.631.

[66]e.g. Dr H.D. Littlejohn, Royal Commission, *BPP*, 1896, vol.xlvi, Qs.1579-84.

[67]Carpenter (Croydon), *BMJ*, 15 Oct. 1881, p.631.

[68]Dr Kammerer (City Physician of Vienna), *BMJ*, 26 Aug. 1882, p.374; Professor Johne (Dresden), *BMJ*, 2 Dec. 1882, p.1098; Ransome on French and German practice, *BMJ*, 22 Mar. 1890, p.648.

[69]W. Field (British Meat Trade spokesman), Royal Commission,*BPP*, 1898, vol.xlix, Q.330.

[70]*Lancet*, 28 July 1888, p.180.

[71]The case-law on these matters is endlessly complicated: *BMJ*, 15 June 1889, p.1359; 29 June, pp.1429, 1479.

[72]*Lancet*, 29 June 1889, p.1314; 1 Mar. 1890, p.484; *BMJ*, 3,10 May 1890, pp.973,1079; *Leeds Mercury* on Dreschfeld's experiments, 26 Apr. 1890.

[73]*BMJ*, 5 Apr. 1890, p.791.

[74]Royal Commission, *BPP*, 1896, vol.xlvi, Qs.1446, 1463; for similar action in Belfast, see Conway Scott, Qs.2911, 2963-8. Sheffield also acted stringently, pp.7-8.

[75]*Lancet*, 3 Feb. 1894, p.295.

[76]Royal Commission report, *BPP*, 1898, vol.xlix, p.20. The crucial evidence was Professor J. McFadyean's, (Principal of Royal Veterinary College) pp.3-4.

[77]These costs were estimated, not very accurately, by T.H. Elliott of the Board of Agriculture, Ibid, Q.179.

[78]W. Field to Royal Commission, Ibid, Qs.379-85.

[79]Ibid, pp.11-12; this also was McFadyean's advice, Q.1323.

[80]Ibid, Q.5753.

[81]*BMJ*, 21 Mar. 1925, p.577; J.M. Armfield in *Veterinary Record*, 4 June 1927, p.507; Gloyne, *Tuberculosis*, p.57.

[82]Francis, *Bovine Tuberculosis*, pp.122-3; *BMJ*, 4 July 1925, p.40.

[83]*BMJ*, 23 Feb. 1924, p.347.

[84]*BMJ*, 25 July 1925, p.179.

[85]R.H. Smythe in *Veterinary Record*, 18 June 1927, p.548.

[86]*Parl. Deb.*, vol.286, col.2026, Walter Elliott, 8 Mar. 1934; Francis, *Bovine Tuberculosis*, p.60.

[87]Gloyne, *Tuberculosis*, p.55.

[88]Francis, *Bovine Tuberculosis*, pp.123-4.

[89]Arthur Latham, *Medical Chronicle*, vol.iii, Apr.-Sept. 1910, p.75.

[90]Memorandum on 'Law on Milk Supplies', n.d. [1913?], Astor Papers, Reading University Library, MS1066/1/1042.

[91]Sheridan Delépine, 'The Share Taken by Human and Bovine Tuberculous Products in the Infection of Young Children', *Transactions of NAPT, 1912*, p.52; E.W. Hope, (Liverpool), *Transactions of NAPT, 1909*, pp.75-6; Sir George Newman, 'Report on Public Health', *BMJ*, 25 Sept. 1926, p.566.

[92]Sir George Newman, 'Report on Public Health', *BMJ*, 25 Sept. 1926, p.566.

[93]Dr Christopher Addison, *Parl. Deb.*, vol.71, cols.2098-2102, 17 May 1915; *BMJ*, 1 July 1922, p.25.

[94]Anon. [Waldorf Astor?], *Campaign for Clean Milk*, 1916, p.11.

[95]*Parl. Deb.*, vol.236, cols.666, 1489-92, 2097-8, 3 Mar. 1930.

[96]William G. Savage, *Milk and the Public Health* , 1912, pp.323-5; Councillor J.S. Pickering (Sunderland), *Transactions of NAPT, 1931*, p.63;*BMJ*, 12 Aug. 1922, p.268.

[97]Savage, *Prevention*, p.42; *BMJ*, 14 Feb. 1925, p.309.

[98]George P. Male (Veterinarian, Reading), William G. Savage (Somerset) *BMJ*, 8 Aug. 1925, p.250-65; Henry Gray, *Veterinary Record*, 23 July 1927, p.634.

[99]Savage, *Prevention*, p.11.

[100]G.S. Wilson, *The Pasteurization of Milk*, 1942, pp.27-8.

[101]J.N. Ritchie, *Proceedings of Royal Society of Medicine*, vol.xxxix, 1945-6, p.218.

[102]*BMJ*, 18 Nov. 1933, p.905;

[103]F.E. Fremantle and Susan Lawrence in *Parl. Deb.*, vol.230, cols.1093-4, 23 July 1929.

[104]*BMJ*, 18 Nov. 1933, p.908; Lord Astor in *BMJ*, 23 June 1934, p.1136; *BMJ*, 26 Jan. 1935, p.163.

[105]Graham Selby Wilson, John W.S. Blacklock and Lilian V. Reilly, *Non-Pulmonary Tuberculosis of Bovine Origin in Great Britain and Northern Ireland*, 1952, pp.5-6.

[106]*BMJ*, 27 Nov. 1920, p.829; Paterson, *Shibboleths*, p.19; Dr John Robertson (Medical Officer of Health for Birmingham), *BMJ*, 14 Feb. 1925, p.309; Dr David Nabarro, *BMJ*, 7 Mar. 1925, p.457.

[107]Williams at National Milk Conference, *BMJ*, 21 Oct. 1922, p.771; see also 'The Milk Supply - What Shall our Policy be?', *Journal of State Medicine*, vol.xxxvi, Feb. 1928, pp.63-78.

[108]Lionel J. Picton, *BMJ*, 2 Dec. 1933, p.1045.

[109]*BMJ*, 18 Nov. 1933, p.908.

[110]Lieut-Col. Brittlebank (Veterinary Officer for Manchester), *BMJ*, 14 Feb. 1925, p.309.

[111]Dr C. Maddock (Certified Milk Producers' Association), *BMJ*, 21 Sept. 1929, p.530; *BMJ*, 11 Oct. 1924, p.676.

[112]Norman C. Wright, *BMJ*, 7 Sept. 1929, p.453; S. Roydhouse Gloyne in *BMJ*, 15 July 1939, p.132.

[113]C. Lee Paterson (Medical Superintendent, King Edward VII Hospital, Sheffield), *BMJ*, 28 Apr. 1928, p.731.

[114]T.M. Clayton and Robert Rutherford (Medical Officer of Health for Wallsend), *Transactions of NAPT, 1931*, pp.62-3; *Annual Abstract of Statistics*, Nos.61,62, Table 40, and No.58, Table 202. On school milk, see Miss M. Gardner (National Union of Teachers), *Transactions of NAPT , 1936*, pp.89-90.

[115]Cameron, *BPP*, 1898, vol.xlix, Qs 2659-62; for confirmation that people disliked boiled milk, but better sense about its digestive qualities, see James Niven, Ibid, Qs 3690-2; Bernard Myers, 'Milk Problems Affecting Child-Life'. *The Child*, vol.ii, Dec. 1911, p.187; on doctors differing, Dr C.M. McNeil, *BMJ*, 3 Aug. 1929, p.194.

[116]Wilson, *Pasteurization*, p.108.

[117]*BMJ*, 9 Dec. 1933, p.1080. A three-year test of 10,000 school children in Lanarkshire revealed no differences in growth or general health between those given Grade A or tuberculin-tested milk and those given pasteurised milk. These results replicated an experiment in the United States completed in 1932. *BMJ*, 2 June 1934, p.995.

[118]*Parl. Deb.*, vol.273, col.906, 20 Dec. 1932.

[119]Macfadyen in *The Times*, 27 Jan. 1937; Wilson, *Pasteurization*, pp.187, 194.

[120]*Shibboleths*, p.19.

[121]T. Williams, *Parl. Deb.* vol.224, col.1161, 31 Jan. 1929; Rabagliati in *Transactions of NAPT, 1931*, p.57.

[122]William S. Stevens, *BMJ*, 23 Jan. 1932, p.172.

[123]Councillor J. Carey, (Easington), *Transactions of NAPT, 1933*, p.197. Councillor R.G. Edwards (Manchester) Ibid, pp.92-3; *BMJ*, 25 Nov. 1933, p.991.

[124]W. Camac Wilkinson, *Treatment of Consumption*, pp.17-18; E. von Behring, *The Suppression of Tuberculosis*, translated by Charles Boldüan, New York 1904, p.31.

[125]Cummins and Nabarro, *BMJ*, 7 Mar. 1925, p.457; Philip and Raw, *Transactions of NAPT, 1931*, pp.51-4.

[126]*BMJ*, 4 July 1931, p.28.

[127]*BMJ*, 11 Nov. 1933, p.892.

[128]H.P. Hughes Gibbs to Lord Astor, 25 Nov. 1920, Astor Papers, MS1066/1/70; J.H. Maggs, Chairman of United Dairies Ltd, *BMJ*, 8 Aug. 1925, p.251; Wilson, *Pasteurization*, p.49.

[129]Savage, *Prevention*, pp.164-71; Ministry of Health Circular No.335, 28 Aug. 1922.

[130]Professor J.M. Beattie and Dr S.R. Douglas, *BMJ*, 12 Dec. 1925, p.1138; H.A. Cookson (Bacteriologist to Sunderland Health Authority), *BMJ*, 9 Oct. 1926, p.637.

[131]Wilson, *Pasteurization*, pp.49-59; 71-3; Department of Health in Scotland, *BMJ*, 30 Dec. 1933, p.1224.

[132]Wilson, *Pasteurization*, p.v.

[133]Milk Nutrition Committee survey, *BMJ*, 19 Nov. 1938, p.1049.

[134]Wilson, *Pasteurization*, pp.49-55.

[135]Wilson in *Transactions of NAPT, 1952*, pp.243-4.

[136]Wilson, Blacklock and Reilly, *Non-Pulmonary Tuberculosis*, p.107.

[137]Wilson, *Pasteurization*, pp.154-5.

[138]Rich, *Pathenogenesis of Tuberculosis*, p.57.

[139]J.B.S. Haldane, *Possible Worlds*, 1927, pp.97-8; Ministry of Health pamphlet on bovine tuberculosis, 1931; John Francis, 'The Work of the British Royal Commission on Tuberculosis', *Tubercle*, vol.xl, 1959, p.131.

[140]C. Guérin, in *Premier Congrès International Du B.C.G. ... 1948*, Paris ND [1950?], p.11.

[141]A. Calmette, *L'Infection Bacillaire et la Tuberculose*, quatrième édition, Paris 1936, pp.309-19.

[142]Guérin, *Premier Congrés*, p.12.

[143]A.S. McNalty to High Commissioner for New Zealand, draft, 7 Apr. 1925, PRO MH55/150.

[144]*BMJ*, 29 Aug. 1925, p.388.

[145]A.S. McNalty to High Commissioner for New Zealand, draft [for Minister?], 7 Apr. 1925, PRO MH55/150.

[146]F.J.H. Coutts, Memoranda, 13 Apr., 29 Sept. 1926, PRO MH55/150.

[147]*BMJ*, 29 Aug. 1925, p.388.

[148]*BMJ*, 27 Mar. 1926, p.581.

[149]*BMJ*, 21 Aug. 1926, p.361.

[150]*BMJ*, 7 May 1927, p.845.

[151]*BMJ*, 12 May 1928, pp.793-4; Greenwood's pursuit of Calmette can be followed in *BMJ*, 27 Mar. 1926, p.581; 14, 28 May 1927, pp.896, 987. Calmette and his disciples seem never to have got their statistics right. The figures in Calmette, *Tuberculose* (1936), pp.952-3 are impenetrable, while Armand-Delille's figures for the Paris Grancher children in *Premier Congrès* (1948) pp.194-5 are at best implausible.

[152]G. Buchanan, memorandum, 11 Oct. 1928, PRO MH55/150; see also *BMJ*, 24 Nov. 1928, p.951. Denmark, Belgium, Germany, Austria, France and the USA attended the conference.

[153]*BMJ*, 16 Feb. 1929, p.302.

[154]Calmette on Austrians and Portuguese at Royal Society of Medicine, *Lancet*, 13 June 1931, p.1299; the Canadian results are reported in *BMJ*, 30 Mar. 1929, p.613; the influence of Petroff and the American allegations can be seen in Savage, *Prevention*, pp.142-5, and *BMJ*, 31 Oct. 1931, p.814; for Petroff, see Pottenger, *Fight*, p.166 and K. Neville Irvine, *B.C.G. Vaccination in Theory and Practice*, Oxford 1949, pp.23, 34, 115. The Americans were still damning BCG, without any effective experimental work, in 1959, see *BMJ*, 6 June 1959 p.1423-30. But it turned out later that BCG was notably less effective in the United States, affording only about 14 per cent protection in the general population, yet it did well among nurses. J.L. Turk, 'Leprosy and Tuberculosis', in Peter Julius Lachmann and D.K. Peters (eds),*Clinical Aspects of Immunology* Oxford 1982, vol.ii, p.1425.

[155]Frank Fenner, 'The Variability of BCG Vaccine', *American Review of Tuberculosis*, vol.lxiii, 1951, p.714.

[156]The *BMJ* provides a good narrative of the affair from German sources, especially in June-July 1931. *The Times* also has sporadic reports commencing 15 Mar. 1930. The American response can be gauged from A. Boquet, 'The Pathogenic Properties of BCG', in *American Review of Tuberculosis*, vol.xxiii, 1931. Renè and Jean Dubos, *The White Plague*, 1953, pp.122-3, are totally misleading, beginning with the date of the affair. Persisting British misapprehensions about Lübeck can be found in the *Lancet* editorial, 12 Jan. 1980, p.73. I have looked into several works which cover the 1931 elections but none mentions the Lübeck trial. My impression is that it is worth more attention: it lowered respect for Republican institutions and fuelled nationalism.

[157]A.S. McNalty and Sir George Newman, memorandum, 21 May 1930; G. Dreher and S.R. Douglas, report, 26 June 1930; Sir George Newman, memorandum, 18 June 1931, PRO MH55/150, 154; P. Freeman, A. Greenwood, S. Lawrence, *Parl. Deb.*, vols 244, 248, cols. 1074, 1080-1, 6 Nov. 1930, 17 Feb. 1931.

[158]*Transactions of NAPT, 1931*, Burrell, p.145; Philip and McGaw, pp.8-12; Gauvain, pp.86-92.

[159]A. Salusbury McNalty, *A Report on Tuberculosis, including an Examination of ... Sanatorium Treatment*, 1932, p.114; Logan and Benjamin, *Tuberculosis Statistics*, p.16; Calmette characteristically damaged his cause by asserting, against a Ministry of Health official memo, that the rate was 6.6 per 100. *Lancet*, 25 Mar. 1933, p.654.

[160]Sir George Newman, memorandum, 18 June 1931, PRO MH55/154; for another proto-BCG supporter, see Reginald C. Jewsbury in *Transactions of NAPT, 1931*, pp.49-50.

[161]Sir George Newman, memorandum, 18 June 1931, PRO MH55/154; Cummins in *Lancet*, 20 Feb. 1932, p.423; McNalty, *BMJ*, 4 May 1935, p.945.

[162]*Transactions of NAPT, 1931*, pp.31-2.

[163]Philip in *Transactions of NAPT, 1931*, pp.31-2. Crofton in *Lancet*, 20 Feb. 1932, p.423; Buchanan in *Lancet*, 25 Mar. 1933, p.654.

[164]Williams, *Requiem*, p.61. See Calmette's passionate, unheeded, appeal for a British trial of BCG, *Lancet*, 19 Mar. 1932, p.643; the Chilean disaster, and another at Ujpest in Hungary in 1930 are recounted in Irvine, *BCG*, pp.42-7.

[165]Irvine, *The BCG Vaccine*, Oxford 1934; E. Rist, *Transactions of NAPT, 1935* , pp.79-82.

[166]Rist, *Transactions of NAPT, 1935*, p.77.

[167]William, *Requiem*, pp.44-5; Irvine in *Transactions of NAPT, 1935*, pp.89-92.

[168]J. Baudouin (Montreal), *Lancet*, 21 Mar. 1936, p.638; *Premier Congrès*, pp.213-8; *Irvine*, BCG, *p.101*; J.D. Aronson, and Armand Frappier, M.E. Perdicologos, Premier Congrès, pp.196-205, 244-6, 294-301; G. Gregory Kayne, 'BCG in Western Europe', *American Review of Tuberculosis*, vol.xxxiv, 1936, p.41.

[169]Kayne, *Control of Tuberculosis, p.130.*

[170]George Gregory Kayne, Walter Pagel and Laurence O'Shaughnessy, *Pulmonary Tuberculosis*, 1939, pp.543-4.

[171]E. Ashworth Underwood, *A Manual Of Tuberculosis clinical and administrative*, Edinburgh 1945, p.75.

[172]T. Dalling, 'The Control of bovine tuberculosis', *Proceedings of Royal Society of Medicine*, vol.xxxix, 1945-6, p.215.

[173]W.H. Tytler (Welsh National School of Medicine), *Premier Congrès*, p.325.

[174]*Transactions of NAPT, 1949*, pp.249, 267.

[175]*Transactions of NAPT, 1952*, pp.137-8. The files dealing with BCG, PRO MH55/1316, 1317, are closed until 1989 and 1991 respectively.

[176]*Tubercle*, vol.xxxvii, 1956, p.142; vol.xxxix, 1958, p.330.

[177]V.H. Springett, 'Effect of BCG Vaccination in Birmingham', *Tubercle*, vol.xl, 1959, p.305.

[178]T.M. Pollock, 'BCG Vaccination in Man', *Tubercle*, xl, 1959, pp.402-3.

[179]*Short History*, p.173.

[180]*Pulmonary Tuberculosis*, 1953 ed., p.702, 1964 ed., pp.364-5, 483.

[181]D.H. Shennan, *Tuberculosis Control In Developing Countries*, Edinburgh 1968, pp.37-8; World Health Organization, *Mass Health Examinations*, Geneva, 1971, p.17; *Tubercle*, vol.lii, 1971, p.304; M.J. Shield, 'The Importance of Immunologically Effective Contact With Environmental Mycobacteria', in Colin Ratledge and John Stanford (eds), *The Biology of the Mycobacteria*, 1983, pp.367-410.

[182]*Tubercle*, vol.lii, 1971, p.303.

The incidence of consumption was closely connected with patterns of employment. Metal workers, tailors and shoemakers, masons, printers, bakers and seamstresses were traditionally subject to high phthisis morbidity and mortality. Many of them worked in small enterprises, beyond the Factory Acts, squatting hunched in fuggy atmospheres in ill-ventilated, dirty workrooms. As Professor W.P. Alison of Edinburgh explained in 1829, the inhalation of deleterious vapours or fine mechanical particles induced 'inflammation in the mucous surfaces ... whence it is propagated to the parenchymatous [soft tissues] structures'.[1] These trades were also peculiarly liable to irregular hours, with frequent long exhausting sessions under insanitary conditions. Compositors, for example, like miners threw the remains of their meals into corners where they accumulated into stinking messes. The London Society of Compositors asserted that these practices bred phthisis: in 1883 nearly a third of their funeral allowances were for phthisis victims.[2] The pervasive dust in many workshops led to habitual hawking and spitting. The hot environment encouraged the wearing of what sanitarians regarded as 'improper' sweaty clothes. Male workers drank too much alcohol, seamstresses, young ones especially, drank great quantities of tea which, according to W.R. Thomas, senior physician to the Sheffield Public Hospital, hurt their gastric mucous membrane, which brought on dyspepsia, which lead to anaemia and malnutrition and hence inevitably to phthisis.[3]

Two major epidemiological studies in the 1890s, by John Tatham of the Registrar-General's office, and by Arthur Ransome, largely confirmed the traditional view.

Occupation	Death-rate
file maker	402
lead miner	380
pottery worker	332
copper miner	331
brass worker	279
stone quarrier	269
mason, bricklayer	225

tin worker	217
cotton worker	202
baker, confectioner	185
agricultural labourer	106
coal miner	97
ironstone miner	90

Male Phthisis mortality in England and Wales by occupation at all age groups standardised at 100, from John Tatham, *Supplement to 55th Registrar-General's Report, 1890-92.*[4]

Tatham also showed that men engaged in the high phthisis risk trades were more likely to die younger, from more severe forms of tuberculosis than agricultural labourers, shopkeepers or professional men.[5] Indeed, the differentials were probably greater than Tatham's table reveals. There is much contemporary comment to suggest that men suffering functional impairment and loss of stamina turned to other jobs or drifted to casual employment or out of the workforce: 'General labourers' had more than three times the phthisis mortality of other occupied males.[6]

Tatham's analyses assumed that dust and dried sputum were fundamental causes of high industrial phthisis rates. But his tentative figures for waged female phthisis rates and some of his statistics for males suggest that airborne droplet infection was very important. Arthur Ransome had already illustrated this connection in 1890. Tatham's figures indicated that domestic servants', cotton operatives and charwomen were 30 to 50 per cent 'healthier' than all women in their age groups, particularly at older ages. This conclusion is open to the objection that it does not count the drop-out of sick women, but Tatham had no way of establishing the size of this group. By contrast, females employed in huddled workrooms were very much at risk. Ransome, following W.H. Greenhow's pioneering research in the 1860s, noted that female lacemakers, home weavers and watchmakers in Coventry, Nottingham and other crowded urban areas had death rates from 'pulmonary affections' that exceeded or equalled those of males in the same areas, and that their rates were around 350 per cent higher than the average for both sexes for the northern and midlands industrial districts. The rates for Birmingham, Southampton, Whitechapel and Newcastle, for example, all showed a male excess of up to 130 per cent, compared with Congleton, Leek, Belper, Buckingham, Sevenoaks, Battle and other rural towns where the female rates exceeded the male by up to 330 per cent. In these places, Ransome observed, the women had paid employment at home, straw plaiting, sewing, cardboard box making and so on, while the men worked in the fresh air as agricultural labourers.[7] Their more adequate diet might also have contributed to the men's better chances. In Dundee, however, where women worked in the same jute and tobacco factories as men, the phthisis rates were about equal.[8]

The classic examples of massive infection among susceptible age groups within closed, insanitary quarters among persons with little exercise and possibly under considerable stress were nuns. Nearly 63 per cent of deaths in Prussian nursing orders in 38 convents between 1864 and 1889 were attributed to tuberculosis. The nuns were examined and declared healthy before their admission as novices: their life expectancy from that time averaged three years.[9] Prisoners had rates approaching those of nuns: men at Chatham developed galloping consumption and died in the cold each winter. One half of the deaths in American prisons in 1890 were ascribed to tuberculosis. Lifers died from tuberculosis after fifteen years of their sentence.[10] Men employed in other closed environments had rates which equalled those of the notorious dust trades. Many of them must have been consumptives who had gravitated to ill-paid sedentary occupations and helped inflate the risks: bookbinders, commercial, law, railway clerks, inn servants, hairdressers, tramway conductors, musicians, tobacconists, drapers, street hawkers and messengers had between 1890 and 1911 a one in four or five chance of dying from phthisis, compared with clergymen, one in 27, physicians and farmers, one in 22, bargemen and navvies, one in 12 and coalminers, one in 11. The average for adult males in 1911 was one in 7.[11]

These differentials generally held through the first half of this century, each having much the same rate of decline. One notable exception was coal miners, whose rates increased up to the Great War, although they still remained well below those of workers in Northampton boot factories, for example.[12] But the dramatically ominous nature of their trade and their union organisation made their risks overshadow those in more dangerous occupations. Less well organised slate and tin miners and quarrymen, whose plight was much worse, did less well in receiving protection against dust and compensation for tuberculosis associated with silicosis.

The problems were and are very complicated. Life chances in some dust industries improved with changes in technology. In the Sheffield metal trades, for example, hooded machine grinding with artificial abrasives replaced sandstone wheels during the early 1920s and the change in tuberculosis morbidity among the workers was almost immediate. Laundresses also showed a reduction of morbidity faster than the national average when machine washing was introduced during the same decade.[13] Among miners of all kinds the tuberculosis morbidity and mortality figures were understated. Consumption developed quickly in adolescents joing the workforce and they left underground mining early.[14] The incidence also varied between kinds of mining, between men with different underground tasks, and in the association between tuberculosis and silicosis. The basic difference was between shale and coal miners: 5.6 per cent with tuberculosis against 1.32 per cent in 1950.[15] Cornish tin and clay miners also had much higher incidences than coal miners, and among them men working machine drills in hard rock had 30 times the respiratory death-rate of their workmates, a rate that equalled that of drill men in the Transvaal.[16] But the South Africans were much readier to introduce dust damping methods than British mine owners, as indeed they needed to, because 33 per cent of underground workers were diagnosed as tuberculous in 1914.[17] Infection there was exacerbated by the barracks housing and stress of the men.

Silicosis is the permanent impairment of the lungs by the desposition and irritation of silica dust. Fibrous scar tissue is formed and the patient is severely debilitated. The process is still not fully understood. It is clear, though, that high exposure brings high risks. Professor Edgar Collis showed in 1921 that men quarrying quartzite rock with 98 per cent silica (Yorkshire ganister) for first-grade fire bricks had a silicosis mortality of 37 per 1000 compared with one per 1000 among men who worked second-grade bricks which mixed fine clay with the crushed quartzite. The clay, he believed, formed a metabolically inert envelope around the sharp silica particles which prevented their irritating the lung surfaces.[18]

Tuberculosis often ensued as a complication. Again the process is unclear. The impaired lung tissues may be less able to withstand reactivated bacilli or fresh infections, while the general debility induced by silicosis probably impairs the immune response.[19] The differences between silicosis and tuberculosis were not easily diagnosed, yet they were important to the victims because silicosis had been scheduled under the Workmen's Compensation Acts since 1918 and tuberculosis had not. (This had the dreadful consequence that nurses, who had very inadequate superannuation, could not claim compensation if they contracted tuberculosis.) Respiratory disability among slate miners was also not scheduled. Even with silicosis, victims found it difficult to prove employers' liability under the Act, and once the initial claim was lost, all subsequent claims to any form of compensation were voided.[20]

Among coal miners, the incidence of pulmonary tuberculosis varied with mining methods, the amount of silica in the dust, and the miners' home conditions and diet.

Coalfield Standardised mortality rates for ages 20-65[21]	Pulmonary tuberculosis
Derby	68.9
Durham	85.5
Nottinghamshire	95.3
Northumberland	98.9
Glamorgan	112.1
Yorkshire	135.9
Lancashire	165.2
West Wales	191.2
All fields	112.2

G. Lissant Cox, Unpublished Report on Tuberculosis among coal miners, 1921-23 (1930)

As the figures for west Wales indicate, Wales, with Ireland, was a redoubt of tuberculosis in the nineteenth and twentieth centuries. The Welsh mortality rate was higher than the English or Scottish and it remained concentrated among young adults decades after it had moved into higher age groups in England.[22] In the 'black spots' of sparsely populated mountain areas of north and west Wales and the slate mining towns, tuberculosis mortality did not show, as in England, a close correlation with the mortality from all causes, but outstripped them, suggesting that special factors, beyond bad hygiene, were implicated.[23] In 1912, 70 per cent of adults and 43 per cent of children were found to be sputum positive. In Swansea in 1914, 57 per cent of sputum specimens contained bacilli. Overall, tuberculosis was the single commonest cause of death.[24]

The Welsh, like the Irish, were a poor semi-urbanised peasantry. In the Gwyrfai slate quarrying district, a 'black spot' in north Wales, Dr Herbert D. Chalke described the people in 1900 as living on tea. They ate their food 'almost raw' and hardly knew fresh meat. In 1932 they still drank too much tea, but tinned meat had replaced salt meat. They still ate hardly any green vegetables and 'good solid meat' was 'scarcely known'. At an educational meeting on tuberculosis in Welshpool in 1931 Mrs David Pryce jumped up after a speech on diet and declared that she 'did not like lettuces, radishes or green cabbage, and she had heard nothing that would induce her to give up ... tea'.[25] In the countryside, as in rural Scotland and Ireland, much of the infection probably came from drinking tuberculous milk. Even in 1945, milk was only 'heat treated' in south Wales.[26] The rural death-rate was on average 12 per cent above that of the towns, especially in south Wales.[27] The rural female rate was also higher than the male. At fifteen the girls generally migrated to the towns to go into service; while there they 'broke down ... and returned home to die.' In 1935 half of all deaths in women 15-20 were caused by tuberculosis. The males had partly moved into the age mortality transition and from the 1920s increasingly were dying at ages 45-65. Some commentators had agreed that the high Welsh rates were the outcome of the belated urbanisation of an unfortified population, but the relatively low incidence in south Wales rather belied this hypothesis.[28] What was clear was that tuberculosis mortality increased with the percentage of Welsh speakers:[29]

	percentage of Welsh speakers	tuberculosis death-rate per 1 million
Anglesey	85	1285
Merioneth	82	1505
Caernarvon	75	1258
Denbigh	48	774
Montgomery	42	619
Flint	33	718

(and two of the worst
black spots)

Gwyrfai	96	2930*
Festiniog	94	1938*

A.C. Watkin, *Transactions of NAPT, 1933*

*These figures come from Linda Bryder in Weindling, *Occupational Health*, p.109.

Doctors Chalke and Watkin despaired of improving the death rate in the Depression. In Merioneth and Caernarvonshire, especially, Chalke asserted, sanitation was poor, cottages were decrepit and damp, the children did not taste milk until they entered school (which could account for Wales's distinctively low rate of infantile, if not young adult, surgical tuberculosis), they huddled indoors throughout most of the year and only ventured out to meet in muggy chapels. Amid the unemployment and short-time work, families changed houses down the scale, especially when tuberculosis progressed in the breadwinner.

The people, as elsewhere in Britain, avoided doctors who notified patients or tried to send them to sanatoria, although some doctors ascribed this behaviour to Welsh deviousness. In Anglesey in 1934, of 206 tuberculosis deaths, only 158 had been notified, including 35 notified within three months of death. The Welsh were said to regard consumption as a disgrace and Heaven-sent affliction rather than a disease. H.D. Chalke summed it up as, 'Poverty, under-nourishment, promiscuity, fatalism and exposure to a dangerous industry [slate mining]; a love of finery that places clothes ... [above] food; and the type of love ... that prefers to shield the victim of phthisis from the doctor's verdict'.[30]

Welsh public men and women made much of the King Edward VII Welsh National Memorial Association, begun in 1910 to commemorate the late king's interest in sanatoria. Over £250,000 had been raised by subscription by 1912 when the Association received its charter. It was a voluntary body. Local authorities, excepting Pembrokeshire, delegated their powers over tuberculosis to it. By 1933 the Association had built five sanatoria and twelve hospitals offering nominally 1400 beds, at a capital cost of £317 each. It had also created a chair of tuberculosis at the Welsh National School of Medicine; the only other one in the nation was at Edinburgh. The Association also claimed to have established a network of dispensaries but, as we have seen earlier, most were moribund.

Basically, the Association had too little money to meet its plans. Many local authorities resented it and refused to back its approach to Westminster in 1925 for capital grants on the English basis, on the ground that it superseded them. English local authorities got an annual bed subsidy of £90; Welsh ones only £30. The Association was a voluntary body and despite its royal charter, could not borrow, like an ordinary local authority. The British Treasury never budged on the issue.[31] The Welsh National Scheme has had a good press from its publicists, but one wonders whether more could have been achieved in other ways: £250,000 would have built a lot of pasteurisation plants and subsidised a lot of milk.

Ireland, like Norway, had late nineteenth- and twentieth-century tuberculosis rates which advanced while the rest of Europe and North America enjoyed their retreat. During the 1880s phthisis and non-pulmonary tuberculosis caused over 100,000 deaths, one-tenth of the total mortality. If 'other respiratory diseases' are added, many of them associated with tuberculosis, the toll rises to a quarter of all deaths. In a population of 5,000,000 subject to heavy emigration of its younger, healthier people, the further loss occasioned by tuberculosis mortality and morbidity amounts to a major hurt to the economy and public morale. Irish phthisis was, like the Welsh, notably acute and febrile.

The mortality was worst among the huddled poor of the towns, especially Dublin.[32] Thirty-six per cent of Edwardian Dublin's dwellings comprised one room, compared with Glasgow's 26 per cent, the next worst in the Kingdom. Over 8 per cent of Dublin's single rooms housed at least five occupants, twice the rate of Glasgow and eighteen times worse than London. The chances of massive droplet infection were worsened by the exclusion of 'hopeless cases' from workhouse infirmaries and general hospitals and the popular preference, abetted by widespread outdoor poor relief, for keeping sufferers at home. The surprising thing is that Dublin's phthisis mortality rate, 329 per 10,000 was only around twice that of Glasgow's and London's. The general tuberculosis death rate rose from 19.5 per 10,000 in 1871-80 to 20.9 per 10,000 in 1881-90 to 21.3 per 10,000 in 1891-1900, to peak at 28.8 per 10,000 in 1904.[33] Only Norway, with a 46 per cent increase over the same period, had a worse record. The decisive fall in the Irish rate to around 16 per 10,000 did not come until 1920 and the decline thereafter was slow, with another rise in 1942-3.[34]

Unlike Wales, Ireland had a high incidence, 21 per cent, of non-pulmonary tuberculosis among children under five.[35] Irish children probably consumed more milk than their counterparts in Great Britain, but the milk was as tuberculous as any in the British Isles. Over 8 per cent of town samples in 1925 contained bacilli.[36] The Free State government, regularly shelved clean milk bills, let alone pasteurisation, throughout the 1920s and 1930s. The farmers saw to it that there was no central milk authority. Ireland had no law to exclude milk producers or vendors repeatedly convicted for gross offences against food cleanliness. Seventy per cent of Irish children were tubercular positive by age twelve in the mid 1920s. In 1930 the Free State had the highest incidence of tuberculosis mortality in young adults among 24 European and North American countries.[37]

The impact of tuberculosis was even worse than the statistics indicated because the population at risk remained the 15-25 years age group, two generations after the transition to older age groups had begun in England and Scotland. Emigration and a relatively low birth rate exacerbated the familial and communal disruption. Female death rates generally slightly exceeded male rates, as in rural Britain, and more so in Dublin and Belfast. In Belfast until the late 1920s women had a reported 50 per cent higher morbidity and a 30 per cent higher death rate than men in the same and older age groups. By 1932 the differential in morbidity rates had narrowed to a 23 per cent excess for women and female deaths had fallen to slightly below those of males. The age transition had also begun, particularly among the men to rising rates at 45 years and over, matching the transition that had begun among poorer English sufferers in the 1870s. The disease also became more chronic and fibrotic, with lengthening periods between diagnosis, incapacity and death.[38]

The preponderance of Dublin and Belfast in the reports obscured the fact that tuberculosis was endemic in the countryside. It was not simply a product of overcrowding and poverty in the towns. 'Overwork, strain, pregnancy and bad health' as Dr W.D. O'Kelly, of University College Dublin, remarked, 'might light up the disease' anywhere. He, like other observers, pondered the old speculation that the Irish were, like the Welsh and other Celts, racially less immune to the disease. This notion had been discussed since Dr John Beddoe, the anthropologist, had popularised it in his *Races of Britain* in 1885.[39] There was considerable evidence for the hypothesis. Irish families in Jarrow in the early 1930s, defined by the birthplace of the father, were found to have a 31 per cent higher tuberculosis death rate than their similarly circumstanced English neighbours.[40] Irish and Welsh nurses in English sanatoria were 250 per cent more likely to develop lesions that were markedly more serious than their equally exposed English colleagues. Brompton Hospital during 1941-3 reported a difference between Irish and English nurses of 900 per cent.[41] Mass radiography in the 1950s revealed a 700 per cent difference between people of Irish and English birth in London and a 200 per cent difference in Birmingham. In the United States, too, Irish, as defined by the birthplace of the mother of the deceased, had a tuberculosis mortality rate three times that of the host population and twice that of their neighbours of English or Scottish origins.[42]

As with the Welsh, sanitarians lamented the people's fatalism and neglect of prophylactic measures; although as Arthur Newsholme recognised in 1908, there was little to be done about the pervasive destitution and overcrowding that underlay the tragedy.[43]

In 1907 the Women's National Health Association of Ireland was founded under the leadership of Lady Aberdeen, whose husband was the Lord-Lieutenant. The Women's Association followed American and Scandinavian models in creating touring educational exhibitions promoting milk, fresh air, sanatoria, rest and so on. It also sponsored the foundation of sanatoria and dispensaries and, like the Welsh National Memorial Association, but even less successfully, they tried to get money from the central government and make policy for local authorities. The outcomes were small, compared with the size of the problem. The Association's greatest achievement, 'a revolution', according to Lady Aberdeen, was to persuade the people to open their windows. More importantly, they created the Dublin Pasteurising Milk Depot in 1910, but it apparently exerted little influence.[44] The Association reinforced the medical profession and politicians in opting to put money into sanatoria and dispensaries, rather than prevention. In 1923 the Free State grant was £21,000, matched with an equal sum from local authorities. By 1930-1 the total expenditure had jumped to about £360,000 and had risen to about £560,000 in 1940-1, nearly all of it going to sanatoria, hospitals and dispensaries. These sums represented a sizeable proportion of the Irish health budget. Meanwhile, assistance with housing for sufferers and maintenance for their families was still being discussed in 1945, as was the possible introduction of BCG.[45]

In 1951 a more prosperous Eire still recorded over 2000 tuberculosis deaths, at the rate of 7.3 per 10,000. With the introduction of streptomycin and its associated drugs the deaths had halved by 1953.[46]

The 'strain' that O'Kelly invoked had in various guises long been accepted as a cause of phthisis. Seventy-two per cent of Edward Smith's cases in the 1860s had 'excitable temperaments'; 19.3 per cent 'had submitted to late hours'; and 22.2 per cent 'had suffered too much anxiety'.[47] Doctors and novelists often marked mental depression as a contributing cause.[48]

The First World War gave a new prominence to strain and overwork. In Britain there were 20,000 more deaths than the figures projected from 1912-13. Tuberculosis was probably the largest single cause of civilian casualties in all the belligerent nations. Germany lost an estimated 280,000 people; one for every ten military casualties. In Britain young women were most affected: their mortality rate jumped from 1.3 per 1000 in 1914 to 1.65 per 1000 in 1918.[49] Those worst hit among them were apparently new industrial workers, overcrowded in factories, overcrowded in lodgings, severely fatigued and newly exposed to dusts and fumes. Between July 1914 and January 1917 nearly 300,000 entered the metal trades, quite apart from transport and office work. The great industrial towns' share of the national tuberculosis mortality jumped from 35 per cent in 1913 to 42 per cent in 1916.[50] In 1919 the rate fell again, but it seems plausible that many of the deaths immediately caused by the Spanish influenza were consumptives whose latent infections had been activated by wartime tensions.

Between 1939 and 1942 tuberculosis mortality rose again by 13 per cent against the twenty-year trend. This time the mortality was among the old. Evacuation of civilians and the early emptying of sanatoria spread active cases through formerly protected rural communities.[51] Tired, anxious people huddled in air raid shelters were also exposed to active cases and to reactivation of lesions, but the authorities contained the former by instituting strict ticket access to deep communal shelters. They also ensured that factory dormitories were less crowded than in 1914-18, and better warmed and heated. The food distribution was well-managed and children received properly pasteurised milk regularly for the first time. Overall, the tuberculosis rate fell during the War by 5 per cent. It was a triumph for preventive medicine.[52] Denmark and Norway, with adequate protein diets and BCG protection, were the only German- occupied countries not to register wartime increases in tuberculosis. The Netherlands, which did not use BCG, showed an increase of 70 per cent between 1940 and 1944.[53] Where starvation and terror became the norm, tuberculosis emerged as the captain of the men of death: one in five survivors of Belsen concentration camp had active tuberculosis and lesions were revealed in a 'very high' proportion of autopsies[54].

The disease often flared up with bereavement or rejection. Mrs F.D. married in 1940, in her early twenties. 'Then my husband contracted tuberculosis. He went to a sanatorium in May. He died in November 1940. Shortly afterwards I felt poorly. I was tired and had pains in the chest. I saw the doctor in October '41. I had an idea that something was cropping up but I didn't want to face it.' Crises in courtship and marriage, part perhaps engendered by incipient tuberculosis in one of the partners, also frequently were cited as causes of galloping infection. Mrs MN, a telephonist, had been in love with a soldier since 1940. Early in 1944 she became engaged to him and at Easter found he was already married. 'This was a great shock to me ... I used to sit indoors and my ... Mummy was not much company. When I told her I was tired she told me I was lazy.' That summer MN began to lose weight. A doctor whom she consulted could find no abnormality and told her that '"people [were] paying pounds for getting slim".' A few weeks later she had a 'terrific pain in the chest', was short of breath, and ran a high temperature. Her tuberculous lesion was then discovered and she entered a sanatorium. On her discharge, her soldier-friend promised to get a divorce. She became pregnant. He refused to seek the divorce. She had an abortion and was soon sputum positive again and back in the sanatorium. While she was there she was introduced to two men friends. They stopped writing to her once they discovered she was a consumptive.

'No one seems to want you when you've got this illness'.[55] The patient's foul breath, smelly sweaty body, enforced sexual abstinence and the male loss of authority in the relationship strained innumerable courtships and marriages.[56] The situation is piercingly analysed in Winifred Holtby's novel, *Land of Green Ginger* (1927). Eric Wittkower, a psychiatrist who interviewed some hundreds of patients after the Second World War, concluded that their outstanding common feature was 'an inordinate need for affection'.[57]

The loss of so many fine young people from all classes in the Great War helped restore the reaction between environment and personal predisposition in etiological explanations and reduce the salience of simple infection. Old romantic notions about phthisis returned to fashion. The literary romantic vision of consumption taking 'the loveliest and most amiable specimens' went back at least to the 1830s and flourished among novelists during the hungry, disturbed 1840s. The writers dwelt upon consumption's insidious, devilishly selective battering on innocence and beauty, depicting it as a ravisher of the pure, seeded from within the body. J.A. Froude in *Shadows of the Clouds* (1847) called consumption, perhaps thinking of his beloved brother, Richard Hurrell, who had perished by it a decade earlier, 'that luxurious feeder on youth and beauty'. Marion Hargrave in Richard Johns's *The Schoolfellows* (1841) 'was a fair and fragile girl, in whom the bloom of youth and beauty seemed as flowers decking a sacrifice, which the destroyer, consumption, would but too surely demand'.[58]Yet the resignation of the victim, cleansed by suffering and ready for judgement, made scrutable the ways of Providence:

> I have been wild and wayward, but you'll forgive me now;
> You'll kiss me, my own mother, and forgive me ere I go;
> May, nay, you must not weep, nor let your grief be wild.
> You should not fret for me, mother, you have another child.
>
> – – –
>
> It seemed so hard at first, mother, to leave the blessèd sun,
> And now it seems as hard to stay, and yet His will be done
> But still I think it can't be long before I find release;
> And that good man, the clergyman, has told me words of peace.

> Tennyson, 'The May Queen',
> 1830, 1842

The vogue for sweet consumptive deaths provoked a reproof: 'we have great doubts', the *Christian Remembrancer* declared in December 1842, 'as to the propriety of this incessant working up our feelings by pictures [in novels] of consumption ... The subject is, to half the families of England, too fraught with painful reality to be thus introduced ... amid dreamy sentiment'.[59]

Before the decade was out, *La Dame aux Camélias* (1847) by Dumas Fils gave romantic consumption a new behavioural stereotype. Marguerite, morally lost but saved by self-abnegation, describes herself as 'nerveuse, malade, triste, ou gaie d'une gaieté plus triste que la chagrin'.[60] She is impetuous, unpredictable, languorous, animated, sensuous, pale yet rosy, amorous, nonchalant, untrustworthy, yet capable of exalted devotion and self-denial. Her moods, hauntingly displayed in *La Traviata*, defined the topos for a century. In 1848 Richard Monckton Milnes published his biography of John Keats, until then largely forgotten, but henceforth to be an 'interesting' young poet of the highest sensuous sensibility. Keats' life and poetry were taken up by D.G. Rossetti, W. Holman Hunt and other young Pre-Raphaelites. They sought out and painted large-eyed, taut-cheeked magnificent women set in contexts of easeful, menacing passages to eternity. W.L. Windus's 'Too Late' (1858), J.E. Millais's 'Ophelia' (1852) and 'The Vale of Rest' (1859), Edward Burne-Jones's 'Fair Rosamund' (1863), together with Alfred Rankley's 'Old Schoolfellows' (1854), H.P. Robinson's 'Fading Away' (1858) and, above all, Alfred Stevens's 'Mrs Young Mitchell and Child' (1851) held an import for their beholders that we, in our tuberculosis and fever-free world, cannot recapture. Tuberculosis had, in the tragic mode, replaced the semi-comic gout of the eighteenth century. It seems that writers and painters draw on one disease and its connotations at a time. Other prevalent chronic, life-threatening illnesses, heart disease, diabetes, cancer, never became aesthetic or emotional devices. However, my colleagues tell me that the tuberculosis topos is absent from the literature of tuberculosis-ravaged East and South Asia, Africa and South America. Their writers and painters introduce sickness as malnutrition or 'fever'.

Noble, sensitive, self-denying consumptives continued to inhabit English novels, notably those of Anthony Trollope and

Mrs Humphry Ward, but by the 1880s other major writers had rather abandoned the disease as a determinant of character and plot, (elsewhere, however, it flourished with Maupassant, especially in *Bel Ami* (1885) and Dostoievsky). Then in 1924 - English translation 1927 - Thomas Mann revised the stereotype again and defined the intelligent, imaginative, often irrational, steadfast, idle, love-starved consumptive of the twentieth century. Brian Bulman's *House of Quiet People* (1939) and A.E. Ellis's *The Rack* (1958), both savagely realistic, might well have been conceived as retorts to *The Magic Mountain*. They are excellent novels, but seem to have had little impact.

Declarations about psychological predispositions to the disease and its mental outcomes came into fashion in the 1920s. The commentators' basic assumption was that neurotic persons were more liable to tuberculosis and that the toxins generated by the bacilli affected the brain and altered behaviour. No other disease, D.G. Macleod-Munro announced in *The Psycho-Pathology Of Tuberculosis* (1926) 'so profoundly modified ... the mental and moral characteristics of the patient' and was 'so constantly associated with ... psycho-neurosis'. He listed variableness of moods, 'eager feverishness of life, rapid alterations of hope and despondency which are such familiar features of the disease', and quoted as clinical proof *La Dame aux Camélias* and Mrs Humphry Ward's *Eleanor*. 'Aesthetic and intellectual' types seemed peculiarly prone to the disease and their 'unusual psychic state' afforded 'convincing testimony' of it contributing to the expression of their 'genius', another preoccupation of the 1920s.[61]

Macleod Munro appended a list which was to become fairly standard until the 1950s. He was among the pioneers in combing through the biographies and histories of medicine for diagnostic evidence and, ignoring the exiguous nature of most of it, attributing to the great dead definitive causes of their morbidity and mortality and, indeed, greatness. Keats and Beardsley, both dead at 26, he concluded had rapid caseating forms, De Quincy and Ruskin suffered intermittent, fibroid attacks, while the fact that Ruskin wrote *Modern Painters* and the *Seven Lamps* between bouts accounted for their occasional disjointedness and extremes of enthusiasms and dislikes, a statement that might worry recent biographers who do not mention tuberculosis in Ruskin's adult life. R.L. Stevenson and J.A. Symonds had 'attenuating forms' of the disease, as did

Francis Thompson. Goethe suffered a haemoptysis in adolescence but thereafter enjoyed a remission and turned serious.

According to Henry Sigerist, the student of medical public policy and historian, tuberculosis provided artists with that necessary separation from common society which enabled their egos to express their imaginings. The heightened temperature and mysterious biochemistry of the disease, stimulated by the greater sensuality of the true artist, drove the ambition and creative faculty.[62] True consumptive genius expressed itself in erotic, rebellious art. In this sense the two archetypal 1920s artists were Modigliani and D.H. Lawrence. Enrolled with them as consumptive, misunderstood geniuses were Balzac (a dubious diagnosis), the Brontës, Samuel Butler (dubious diagnosis), Calvin (ditto), Chekhov, Cherubini (ditto), Chopin, Dostoievsky (ditto), Goldsmith, the Goncourts (ditto - 'consumption' seems often to have replaced syphilis as a more acceptable artists' disease), Thomas Hood, Kafka, Laënnec, Locke, Mansfield, Mérimée (ditto), Molière, Murger, Eugene O'Neill, Proust, Purcell (ditto), Schiller, Sterne (ditto), Weber and Whitman (ditto) amongst dozens of other lesser figures.[63] Botticelli was said by Dr Camac Wilkinson, following Venturi, Richter and other connoisseurs - to have used a consumptive model, Simonetta Catanea (or Vespucci), for one of the favourite pictures of the era, *The Birth of Venus;* thereby Botticelli prefigured the Pre-Raphaelites and Elizabeth Siddall.[64] Great minds, Wolfgang Hildesheimer argued, apropos Mozart, needed sickly bodies in order to confront weakness and overcome it, again and again.[65] Curiously, in light of this remark, Ireland, with a higher incidence of tuberculosis and a Celtic Twilight, never produced a romantic tuberculosis fashion; only the half-forgotten John Field was sometimes adduced and his real cause of death appears to have been alcoholism, seconded by fistula.

The prodigious output of otherwise debilitated geniuses was explained in the 1920s by reviving the largely forgotten 'spes phthisica', a grandiose hopefulness, even in extremis.[66] Sir Farquhar Buzzard, Regius Professor of Medicine at Oxford, defined it by analogy with Korsakow's psychosis, a condition associated with alcoholics and syphilitics, exhibiting euphoria, want of insight coupled with the ability to talk plausibly, often about elaborate visits to imagined places. Consumptives showed the same lowered threshold of inhibition, the same brilliance, interspersed with hysteria and senseless likes and dislikes.[67] The prevalence of consumption among the Celts, accompanied by mass 'spes phthisica febrile' might even account for their febrile behaviour and ready, overblown rhetoric. Nonetheless, there was no clinical evidence for this kind of toxaemia. A decade earlier, Bernard Miall had quietly pointed out that such behaviour might be true of wealthier patients, 'but in the working classes many a sufferer has been killed by sheer panic and despondency rather than by consumption',[68] but this view had few supporters in the 1920s and 1930s. Only in 1945 did the experts rank consumption as a 'disease of discouragement', or as another expert, herself a consumptive, expressed it, a game of chess in which the victim 'is checkmated ... by a dangerous opponent ... without haste, without remorse'.[69] Moreover, the victims, Wittkower and later psychiatrists conceded, had no uniform set of pre-disposing personality traits. But once they developed it, they almost uniformly revealed a hunger for love lost or denied them by the disease.[70]

A disease so ubiquitous and so unhurried readily accommodated writers and painters among its victims, but other creative people who needed greater amounts of time to accomplish their pursuits, scholars, scientists, engineers, entrepreneurs, were both less romantic and less prone, it might seem, to fall consumptive.

O'Kelly had also defined 'strain' to include pregnancy. Thereby he echoed a sudden break with an opinion that had prevailed since Hippocrates, that pregnancy was good for consumptives. As S. Gower, surgeon of High Wycombe, put it in 1831, the counter-irritation occasioned by the foetus released pressure on the lungs, although, he added that after birth 'the disease advances with a fearful rapidity', although others held that childbearing improved the health of the mother.[71]

Even before Koch and infection theory, French medical opinion was moving to assert that both pregnancy and confinement were very dangerous.[72] During the 1880s British doctors began to advise consumptives against marriage: they did not, publicly at least, advise contraception, although the fall in the birth-rate that began after 1876 suggests that contraceptive practice was spreading. There was also a spread of termination of pregnancies among consumptive women by registered practitioners on the grounds of preserving the woman's health. The issue was debated at the Obstetrical Society of London in 1890. It emerged that termination was already usual in difficult cases likely to develop eclampsia (convulsions late in pregnancy). Few of the contributors were opposed to abortion as such: most preferred to avoid it as long as the effects of pregnancy or childbirth on consumptives remained uncertain.[73] Medical opinion stayed divided, but abortions continued into the mid 1920s. A large proportion of the women submitting themselves to illegal termination or trying abortifacients may also have been consumptives.[74]

This period of laissez-faire ended in 1925 when Dame Louise McIlroy, of the London School of Medicine for Women, called for contraceptive advice for consumptives and provoked a row. She declared that doctors had no right to dissuade young people from marriage while withholding information about birth control.[75] Pregnancy was dangerous, but so was abortion. Dr Ernest Ward supported Dr McIvoy in a roundabout way by estimating that 50 per cent of cases in his experience were 'made worse' by termination, but he had not kept figures.[76]

Those really at risk were women of the 'hospital class', in their second or third pregnancy. Wealthier women entered sanatoria and convalesced during their pregnancies and usually had confinements which did not damage them in the short term.[77] An attempt in 1930 by Dr McIlroy and Dr Jane Walker to place all pregnant women from the London County Council area in sanatoria foundered on the opposition of the women: an earlier trial scheme in Shropshire had incorporated the removal of the babies and the women simply refused to budge. Their situation was worsened because they were frequently victims of inefficient contraceptive practices. Termination continued to be the standard solution.[78]

Alderman W. Taylor of Deptford declared that obstreperous consumptives ought to be sterilised: they and their offspring only 'caused trouble'.[79] Fortunately, Taylor's alarmism was undermined by some pioneering research by Dr Andrew Trimble, of Belfast. He showed, to everyone's surprise, that the infantile mortality rate among tuberculous mothers was about 93 per 1000 in Belfast, Lancashire and Leeds, compared with 102 per 1000 for the general population. Trimble attributed the outcome to the supervision of visiting nurses, but I suspect that tuberculous families were smaller, partly because of abortion and partly because, as it emerged in 1933, it was standard practice to sterilise the woman, without consulting her (most objected, if they were asked), often at the first pregnancy and normally at the second or third.[80] It was about this time, with the collapse of the world economy and a fall in the European birthrate, that the Catholic hierarchy first became comminatory about abortion. The papal encyclical, *Custi Connubii*, was issued at the end of of 1930. Catholic spokesman, D.G. Logan, a Labour member for Liverpool in the House of Commons, and Dr R.H.J.M. Corbet of Dublin at the Annual Meeting of the British Medical Association in 1932, echoed the rescript in describing terminations as 'murders', but won little support. Demand for abortion for therapeutic and social reasons had, doctors said, 'increased enormously since the War'. Dame Louise McIlroy answered Corbet by stating that 'the lay public was demanding abortion and women were asserting categorically that pregnancies belonged to them and they could do as they thought fit'.[81] The Irish hierarchy was possibly the more upset because it appears to have been common practice in Britain to advise Irish consumptive women to practise contraception and seek terminations after the first pregnancy.[82]

The real problem, as the tuberculosis specialists Kayne, Pagel and O'Shaughnessy acknowledged in 1939, was that weak, malnourished pregnant consumptives already had a bad prognosis. Among wealthy women pregnancy might even help by elevating the diaphragm and thereby diminishing the volume of the lungs; but among all classes of consumptives the strain involved in labour and the sudden descent of the diaphragm was damaging to their chances. The increased resort to extensive X-rays during the pregnancy could not have helped the foetus either.[83] But careful contraception was spreading: it must have been a main cause of the 50 per cent fewer pregnancies among active tuberculous women - together with debility and probably abstinence - compared with quiescent tuberculous women between 1937 and 1950. Moreover, terminations and sterilisations were still being performed at the advent of streptomycin and PAS and isoniazid.[84] The terminations must have been recorded, but I could not find consolidated figures. The unpublicised resort to therapeutic abortion on what must have been a considerable scale is a remarkable instance of lay and medical cooperation in the face of clerical and political obstruction. Contraception, meanwhile, must have buoyed many a foundering marriage and unobtrusively contributed to the reduction of tuberculosis mortality among a vulnerable group.

NOTES

[1]*Lancet*, 5 Dec. 1829, p.354; see also J.E. Pollock (Brompton), *Lancet*, 1 Apr. 1876, p.487.

[2]*Lancet*, 9 Feb. 1884, p.265.

[3]*BMJ*, 4 Feb. 1888, p.239.

[4]*Supplement to 55th Registrar-General's Report, 1890-92, BPP*, 1897, vol. xxi, p.xcvi.

[5]Ibid, p.iii.

[6]Ibid, p.lxxxvii.

[7]*BMJ*, 8 Mar. 1890, p.525-8.

[8]Scurfield (Edinburgh), *Transactions of NAPT 1910*, pp.94-5,

[9]Bulstrode, *Report*, p.63.

[10]Chatham prisoners in *BMJ*, 29 Apr. 1882, p.630; Americans, *BMJ*, 29 Nov. 1890, pp.1257-8.

[11]Moore, *Dawn*, pp.201,119.

[12]Gloyne, *Tuberculosis*, quoting E.A. Cheeseman, *J. Hygiene*, 1941, pp.100-1; Alice Stewart and J.P.W. Hughes on Northampton boot and shoe industry, *Proceedings of Royal Society of Medicine*, vol. xli, 1948, p.501; Margaret Cairns and Alice Stewart, 'Pulmonary Tuberculosis Mortality In the Printing And Shoemaking Trades ... 1881-1931', *British Journal of Social Medicine*, vol. v, 1951, p.79.

[13]Sir Thomas Oliver in *BMJ*, 12 Oct. 1929, p.674; Edgar L. Collis and Major Greenwood, *The Health of the Industrial Worker*, 1921, p.135.

[14]Tatham, *Supplement*, pp. lxxvi-lxxvii.

[15]C.L. Sutherland, *Transactions of NAPT, 1952*, p.296.

[16]Bulstrode, *Report*, pp.93-4.

[17]Brian Kennedy, *Silver, Sin and Sixpenny Ale*, Melbourne 1978, pp.151-3; *Lancet*, 21 Mar., 18 Apr. 1914, pp.853, 1147.

[18]*Lancet*, 22 Jan. 1921, p.179.

[19]Rich, *Tuberculosis*, pp.664-5.

[20]There is an excellent coverage of these points by Linda Bryder, 'Tuberculosis, Silicosis, And The Slate Industry In North Wales 1927-1939', in Paul Weindling (ed.), *The Social History of Occupational Health, 1985*, pp.108-26; *BMJ*, 29 Mar. 1924, p.612 on difficulties of proving claims.

[21]PRO MH 75/12.

[22] S. Lyle Cummins (?) Memorandum, 28 Sept. 1931, PRO MH 75/13.

[23] S. Lyle Cummins, *BMJ*, 4 Apr. 1922, p.339.

[24] Glynne R. Jones, 'The King Edward VII Welsh National Memorial Association 1912-1948', in John Cule (ed.), *Wales and Medicine*, Cardiff 1975, pp.30-1.

[25] Chalke, 'Report on tuberculosis in North Wales', Dec. 1932, PRO MH75/15; Mrs Pryce, cutting from *Montgomeryshire County Times*, 24 Oct. 1931, PRO MH55/148.

[26] Wilson, Blacklock and Reilly, *Non-Pulmonary Tuberculosis*, pp.12-13.

[27] H. Old, 'Statement' on Wales to Ministry of Health, Mar. 1927, PRO MH96/1111.

[28] Ibid.; J.E. Tomley, *BMJ*, 24 Aug. 1935, p.354.

[29] A.C. Watkin (Tuberculosis Officer for Salop County Council), *Transactions of NAPT, 1933*, p.177.

[30] Tomley, on Anglesey, *BMJ*, 24 Aug. 1935, p.354; Bryder in Weindling, *Occupational Health*, p.116; Chalke in *BMJ*, 30 Sept. 1933, p.614.

[31] D.W. Evans, Memorandum on Welsh National Memorial Association, [June? 1924], PRO MH 75/1; Report of Deputation from Welsh NMA to Ministry of Health, 21 Mar. 1928, PRO MH 75/2, Llandinam, *BMJ*, 22 July 1933, p.165; Lord Davies of Llandinam, *Transactions of NAPT, 1933*, pp.11-12; Jones, 'Welsh National Memorial Association', in Cule (ed), *Wales and Medicine,,* pp.30-41.

[32] T.W. Grimshaw (Registrar-General for Ireland), *BMJ*, 2 July 1887, p.23.

[33] *Supplement to 32nd Report of Registrar-General for Ireland , BPP*, 1904, vol. xiv, p.36, *51st Annual Report of Registrar-General for Ireland, BPP*, 1914-16, vol. ix, p.xxxviiii, Department of Local Government and Public Health, Eire, *Tuberculosis*, Dublin [1945?], p.5; Arthur Newsholme, 'Poverty and disease; as illustrated by the course of ... phthisis in Ireland', *Proceedings of the Royal Society of Medicine*, vol. 1, pt.1, 1907-8, pp.24, 37.

[34] Department of ... Public Health, *Tuberculosis*, p.5.

[35] Newsholme, 'An Inquiry', *Journal of Hygiene*, vol. vi, 1906, p.313; *54th Report of Registrar-General for Ireland, BPP*, 1909, vol. xi, table xiv.

[36] Dr W.D. O'Kelly (University College, Dublin), *BMJ*, 14 Nov. 1925, p.920.

[37] R.C. Geary, *BMJ*, 12 July 1930, p.77; *BMJ*, on failures of Clean Milk Bills, 4 Apr. 1931, p.602; Dr Arthur Trimble (Chief Tuberculosis Officer, Belfast), *BMJ*, 28 May 1932, p.1002.

[38] Newsholme, 'An Inquiry', *Journal of Hygiene*, vol. vi, 1906, p.378; Trimble, *BMJ*, 23 Sept. 1933, p.583; Sir William Thomson (Registrar-General for Ireland), *Transactions of NAPT, 1913*, p.196; Michael P. Flynn and J. Cyril Joyce, 'Migration and Tuberculosis - The Irish Aspect', *Tubercle*, vol.xxxvi, 1955, p.338.

[39] *BMJ*, 14 Nov. 1925, p.920; Bulstrode, *Report*, pp.5-6.

[40] F.C.S. Bradbury on Tyneside surveys, *Transactions of NAPT, 1933, 1937*, pp.112-133, 57-8; Henry A. Mess, *Transactions of NAPT, 1929*, pp.10-13.

[41] Daniels, *Tuberculosis In Young Adults*, p.161; Anon., 'Incidence of Tuberculosis Among the Nursing Staff', *Brompton Hospital Reports*, 1944, vol. xiii, p.160.

[42] V.H. Springett, J.C.S. Adams et al., 'Tuberculosis In Immigrants In Birmingham, 1956-57', *British Journal of Social & Preventive Medicine*, vol. xii, 1958, pp.137-8.

[43] Newsholme, 'Ireland'. *Proceedings of the Royal Society of Medicine*, vol.1, pt.1, 1907-8, p.36. See also James Craig, *Consumption In Ireland.*, Dublin 1900, p.4.

[44] Dr Stafford (Local Government Board for Ireland), *Transactions of NAPT, 1910*, p.75; Countess of Aberdeen, *Transactions of NAPT, 1911*, pp.169-75; Miss L. Thompson, 'Child Welfare Work in Ireland', in T.K. Kelynack (ed.), *Child Welfare Annual*, vol.i, 1916-17, p.95.

[45] Department of ... Public Health, *Tuberculosis*, pp.12-17.

[46] *Lancet*, 11 June 1955, p.1221.

[47] Smith 'One thousand patients', *Report of British Association ... 1862*, p.175.

[48] e.g. Dr J.C. Thorowgood, at West-London Medico-Chirurgical Society, *BMJ*, 22 Jan. 1887, p.160; Squire, *Consumption*, p.37; Mrs Humphry Ward's *Eleanor* (1900) offers a standard narrative of anxiety, impulsiveness, heart disease and consumption.

[49] T.D. Lister (Mount Vernon Sanatorium), *Lancet*, 17 Nov. 1917, p.739; Edgar Collis (Professor of Preventive Medicine, Welsh National Medical School), *Transactions of NAPT, 1927*, p.78; P. D'Arcy Hart, *BMJ*, 30 Dec. 1939, p.1295; T.H.C. Stevenson, *Registrar-General's Report, 1917, BPP*, vol.x, 1919, p.lvii.

[50] Report of Local Government Board, *BMJ*, 31 Jan. 1920, p.164; Collis and Greenwood, *Health Of The Industrial Worker*, p.132.

[51] *BMJ*, 4, 11 Nov. 1939, pp.922, 979; Bankoff, *Conquest of Tuberculosis*, pp.153-5.

[52] Ibid; Neville M. Goodman, *Wilson Jameson*, 1970, p.104.

[53] Kissen, *Emotional Factors*, p.129.

[54] F.M. Lipscombe, 'Medical Aspects of Belsen Concentration Camp', *Lancet*, 8 Sept. 1945, p.315; Brockington, *Health of Community*, p.261, says 'one in three'.

[55] Eric Wittkower, *A Psychiatrist Looks At Tuberculosis*, second ed., 1955.

[56] Dr Edmund Sharkey (Dublin), *Lancet*, 25 Feb. 1832, p.765. An earlier pre-Romantic example is the epitaph in a Suffolk churchyard on the Clark family of two sisters who died aged seventeen and their brother who died aged twenty in 1786-7:

> A pale consumption gave the fatal blow
> The stroke was certain but the effect was slow,
> With wasting pain, death saw us sore oppressed,
> Pitied our sighs and kindly gave us rest.

Quoted by Alderman P. Astins (Essex County Council) in *Transactions of NAPT, 1939*, P.115. Jane Austen's view in *Mansfield Park* and *Sanditon* was equally straightforward: consumption was a nasty indiscriminate killer.

[57]Wittkower, *A Psychiatrist*, p.138; his view is supported by D.M. Kissen (Strathclyde Chest Clinic), *Transactions of NAPT, 1958*, p.165.

[58]The Froude and Johns extracts come from M. Brightfield, *Victorian England in its novels 1840-1870*, vol.ii, p.214, vol.iv, p.486.

[59]*Christian Remembrancer*, Dec. 1842. I owe this reference to the kindness of Professor Oliver MacDonagh.

[60]Alexandre Dumas, *La Dame aux camélias*, 1847. His dramatisation was finally staged in 1852 and held the stage thereafter. Marguerite's self-description comes from act 1, scene 10.

[61]D.G. Macleod Munro, *The Psycho-Pathology of Tuberculosis*, Oxford 1926, p.2.

[62]Henry Sigerist, *Civilization and Disease*, New York 1945, p.79. There was a widespread idea that consumption made its victims more sexually active. H.G. Wells suscribed to it in his *Autobiography* (vol.i, p.300). Men boasted their prowess, women bought frilly underwear and nightdresses. The reality was sadly different. Potency and sexual drive usually diminished as the disease advanced. Sexual intercourse often brought on haemoptysis. Patients could not achieve their expectations and were reduced to talking about 'living rapidly' which meant indulging in erotic daydreams. Macleod Munro, *Psycho-Pathology*, pp.32-6; Wittkower, *A Psychiatrist*, p.77.

> And how I strive and strive
> And there is nothing. For I am barren now
> Who once abounded to the point of waste.
> I who have known the high intoxication,
> Such lavish ecstasy that I have said
> 'There will be other moments', and postponed expression.
> Harry Fitzgerald (Midhurst Sanatorium 1935)
>   *Thanksgiving and other poems*, 1938, p.22.

[63]Macleod Munro, *Psycho-Pathology*, pp.3, 43-6; for other examples see Huber, *Consumption*, p.17; and L.J. Moorman, *Tuberculosis and Genius*, 1940.

[64]Wilkinson, *Treatment*, p.98. Horne, *Botticelli*, 1908, dismissed the story as 'legend' but it survived.

[65]Hildesheimer, *Betrachtungen über Mozart* (1963), quoted in *Times Literary Supplement*, 8 Apr. 1983, p.343.

[66]Guy, *Tuberculosis*, pp.88-9.

[67]Buzzard, *BMJ*, 11 May 1929, p.839. See also Holden (1922) quoted in Wittkower, *A Psychiatrist*, p.43. There is a jokey, ill-informed discussion of these issues by a panel of five leading British psychiatrists in *Transactions of NAPT, 1938*, pp.168-206.

[68]Bernard Miall, additional chapter to translation of J. Héricourt, *The Social Diseases*, 1920, p.222.

[69]Williams and Harbert, *Social Work*, p.26; Betty Macdonald, *The Plague and I*, 1949, p.98.

[70]Wittkower, *A Psychiatrist*, p.143; Kissen, *Emotional Factors*, p.91; Dr James Brown (Psychiatrist, St. Lawrence's Hospital, Bodmin), *Transactions of NAPT, 1958*, p.161.

[71]'Pregnancy and Phthisis', *Lancet*, 22 Oct. 1831, p.119; cf. Silvester, *Physiological Method*, p.16.

[72]J.G. Sinclair Coghill in *BMJ*, 20 Aug. 1881, 316.

[73] *Lancet*, 18 Jan. 1890, pp.134-5.

[74]Sir Thomas Oliver, 'Pregnancy and Tuberculosis', *Practitioner*, vol.cxv, 1925, p.373.

[75]*Transactions of NAPT, 1925*, pp.82-4; *BMJ*, 26 Feb., 8 Aug. 1926, pp.377, 295-6.

[76]*BMJ*, 17 Apr. 1926, p.723.

[77]Discussion at Cambridge Tuberculosis Society, *Lancet*, 7 Aug. 1926, pp.297-8.

[78]*Lancet*, 24 Jan. 1931, p.188; T.R. Elliott (Tuberculosis Officer, Salop County Council), *Transactions of NAPT, 1931*, pp.99-100.

[79]Ibid, p.109.

[80]*BMJ*, 5 Dec. 1931, p.1059, p.1059; Cecil Wall in *Lancet*, 4 Nov. 1933, p.1056.

[81]D.G. Logan *Parl. Deb.*, vol. 266, cols. 532-3 (26 May 1932). The minister, Sir Hilton Young, stonewalled. *BMJ*, 4 June, 6 Aug. 1932, pp.1059, 254-5.

[82]W. Stobie (Radcliffe Infirmary, Oxford), *BMJ*, 25 Mar. 1933, p.508.

[83]Kayne, Paget and O'Shaughnessy, *Tuberculosis*, 1939 ed., pp.168, 542.

[84]Charles J. Stewart, *Transactions of NAPT, 1952*, pp.329-30.

8 CONCLUSION

Recorded tuberculosis mortality declined steadily in England and Wales after 1840 and in Scotland from 1870. Irrespective of medical or political interventions, the annual rate of decline was 1.78 per cent in the nineteenth century and 1.79 per cent in the twentieth. Fifty-seven per cent of the total fall in mortality between 1850 and 1950 occurred before 1900. The share of tuberculosis among the causes of death, within a general retreat of infectious diseases, fell from about one-sixth in 1870 to about one-ninth in the 1920s.[1]

Table V

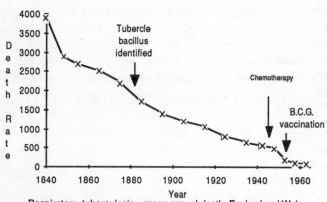

Respiratory tuberculosis - mean annual death: England and Wales
From Thomas McKeown, *The Role of Medicine*, 1976, p. 9

Note: Death rate per million

Mortality from non-pulmonary forms was halved in England and Wales between 1917 and 1930, coincident with a decline in enteric fever, scarlet fever and tertiary syphilis. The incidence of tuberculous spinal caries declined noticeably during the same period.[2] From the early 1920s increasing proportions of new patients showed evidence of rapid fibrosis, with better prognoses; doctors agreed in the late 1920s that pulmonary tuberculosis had become generally 'less acute' and profuse haemoptyses rarer. For every 100 persons who had died from tuberculosis of all forms in 1880, eighteen died in 1937.[3] After 1944 up to 50 per cent of cases were surviving at least five years beyond the initial diagnosis, compared with about 27 per cent in the 1930s and, possibly as low as 10 per cent in the 1880s. This prolongation of existence was linked with the gradual equalisation of female and male mortality rates and the shift of mortality, for males especially, from young adulthood to old age.[4] Nonetheless, in 1939 tuberculosis was still killing more people aged between 10 and 40 in the United Kingdom than any other disease.[5]

The link between morbidity and the decline of mortality is less clear. In some places, Birmingham for example, notification decreased by 80 per cent between 1913 and 1938, while mortality fell by 40 per cent and moved to older age groups.[6] But when mass radiography was introduced in 1941 among the civilian population at risk, notably those in large public air raid shelters, 4 per 1000 were found to have active disease, with another 50-80 per 1000 showing signs of past infections. With the death rate at 0.6 per 1000, this discovery-rate suggests an overall proportion of roughly 100 diagnosable cases for every death. Eighty-five per cent of young people in 1946-7 were sensitive to the Mantoux test, with females and males showing roughly equal rates of infection.[7] It is hazardous to generalise, but it seems that while exposure remained widespread, and many members of older age cohorts had at least periodically active periods of disease, younger people were becoming more resistant.

The pattern of falling mortality was repeated in western and central Europe, the United States and Japan, from various recorded starting dates and at differing rates. The decline began about 1870 in the United States and accelerated after about 1916, in New Zealand it began about 1880, in Bavaria and Switzerland about 1890, in Hungary about 1901-5, in Czechoslovakia about 1905 and in Japan about 1909. Nearly all of these nations began at mortality levels much higher than those prevailing in Great Britain.[8]

British spokesmen on tuberculosis paid little attention to the foreign successes. Their object was to claim the credit for their particular intervention. The first obstacle, the enormous decline during the nineteenth century before the advent of 'scientific procedures', when medical ministrations damaged rather than preserved patients, was avoided by collective amnesia.

Acknowledging the longterm trend meant acknowledging the primacy of environmental factors in reducing the disease. Dr H.C. Wilbur's prediction in 1908, from the United States Census office, that tuberculosis would disappear in 1945 if the nineteenth-century trend was projected, was ignored or ridiculed.[9] 'The scoffer who tells us that the decline so evident in Great Britain to-day', Sir Robert Philip declared in 1931, 'is referable to causes acting uniformly throughout the world [which was not Wilbur's point] does not know ... the facts'.[10] The decline had come about, Philip asserted, from the 'intelligent action' of medical experts and the 'co-operation ... of the inhabitants'. Infectious cases had been traced in their homes, contacts identified; public taxation and private philanthropy had created sanatoria and dispensaries and patients had been educated to contain droplet infection and value the 'marvellous influence of open air and sunlight'.[11] His fellow sanatorium promoter, Dr Noel Bardswell, made a similar claim in 1934: 'although other factors were concerned in this falling incidence, which had, indeed, been observable since 1875 ... the special efforts directed towards the prevention of tuberculosis [notification, the "march past", dispensaries, sanatoria] ... had materially contributed to the diminution of the disease'.[12]

Leaving aside the fact that tuberculosis was retreating before sanatoria and dispensaries began, Philip's claims for them were egotistical fantasy, as Dr J. Crocket (Bridge of Weir Sanatorium) pointed out as early as 1926. The 47,000 annual deaths implied 470,000 other potential cases. Sanatoria did not have the beds to cope, nor were there sufficient dispensaries, particularly when they were only available during working hours.   The 420 tuberculosis officers in Great Britain were simply too few to supervise home conditions, search out contacts, do laboratory tests, sort cases, give domiciliary treatments, attend to after-care and, above all, keep the records.[13]

The one agency which isolated advanced cases from the community and provided a bed and care, however grim, for the dying, was the unsung network of Poor Law infirmaries. As Dr Newsholme demonstrated as early as 1906, Brighton, Sheffield and Salford, with around 25 to 33 per cent of all their phthisis deaths in Poor Law institutions by 1901, recorded among the fastest decreases in phthisis death rates in the kingdom.[14] In 1910, 4000 consumptives were admitted to London workhouse infirmaries alone, for stays that were frequently terminal; in the same year there were only 4000-5000 sanatorium beds, with a possible annual occupancy rate of 12,000-14,000 patients in the British Isles.[15] These relativities held until the Second World War: consumptives filled the former Poor Law hospitals of England and Wales in 1938 and about one-third of them died there.[16] Their continuing service since the 1840s might well make the Poor Law institutions a major contributor to the retreat. The diversion of money and medical resources into sanatoria during the Edwardian period represented a tragedy for the impoverished victims who suffered and died uncherished and stigmatised, amid unnecessary austerity. The alternative of pouring Lloyd George's National Insurance money into them was not unthinkable: Dr Nathan Raw had called for it in 1911, but his argument passed unnoticed: philanthropists, doctors and aldermen could hardly ask the King to open a workhouse, however refurbished.

The sanatoria were models of streamlined, clean design and they undoubtedly influenced domestic taste and habits. But their specific educational activities together with those of the National Association, seem to have produced small results. Spitting in public and at home was still prevalent in the mid 1930s. The tuberculosis activists failed to have it made a legal offence, as it had long been in several Continental countries.[17] Care committees remained ill-informed and censorious. The scare tactics of the National Association's travelling exhibitions often frightened children and families into concealment and suspicion of their neighbours. Dr Stella Churchill, a member of the London County Council and former deputy Medical Officer of Health for St Pancras, suggested in 1928 that the National Association, then appealing for £100,000 to extend its education schemes, 'follow up' its exhibitions to discover their impact, but apparently no such investigation was made.[18] In 1950 28 per cent of respondents in Bermondsey, Tottenham and Wandsworth said that they did not know 'the main cause of tuberculosis'; another 19 per cent settled for 'cold and chills'.[19]

When the achievements of sanatorium exercise and rest therapies came into question, their promoters hailed the new chest surgery. Dr Noel Bardswell declared in 1934 that 'collapse therapy had effected some remarkable successes' but, he added, it had not yet 'affected the statistics of the ultimate results of treatment'.[20] The good news statistics never eventuated, but this did not stop chest surgery passing into history as a contributor to the retreat. According to one standard authority, 'a great part of the credit for a steady reduction in the tuberculosis death rate must be awarded to the medical profession, which had evolved new methods ... sanatorium regime ... lung collapse ... operating theatres and X ray apparatus ... The introduction of chest surgery ... brought ... an added interest to the lives of those who were employed in this Service'.[21] X-ray procedures were too little used and mass radiography arrived too late to make a direct impact upon the decrease. In 1933 X-rays were used 'rarely' in diagnosis in England; the London County Council refused to support them in its dispensaries in 1934 and the Welsh National Memorial dispensaries did not begin to instal X-ray apparatus until 1935.[22] By 1937 only three X-ray examinations were made for every five new cases: half the 50 county administrative districts and 30 of the 76 county boroughs had no apparatus and no provision for having cases X-rayed elsewhere. X-rays were too expensive and their results too unspecific.[23] Mass radiography did reveal a vast, hitherto unsurveyed amount of mostly non-threatening morbidity, but while treatment facilities remained inadequate and ineffectual it is difficult to see that the programme represented any major advance, particularly when it was operating in the context of a continuing reduction in the incidence of active disease. The National Association and the specialists were enthusiastic about the campaign but yet again it seems they devoted themselves to showy efforts which diverted money and energy from more efficacious procedures. As Dr J.M.G. Wilson remarked about a group of nations, including Britain, which had followed this path, the 'decline ... is not attributable to any great extent to the use of mass radiography'.[24] Mass radiography probably was only important in 1942-4 and again around 1950 when the cases it revealed could be given chemotherapy.[25]

Most commentators on the retreat invoked general environmental factors, but usually as passing unsubstantiated assertions. Housing, nutrition and comfort are important, but impossible in our present state of knowledge to quantify or explain in relation to individual cases.

One large element which must have assisted United Kingdom tuberculosis figures was emigration, particularly in the nineteenth century.   Between 1861 and 1911 10,000,000 people left the British Isles: 6,000,000 of them embarked from English ports, 1,000,000 from Scottish and 3,000,000 from Irish ports. Most were probably within the high risk age groups. We know that an average of about 78 per cent of the Irish emigrants between 1871 and 1900 were aged between 15 and 35.   Apart from reducing the risk factor and probably enhancing the life chances of those with dormant infections, the emigrants included active cases who were to die abroad. About 1911-12 Dr W.H. Hamer, Medical Officer to the London County Council, asked his colleagues to review their recent terminal cases aged 15-55. These amounted to 118, most of them probably among the comfortable classes - one-quarter of them died overseas. There is no reason to think that Hamer's sample is unrepresentative of consumptive exiles among the upper classes during the four decades before 1914, with the implication that the British death rate and incidence of advanced cases within those classes, at least, was considerably reduced.[26] But we know little about the composition of the emigration from the British Isles during this period.   Similarly, the wartime deaths of 740,000 men in the high risk age groups, followed by the 185,000 deaths ascribed to influenza in 1918-19, many of whom would have been weakened by consumption, possibly reduced the tuberculosis death-rate by 10 to 12 per cent and might well have influenced the apparent acceleration of the decline through the 1920s and 1930s.[27]

Some medical explanations of the longterm decline depend upon assumptions about acquired immunity among the populations at risk.   There is general agreement that the bacterium has been stable in its virulence through time and space, although the incidence of peak mortality tends to be concentrated among the young in regions and periods of high prevalence and among the old in regions and periods of reducing or low prevalence.[28] Changes in the relation between the micro-organism and its hosts seem, it is also generally agreed, to have occurred only on the side of the hosts. Sims Woodhead broached the idea in 1888, arguing from Metchnikov's propositions about the struggle between tissue and invading bacilli, that a similar concept of infection processes in tuberculosis would explain variability in susceptibility between individuals.[29] Medical scientists went on to assume that minor tuberculosis infections must produce antibodies and that early infection could confer immunity. It followed that the growth of the great towns both increased the chances of infection and the opportunities to extend immunity. Hence the earlier development of large cities in England than in Scotland explained the 20 to 30 years earlier start of the decline in England, while Ireland, which never industrialised and lacked great concentrations of people, did not begin its decline until around 1907.[30] Certainly it was true that formerly isolated communites, Pacific island populations for example, were formerly free of tuberculosis and devastated by it when it was introduced, as were West African labourers brought to France during the Great War. Through time, perhaps a century, the death-rate among these populations dropped, as in Mauritius, apparently because the inhabitants developed greater resistance, because the incidence of latent infection remained high.[31]

A few eugenically-minded commentators postulated that because tuberculosis was such a savage killer among the young, it weeded out the susceptibles and, over time, left a more resistant host population, who in turn like good cattle, according to Dr J.J. Thompson in 1926, 'bred truer'. He asserted that 'the main factor in the reduction ... [was] the more sensible age at which people marry' by which he meant, it seems, younger. Thompson wanted doctors to forbid marriage among the tuberculous, to prevent 'deterioration arising from the infringement of inevitable law'.[32] The main objections to this argument, which persists today, is that tuberculosis hits selectively, by social class, at enormous differential rates. Shoemakers, for example, with rates nearly four times those of coal miners in England and Wales in 1910-12, ought to have become extinct. The Irish and the Welsh ought to have bred out their tuberculosis before the English and the Scots. If, as seems probable, consumption had been a major killer in English towns since the late seventeenth century, susceptibles ought to have been weeded out and resisters multiplied in the population well before 1800. Foreign cities with rates higher than any in the British Isles should have registered faster or at least equal declines with London or Liverpool. And the argument ignored the massive, apparently age-old incidence of tuberculosis in India and South-East Asia. Moreover, one early attack, unlike smallpox or mumps, did not confer immunity against subsequent infections from the same type of human bacillus, although attack by some forms of the bovine bacillus might confer some immunity.[33] The balance of these complex factors is delicate and still little understood. While a third of the infants died in the Lübeck disaster, two-thirds, who had received near identical doses, survived up to twelve years presumably because of their superior genetic inheritance. The tubercle bacillus appears to form no discernible toxin, it develops no single antigen or other component that might account for its virulence. One authority concludes that 'for a given microorganism there are almost as many different diseases as there are susceptible individuals'. The eruption of infection in older individuals may be an outcome of progressive loss of cell mediated immunity.[34]

Nonetheless, resistance is enhanced by adequate nutrition and comfort, and real wages are a good indicator of access to them. Dr R.J. Ewart pointed out in 1923 that the longterm rising trend of real wages from 1851 matched the longterm decline in tuberculosis mortality. Moreover, the occasional falls in wages and jumps in unemployment were, Ewart argued, softened so far as consumption mortality was concerned by the provision of Poor Law infirmaries and, from the mid 1870s, by a reduction of the birth-rate which produced smaller, more resistant families.[35] Potatoes, sugar, butter, meat, flour, fruit, woollen and cotton goods, coal and gas, became more widely available, sometimes strikingly, between the 1840s and 1940s. Annual per capita consumption of meat, for example, rose from 109 pounds in 1880 to 132 pounds in 1900.[36] Other nations with burgeoning economies, such as Belgium and the United States for instance, were also among the leaders in recording falling tuberculosis rates.

In the 1860s Dr C.R. Drysdale and Dr Edward Smith argued that the higher phthisis rate in the English countryside relative to the towns was the result of the 'wretched diet', especially among very large families.[37] Poor sanitation and overcrowding made gastrointestinal infections and infestations endemic and these in turn depressed digestive competence. The drainage, cleansing and enlargement of cottages that observers noted between the 1840s and 1880s must have helped the chances of their inhabitants, particularly the women.[38] Wider access in the countryside to refined sugars, fats, and oils, to foods other than potatoes and coarse milled grains, would have made the diet less bulky, that of children and women especially, and enabled an increased energy intake.[39] This change in nutrition, particularly during the last 30 years of the nineteenth century, would help to explain the narrowing of the differences in rates between countryside and town, between England, Wales and Scotland, and later, Ireland, and between females and males. It would also have contributed to the shift from younger to older age groups. Overall, it seems reasonable, particularly when we scrutinise current phenomena in the poorest parts of the world, to assert that improvements in the living conditions of the poorer classes, the masses most at risk, together enforced the retreat of tuberculosis. Better nutrition, housing, nurture, lessening of fatigue, smaller family size acting synergistically in varying permutations through time and place hold the answer, although that answer remains vague because its chronology and linkages are little traced or understood. Only detailed local studies and full-scale investigations of Wales and Ireland especially, will make these assertions convincing.

Sadly, preventive innovations such as pasteurisation and BCG vaccination, which could have helped decisively, were implemented too late to have much impact on the retreat. The delay highlights the unnerving dogmatism of self-declared experts with interests to protect. A want of scientific rigour prevailed almost throughout: statistical investigations, with notable exceptions such as the Tyneside surveys, were simplistically designed and coarsely mounted: time-scales were too brief, cells were too small and dubiously comparable, claimed outcomes were too grand and unrelated to the analysis. The vast accumulation of dispensary records was too rarely combed through to test policy choices. There was also a continuing failure to conduct effective local trials, notably of BCG, but also of various therapies. And this in a nation whose regional divisions, population distribution and pattern of local government invited such innovations.

It was unfortunate that a coterie of medical practitioners captured the tuberculosis speciality in the late 1880s and thereafter set the terms by which the disease was comprehended. The coterie and their pupils dominated their general practitioner and specialist colleagues who were usually little interested in such a commonplace intractable malady. Lay parliamentarians, ministers of health, philanthropists, local aldermen, Poor Law guardians and trade unionists, who from their own diverse experiences had much to question and to offer, remained passive throughout, excepting the brief revolt at the National Association meeting in 1931. Even then, they had no consistent idea of challenging prevailing therapeutic methods and the allocation of resources that underpinned them, and no considered alternative policies to advance. Public money could and should have been diverted to trying preventive measures and to helping severe impoverished cases and their families. Neither of the main political parties had a policy on tuberculosis, excepting the Conservatives' resolve to thwart attempts to curb milk producers, and the Labour members' pursuit of compensation for miners' silicosis and additional sanatorium 'benefit'. Cranky parliamentarians and aldermen occasionally unleashed their suspicion of medical pretensions by backing worthless charlatans, but none appears to have thought beyond this exhibitionism or sought the information that might have led to fresh trials and programmes. Despite the educative efforts of Dr G.C.M. McGonigle, Medical Officer of Health for Stockton-on-Tees and main author of *Poverty And Public Health* (1936), and a few other medical practitioners, the laity seem to have kept health issues separate in their minds from everyday political concerns.

This ignorance helped maintain the hegemony of the tuberculosis experts and their lay allies but it endured also because their subjects were so weak. Consumptives and surgical cases were, until the 1930s, mostly young, enfeebled, poor, stigmatised, listless, and politically unorganised. They and their kin never formed a pressure group, unlike say, diabetes sufferers. Legislators, minstry officials, municipal officers, trade union officials, were all more concerned with the maladies which struck their age group, hypertension, heart disease and cancer.[40]

One potentially powerful group, ex-soldiers, died off too soon. Another group, insured workers, were pacified by Lloyd George's sanatorium 'benefit'. The appropriation of this word by the state lost the term its traditional connotation of a mutually supportive association between individuals at risk in a voluntary organisation that was their creation. 'Sanatorium benefit' became a claim for maintenance from a bureaucratic state, bestowed indiscriminately upon members of a class of victim recipients. The victims and his or her associates were by implication disfranchised from participating in the determination of the policy governing the bestowal of the benefit. Altogether, between 1912 and 1919, the administration of the benefits cost £25 million, from £99 million paid out in 'benefits' of all kinds, but which included a large portion going straight to sanatoria cases.[41]   One wonders whether a better result might have been achieved by distributing the money on subsidised rents or food. Had 'enablement' been substituted for 'benefit' the course of British social policy might have been more efficient. 'Benefits' entailed bureaucratic secrecy in order to maintain a semblance of equality between applicants. Full annual reports on the operation of the system were not issued and in 1934 the claim by the Ministry of Health that the scheme had to be kept anonymous helped fend off a unique call for a full inspection of the nation's tuberculosis schemes and services.[42]   With this failure went the last chance, until the War intervened, of moving the focus of expenditure from curative to preventive science.   One post-war criticism of tuberculosis schemes in poor countries is apt for Britain before 1947: 'the literature is strikingly deficient in descriptions of realistic ... schemes, and it is especially difficult to find references to built-in arrangements for measuring results'.[43]

Dr Selman Waksman's great discovery, streptomycin, was a long time in the making. He was a soil bacteriologist, not medically qualified, and this made difficulties in arranging clinical trials. His search developed from the old observation that the soil must contain microorganisms which destroy tuberculosis bacilli. He and his colleagues isolated streptomycin in 1943 from *Streptomyces griseus*, a strain he had himself discovered in 1915. Exhaustive tests proved streptomycin to have spectacular effects on previously terminal   attacks of miliary tuberculosis and tuberculous meningitis.[44]

Streptomycin was first heard of in the United Kingdom in 1946 and in the following year the Medical Research Council organised a trial. This was successful and the drug was distributed in small quantities in 1947. Two powerful adjuvants - P.A.S., para-amino-salicylic acid - a Swedish discovery by Lehmann - and isoniazed, were introduced in 1948 and 1952. They were joined later by the powerful rifampicin, derived from *Streptomyces mediterranei*. Initially there was much uncertainty. Courses were short, four to six weeks, and the dosages were small, partly in reaction from the heroic dosages of sancrysin, for example, of the previous generation, and partly because supplies were short.   Some ambiguous early results encouraged a few British surgeons to continue with resections and thoracoplasties, and to regard chemotherapy as 'supplemental'.[45]   There were severe adverse reactions. Isoniazid can cause hepatitis and damage the optic nerve, while streptomycin, apart from the difficulty that organisms rapidly develop resistance, also has toxic effects on the hearing and balance nerves. The French seized the opportunity to denounce streptomycin and uphold BCG, while until at least 1960 the Swiss continued to proclaim as preferable sanatorium treatment and surgery.[46] Still, the shortage of streptomycin between 1948 and 1952 had the unlooked for benefit of permitting careful clinical trials which proved its worth.[47]

The much larger Madras Experiment conducted under Medical Research Council direction in 1959-61 finally made it clear that patients, however malnourished, overcrowded, fatigued and heavily infected, could be treated while living at home and recover, with no greater risk to their families than if they had been institutionalised - had that been possible.[48] A vast lessening of human misery and a vast saving in public and domestic expenditure had been made and even greater savings were in prospect. The Madras Experiment also helped solve the complexities in assigning streptomycin dosages for individuals and setting effective terms of treatment, up to two years or more for patients with large cavities and extensive fibrosis, in order to extirpate inactive bacilli.

In England and Wales mortality among young women fell by 90 per cent in five years and by 99 per cent from 1951 to 1961. The reduction in higher age groups of both sexes, especially among chronic cases, was less dramatic but still successful, despite the emergence of bacterial resistence to streptomycin after 1951. By 1961 the death-rate had plunged to under two per million.[49]   Between 1948 and 1971 streptomycin and its associated drugs reduced the number of deaths by 51 per cent, a saving of about 140,000 lives.[50]   The longterm effects of improved nutrition, shelter, employment and life chances since the War, particularly among younger age cohorts probably helped, but the victory belonged to streptomycin. The slowly retreating white plague was at last routed.

NOTES

[1]C.R. Gibson, *BMJ*, 20 Mar. 1926, p.547; Thomas McKeown, *The Modern Rise of Population*, 1976, pp.56-8; Hubert Campbell, *Changes In Mortality Trends: England and Wales, 1931-1961*, Washington 1965, p.22.

[2]C.E.S. Fleming, 'Disappearing Diseases', *BMJ*, 20 Feb. 1926, p.321; Sir George Newman, *BMJ*, 12 July 1930, p.72; Sir Farquhar Buzzard, *BMJ*, May 1929, p.841.

[3]*BMJ*, 4 Feb. 1939, p.207; Cecil Goodman on early fibrosis in *BMJ*, 23 Nov. 1929, p.980. Muthu, *Tuberculosis*, p.308.

[4]C.R. Lowe, 'Recent Trends In Survival Of Patients With Respiratory Tuberculosis', *British Journal of Preventive and Social Medicine*, vol.viii, 1954, pp.91-2; Dr.J. Williamson, *BMJ*, 17 Apr. 1920, p.552. Sir James Clark, *Lancet*, 29 July 1843, p.609.

[5]Herbert, *Britain's Health*, p.162.

[6]Lowe, 'Recent Trends', *British Journal of Preventive and Social Medicine*, vol.viii, 1954, p.91.

[7]Williams and Harbert, *Social Work*, p.30; Edna Mawson, *Transactions of NAPT, 1955*, pp.27,36; Brockington, *Short History*, p.173. Daniels, *Tuberculosis in Young Adults*, p.207.

[8]League of Nations Health Section Report, quoted in *BMJ*, 27 June 1971, p.1127; Gloyne, *Tuberculosis*, pp.80-1.

[9]Paterson, *Shibboleths*, pp.216-7. Wilbur's calculation has a particular pathos: he was a consumptive who died from the disease.

[10]'The Outlook on Tuberculosis', *BMJ*, 10 Jan. 1931, p.47.

[11]'Cause of Decline in Tuberculosis Mortality', *BMJ*, 28 Apr. 1928, p.705.

[12]*BMJ*, 23 June 1934, p.1136.

[13]*Lancet*, 10 July 1926, p.91.

[14]Newsholme, 'An Inquiry', *Journal of Hygiene*, vol.vi, 1906, p.370; Nathan Raw, 'The Use of Existing Accommodation In Dealing with Tuberculosis', *Transactions of NAPT, 1911*, p.208.

[15]Garland, *Transactions of NAPT, 1911*, p.122; Latham and Garland, *Conquest*, pp.74-5.

[16]J.E. Chapman, 'T.B. Analysis and Progress 1936-1944', PRO MH 55/1120.

[17]G.A. Powell Tuck, *BMJ*, 24 Aug. 1935, p.364.

[18]Stella Churchill, *Health Services And The Public*, 1928, p.31.

[19]S.T. David, 'Public Opinion Concerning Tuberculosis', *Tubercle*, vol.xxxiii, 1952, p.82.

[20]*BMJ*, 23 June 1934, p.1136.

[21]W.M. Frazer, *A History of English Public Health, 1834-1939*, 1950, p.425.

[22]Bradbury, *Casual Factors*, p.87; Councillor Mrs F.A. Powell (Bermondsey) and Alderman A.E. Cross (Denbighshire), *Transactions of NAPT, 1934* , pp.123, 119.

[23]Kayne, *Control*, p.166.

[24]J.M.G. Wilson, 'Mass Health Examinations', in World Health Organization, *Mass Health Examinations*, Geneva 1971, p.11; on NAPT and mass radiography, see Williams, *Requiem*, pp.66-8.

[25]Rosemary Mulligan, 'The ... chest service ... within the National Health Service', in Gordon McLachlan (ed.), *Specialized Futures*, Oxford 1975, p.85.

[26]W.H. Hamer, 'The Influence of Migration upon the Phthisis Death-rate', *Proceedings of the Royal Society of Medicine*, vol.vi, pt.11, 1912-13, pp.20-4.

[27]The argument about this demographic result of the wartime losses was put, uniquely so far as I can discover, by Camac Wilkinson in the *BMJ*, 4 June 1927, p.1029. *BPP*,1920, vols.x,xi.

[28]F. Macfarlane Burnet, *The Natural History of Disease*, third ed., 1962, p.298; Thomas McKeown, 'Medical Issues in Historical Demography', in Edwin Clarke (ed.), *Modern Methods in the History of Medicine*, 1971, p.65.

[29]*Lancet*, 28 July 1888, p.170.

[30]Louis Cobbett, *The Causes of Tuberculosis*, Cambridge 1917, p.22; S. Lyle Cummins, *BMJ*, 4 Mar. 1922, p.339.

[31]*BMJ*, 13 Dec. 1930, p.1010; Burnet, *Natural History*, pp.300-1.

[32]Thompson, *BMJ*, 11 Sept. 1926, p.501; Burnet, *Natural History*, p.300; René Dubos, *Man Adapting*, new ed. New Haven, 1980, p.187.

[33]*BMJ*, 16 Apr. 1921, p.570; Guy, *Pulmonary Tuberculosis*, p.22; Sir Robert Philip, *BMJ*, 28 Apr. 1928, p.702; Nathan Raw, *BMJ*, 27 Mar. 1926, p.566.

[34]Cedric A. Mims, *The Pathogenesis of Infectious Disease*, second ed., 1982, pp.180, 228, 240; Lefford 'Immunology of *Mycobacterium tuberculosis*', in Nahmias and O'Reilly, *Immunology*, p.349.

[35]*BMJ*, 4 Nov. 1922, p.868; 'Economics and Tuberculosis', *Proceedings of the Royal Society of Medicine*, vol.xvi, pts 1-11, 1922-23, p.13.

[36]The statistics underpinning these assertions are conveniently gathered in B.R. Mitchell and Phyllis Deane, *Abstract of British Statistics*, Cambridge 1962. The figures on meat consumption come from F.B. Smith 'Health', in John Benson (ed.), *The Working Classes in England*, 1985, p.51. See also Bostock Hill (Professor of Hygiene, University of Birmingham), *Conference on Destitution*, 1911, pp.41-2.

[37]Drysdale in *Transactions of St Andrews' Medical Graduates' Association, 1867, p.141.*

[38]Dr Armistead at Cambridge Medical Society, *BMJ*, 3 Mar. 1883, p.415; Arthur Ransome, 'Consumption: A Filth Disease', in *Medical Chronicle*, vol.viii, Oct. 1897-Mar. 1898, p.163.

[39]see David Morley, 'Severe Measles', in N.F. Stanley and R.A. Joske (eds), *Changing Disease Patterns and Human Behaviour*, 1980, p.125.

[40]Dr W.M. McPhail, (Barrow Hill Colony), *Transactions of NAPT* , *1937*, p.97; J. Greenwood Wilson (Medical Officer of Health, Cardiff), *Tubercle*, vol. xxxiii, 1952, p.215.

[41]Geoffrey Drage, *Public Assistance*, 1930, p.37; on the new concept of 'benefit', see J.G. Legge (Director of Education, Liverpool), *Prevention of Destitution*, 1911, p.699.

[42]G. Lissant Cox, *BMJ*, 10 Feb. 1934, p.261.

[43]D.H. Shennan, *Tuberculosis Control In Developing Countries*, Edinburgh 1968, pp. 2-3.

[44]Selman A. Waksman, *The Conquest of Tuberculosis*, 1965; H. Boyd Woodruff (ed.), *Scientific Contributions of Selman A. Waksman*, New Brunswick, 1968, pp.287-305.

[45]Pagel, *Pulmonary Tuberculosis* (1964 ed.), p.364.

[46]Etienne Bernard and B. Kreis (Paris), 'Comparaison entre la Prevention de la Tuberculose Experimentale par la Streptomycine et par le BCG', *Premier Congrés*, pp.25-30; The Swiss Symposium at Davos is reported in *Tubercle*, vol. xli, 1960, p.154.

[47]F.H.K. Green, 'The Clinical Evaluation of Remedies', *Lancet*, 27 Nov. 1954, p.1089; Ffrangcon Roberts, *The Cost of Health*, 1952, p.104.

[48]Pagel, *Pulmonary Tuberculosis* (1964 ed.), p.364.

[49]Campbell, *Changes In Mortality Trends*, p.22,38.

[50]Thomas McKeown, *The Role of Medicine*, 1976, pp.81-2; see also Colin Dollery, *The End Of An Age Of Optimism*, 1978, p.14.

BIBLIOGRAPHY

Unpublished Papers
Astor Papers, Reading University Library
Australian negotiations with Henri Spahlinger, Files numbers
  PM Dept 501/1/58-88 Australian Archives
W.J. Braithwaite Collection, British Library of Political and
  Economic Science
Clive Fitts Collection, University of Melbourne Archives
Lloyd George Papers, House of Lords Records Office
Ministry of Health correspondence and reports about
  tuberculosis and dispensaries and sanatoriums, MH52, 48, 55,
  96, Public Record Office

Parliamentary Reports and Papers
First Report of Commissioners on the State of Large Towns,
  1844, vol.xvii
Royal Commission on ... Food from Tuberculous Animals,
  1895, vol.xxxv; 1896, vol.xlvi; 1898, vol.xlix
Report of British Delegates at the International Congress,
  Berlin, 1899, vol.xlv
Royal Commission on ... Bovine Tuberculosis 1904, vol.xxxix;
  1907, vols.xxxviii, xxxix, lvii; 1909, vol.xlix, 1911, vols xlii,
  xliii, xliv; 1913, vol.xl; 1914-16, vol.xxxvii
Departmental Committee on Tuberculosis (Astor), 1912-13,
  vol.xlviii
Tuberculosis (Sanatoria for Soldiers), 1919, vol.xxx
Tuberculosis, (J.P.Younger), Department of Health, Scotland
Committee on *Conditions in Air Raid Shelters*, 1939-40, vol.iv

Periodicals
Annals and Transactions of the British Homeopathic Society
British Journal of Preventive & Social Medicine
British Medical Journal
Brompton Hospital Reports
The Child
Child Welfare Annual
Colonist [Papworth]
Glasgow Medical Journal
Guy's Hospital Reports

Journal of Hygiene
Journal of Public Health
Journal of the History of Medicine
Lancet
Medical Chronicle
Medical Circular
Medical Magazine
Medical Press
Papworth Research Bulletin
Practitioner
Proceedings of the Royal Society of Medicine
St Bartholomew's Hospital Journal
Sanitary Review
Transactions of the Epidemiological Society of London
Transactions of the National Association for the Prevention of Tuberculosis
Tuberculosis Year Book 1913-1914
Tubercle
Veterinary Record

Articles and Monographs
All were published in London, unless otherwise stated.

'A Glasgow Physician', *Tuberculosis and its Treatment* (Glasgow, 1891)

Anon. (Waldorf Astor?) *Campaign for Clean Milk* (1916)

Anon. *National Conference on The Prevention of Destitution* (1911)

Anon. *40 Years of Progress and Development at Papworth* (Papworth, 1956?)

Abercrombie, Robert *The Solvent Process Cure of Consumption, Diseases of the heart, Bronchitis, Asthma, Dropsy, and Tumours* (1892)

Anderson, A.W. and B. Benjamin et al. 'Control of Tuberculosis. Importance of Heredity and Environment', *British Journal of Preventive & Social Medicine*, vol.ii (1957)

Ayres, Leonard P. *Open Air Schools* (New York, 1911)

Ball, F.C. *One of the Damned* (1973)

Bankoff, George *The Conquest of Tuberculosis* (1946)

Bardswell, Noel Dean *Advice to Consumptives* (1910)

von Behring, E. *The Suppression of Tuberculosis* (New York, 1904)

Bell, Clark (ed.) *The American International Congress on Tuberculosis* (New York, 1905)

Bennet, J. Henry *Winter in the South of Europe*, 3rd edn (1865)

Bennett, John Hughes *The Pathology and Treatment of Pulmonary Consumption*, 2nd edn (Edinburgh, 1859)

Bickerton, Thomas H. *A Medical History of Liverpool From the Earliest Days to the Year 1920* (Liverpool, 1936)

Bignall, J.R. *Frimley: The Biography of a Sanatorium* (1979)

Bodington, George *An Essay on the Treatment and Cure of Pulmonary Consumption, on Principles Natural, Rational, and Successful* (1840 reprinted 1901)

Brackenridge, R.D.C. *The Medical Aspects of Life Assurance* (1962)

Bradbury, F.C.S. *Causal Factors in Tuberculosis* (n.d., 1933)

Brand, Jeanne L. *Doctors and the State* (Baltimore, 1965)

Brieger, E.M. *The Papworth Families* (1944)

British Medical Association *National Formulary for National Health Insurance Purposes*, 2nd edn (1933)

Brockington, C. Fraser *The Health of the Community* (1956)

—————*A Short History of Public Health* (1956)

Brown, Lawrason *The Story of Clinical Tuberculosis* (Baltimore, 1941)

Brown, Junior, I.B. *Australia for the Consumptive Invalid* (1865)

Bryden, Linda 'Papworth Village Settlement - A Unique Experiment in the Treatment and Care of the Tuberculous', *Medical History*, vol.28 (1984)

Bulman, Brian *The House of Quiet People* (1939)

—————*Four Years* (1939)

Bulstrode, H. Timbrell *Report on Sanatoria for Consumption* (1908)

Burnet, F.M. *Natural History of Infectious Disease*, 3rd edn (1962)

Burrell, L.S.T. and A. Salusbury MacNalty *Report on Artificial Pneumothorax* (1922)

Calmette, A. *L'Infection Bacillaire et la Tuberculose* quatrième édition (Paris, 1936)

Campbell, Hubert *Changes in Mortality Trends: England and Wales, 1931-1961* (Washington, 1965)

Candler, C. *The Prevention of Consumption* (Melbourne, 1887)

Canetti, Georges *The Tubercle Bacillus* (New York, 1955)

Castiglioni, A. *History of Tuberculosis* (1933)

Carton, Paul *Consumption Doomed ... by Vegetarianism* (1913)

Churchill, Stella *Health Services and the Public* (1928)

Clutterbuck, Henry *An Inquiry into the Seat and Nature of Fever*, 2nd edn (1825)

Cobbett, Louis *The Causes of Tuberculosis* (Cambridge, 1917)

Collis, Edgar L. and Major Greenwood *The Health of the Industrial Worker* (1921)

Copland, James *Consumption and Bronchitis* (1861)

Craig, James *Consumption in Ireland* (Dublin, 1900)

Creighton, Charles *Bovine Tuberculosis in Man; an Account of the Pathology of Suspected Cases* (1881)

Crisp, Edwards 'On Tuberculous Affections in Man and in the Lower Animals ...', in *Transactions of St Andrews Medical Graduates' Association* (1867)

Cronjé, Gillian *'Tuberculosis and Mortality Decline in England and Wales, 1851-1910'* in Woods, Robert and John Woodward (eds) *Urban Disease and Mortality* (1984)

Culyer, A.J. *Need and the National Health Service* (1976)

Cummins, S. Lyle *Tuberculosis in History* (1949)

Daniels, Marc et al., *Tuberculosis in Young Adults: Report on the Prophit Tuberculosis Survey 1935-1944* (1948)

Dollery, Colin *The End of an Age of Optimism* (1978)

Drage, Geoffrey *The State and the Poor* (1914)

——*Public Assistance* (1930)

Drysdale, Charles R. 'An Essay on Some Disputed Points in the Nature and Antecedents of Tuberculosis', in *Transactions of St Andrews Medical Graduates' Association* (1867)

Dubos, René and Jean *Man Adapting*, new edn (New Haven, 1980)

——*The White Plague* (1953)

Elderton, W. Palin and Sidney J. Perry 'A Third Study of the Statistics of Pulmonary Tuberculosis' in *Studies in National Deterioration* (1910)

——'The Mortality of the Tuberculous' in *Studies in National Deterioration* (1913)

Ellis, A.E. *The Rack*, Penguin Books (1979, first pub. 1958)

Ewart, R.J. 'Economics and Tuberculosis' *Proceedings of the Royal Society of Medicine*, vol.xvi, parts i and ii (1922-23)

Fearis, Walter H. *The Treatment of Tuberculosis by Means of the Immune Substances (I.K.) Therapy* (1912)

Fenwick, W. Soltau *The Dyspepsia of Phthisis* (1894)

Ferriar, John *Medical Histories and Reflections*, 2 vols. (1795)

Fitzgerald, Harry *Thanksgiving and Other Poems* (1938)

Forbes, Thomas R. 'By What Disease or Casualty: the Changing Face of Death in London', in Charles Webster (ed.) *Health, Medicine and Mortality in the Sixteenth Century* (Cambridge, 1979)

Francis, John *Bovine Tuberculosis including a contrast with Human Tuberculosis* (1947)

Frazer, W.M. *A History of English Public Health, 1834-1939* (1950)

French, Roy L. *Home Care of Consumptives* (New York, 1916)

Gibson, James Arthur 'The Open-Air Cure of Consumption', *Nineteenth Century* (Jan. 1899)

——'The Nordrach Cure Practicable in This Country', *Nineteenth Century* (Mar. 1899)

——*The Nordrach Treatment* (1901)

Gloyne, S. Roodhouse *Social Aspects of Tuberculosis* (1944)

Glynne, R. Jones 'The King Edward VII Welsh National Memorial Association 1912 -1948' in John Cule (ed.) *Wales and Medicine* (Cardiff 1975)

Goldschmidt, S. *The Prevention of Disease* , English translation (London, 1902)

Goring, Charles 'On the Inheritance of the Diatheses of Phthisis and Insanity. A Statistical Study Based Upon ... 1500 Criminals', in *Studies in National Deterioration* (1909)

Gorst, John E. *The Children of the Nation* (1906)

de Gouvea, Hilario (ed.) *A Conferencia Internacional de Copenhague Sobre a Tuberculose* (Paris, 1905)

Grancher, J. *Diagnostic Precoce de la Tuberculose Pulmonaire* (Copenhague, 1886)

Greenwood, Major, *Epidemics and Crowd Diseases* (1935)

Greenhow, E. Headlam *On the Prevalence of Certain Diseases in ... England and Wales* (1858)

Guérin, Camille et.al *Premier Congrés International Du B.G.G.* (Paris, n.d., [1950?])

Guinard, L *La Pratique des Sanatoriums* (Paris, 1925)

Gunter, F.E. *Tuberculin in Practice* (1928)

Guy, John *Pulmonary Tuberculosis* (Edinburgh, 1923)

Haldane, J.B.S. *Possible Worlds* (1927)

Harraden, Beatrice *Ships that Pass in the Night* (1893)

Harris, Vincent D. and Edwin C. Beale *The Treatment of Consumption* (1895)

Hart, P.D'A. *The Value of Tuberculin Tests in Man, With Special Reference to the Intracutaneous Test* (1932)

——and G. Payling Wright *Tuberculosis and Social Conditions in England* (1939)

Hartz, Jerome 'Psychological Aspects of Pulmonary Tuberculosis' in Eric D. Wittkower and R.A. Cleghorn (eds), *Recent Developments in Psychosomatic Medicine* (1954)

Hastings, John *Pulmonary Consumption Successfully Treated With Naptha* ... (1845)

Hawes, John B. *Consumption* (Boston, Mass., 1915)

Haybittle, J.L. 'Mortality Rates From Cancer and Tuberculosis', *British Journal of Preventive & Social Medicine*, vol.17 (1963)

Heaf, F.R.G. and J.B. McDougall, *Rehabilitating the Tuberculous* (1945)

Hecht, Charles E. (ed.) *Rearing an Imperial Race* (1913)

Herbert, S. Mervyn *Britain's Health* (1939)

Hill, A. Bradford 'The Recent Trend in England and Wales of Mortality from Phthisis at Young Adult Ages', *Journal of the Royal Statistical Society*, vol.xcix (1936)

Hirsch, August, *Handbook of Geographical and Historical Pathology*, 2nd edn, 2 vols (1885)

Holtby, Winifred *The Land of Green Ginger* (1927, new edn, 1983)

Huber, John Bessner *Consumption: Its Relation to Man and His Civilization* (Philadelphia, 1906)

Hudson, Bernard 'Davos-Platz as a Health Resort', *St Bartholomew's Hospital Journal* (Nov. 1913)

Humphreys, Noel A. 'Class Mortality Statistics' *Journal of the Royal Statistical Society* vol.L (1887)

Hunt, Agnes *Reminiscences* (Shrewsbury, 1935)

Irvine, K. Neville *The B.C.G. Vaccine* (Oxford, 1934)

———B.C.G. Vaccine in Theory and Practice (Oxford, 1949)

Kayne, G. Gregory *The Control of Tuberculosis in England* (1937)

——— G. Gregory, Walter Pagel and Laurence O'Shaughnessy *Pulmonary Tuberculosis* (1939, new editions in 1948, 1953, 1964)

Kelynack, T.N. (ed.) *Defective Children* (1915)

Kissen, David M. *Emotional Factors in Pulmonary Tuberculosis* (1958)

Klein, Jan *Immunology* (New York, 1982)

Lanza, A.J. *Silicosis and Asbestosis* (1938)

Latham, Arthur and C.H. Garland *The Conquest of Consumption* (1910)

Leared, Arthur *New and Successful Treatment of Consumption* (San Francisco, 1875)

Lefford, Maurice J. 'Immunology of *Mycobacterium tuberculosis* ' in Andre J. Nehman and Richard J. O'Reilly (eds) *Immunology of Human Infection* (New York, 1981)

Lewis, J.G. and D.A. Chamberlain 'Alcohol Consumption and Smoking Habits in Male Patients with Pulmonary Tuberculosis', *British Journal of Preventive & Social Medicine*, vol.17 (1963).

Lister, Thomas D. *Medical Examination for Life Insurance* (London, 1921)

Littler, J.R. *Progress of the British Empire* (1903)

Loewy, A. and E. Wittkower *The Pathology of High Altitude Climate* (Oxford, 1937)

Logan, W.P.D. 'Mortality in England and Wales from 1849 to 1947', *Population Studies*, Vol.4 (1950-51)

―――― and B. Benjamin *Tuberculosis Statistics for England and Wales* (1938-1955, 1957)

Long, E. *A History of the Therapy of Tuberculosis and the Case of Frederic Chopin* (Lawrence, 1956)

Lovell, R. Goulburn *Why Tuberculosis Exists how it may be and has been Cured And Prevented* (n.d., 1926?)

Lowe, C.R. 'Recent Trends in Survival of Patients with Respiratory Tuberculosis', in *British Journal of Preventive & Social Medicine*, vol.viii, (1954)

Macassey, Sir Lynden and Dr C.W. Saleeby (eds.) *Spahlinger contra Tuberculosis* (1934)

MacDonald, Betty *The Plague and I* (1949)

Macintosh, J.M. *Trends of Opinion about the Public Health 1901-51* (1953)

Mackenzie, William L. 'The Administrative Aspects of Tuberculosis' in Walter Bullock (ed.) *Studies in Pathology* (Aberdeen, 1906)

McKeown, Thomas and C.R. Lowe *An Introduction to Social Medicine* (1974)

―――――*The Modern Rise of Population* (1976)

―――――*The Role of Medicine* (1976)

McLachlan, Gordon (ed.) *Specialized Futures* (Oxford, 1975)

MacNalty, A. Salusbury *A Report on Tuberculosis, including an Examination of the Results of Sanatorium Treatment* (1932)

Main, Alexander *Sir James MacKenzie, M.D.* (1973)

Masters, David *How to Conquer Consumption* (1930)

Mattéi, Charles *Traitement Actuel de la Tuberculose Pulmonaire* (Paris, 1960)

Miall, Bernard additional chapter to his translation of J. Hericourt, *The Social Diseases* (1920)

Miller, D.L. and R.D.T. Farmer (eds.) *Epidemiology of Diseases* (Oxford, 1982)

Miller, F.J.W. et al. *Growing Up in Newcastle Upon Tyne* (Oxford, 1960)

Moore, Benjamin *The Dawn of the Health Age* (1911)

Moorman, L.J. *Tuberculosis and Genius* (1940)

Much, Hans *Tuberculosis of Children* (New York, 1921)

Munro, D.G. Macleod *The Psycho-Pathology of Tuberculosis* (Oxford, 1926)

Muthu, David J.A.C. *Pulmonary Tuberculosis and Sanatorium Treatment* (1910)

——— *Pulmonary Tuberculosis, its Etiology and Treatment* (1922)

Newman, Sir George *The Building of a Nation's Health* (1939)

Newsholme, Arthur 'Public Health Authorities in Relation to the Struggle Against Tuberculosis ...', *Journal of Hygiene*, vol.iii (1903)

Niemeyer, Felix *Clinical Lectures on Pulmonary Consumption* (London, 1870)

Nolan, Cynthia *Open Negative* (1967)

Oliver, Thomas *Diseases of Occupation* 3rd edn (1916)

Osborne, John *A Better Class of Person* (1981)

Owen, David *In Sickness and in Health* (1976)

Parker, Rowland *On the Road* (Papworth, 1977)

Paterson, Marcus *Auto-Inoculation in Pulmonary Tuberculosis* (1911)

——— *The Shibboleths of Tuberculosis* (1920)

Pearson, Karl 'A First Study of the Statistics of Pulmonary Tuberculosis' in *Studies in National Deterioration* (1907)

Pearson, S. Vere *The State Provision of Sanatoriums* (Cambridge, 1913)

Pope, Ernest G. and Karl Pearson and Ethel M. Elderton 'A Second Study of the Statistics of Pulmonary Tuberculosis:

Marital Infection', *Drapers' Company Research Memoirs* (1908)

Pottenger, Francis Marion *The Fight Against Tuberculosis* (New York, 1952)

Preston, Samuel H. and Etienne van de Walle 'Urban French Mortality in the Nineteenth Century', *Population Studies*, vol.32 (1978)

Puranen, Britt Inger *Tuberkulos En sjukdoms forekomst och dess orsaker. Sverige 1750-1980*, with English summary (Umea, 1984)

Rafferty, T.N. *Artificial Pneumathorax in Pulmonary Tuberculosis* (1947)

Ratledge, Colin and John Stanford *The Biology of the Mycobacteria* (1983)

Reid, Thomas *An Essay on the Nature and Cure of the Phthisis Pulmonalis* (1785)

Rich, Arnold R. *The Pathogenesis of Tuberculosis*, 2nd edn (Oxford, 1951)

Rivers, D. et al. 'The Prevalence of Tuberculosis at Necropsy in Progressive Massive Fibrosis of Coalworkers', *British Journal of Industrial Medicine*, vol.ix (1957)

Roberts, Ffrangcon *The Cost of Health* (1952)

Robertson, John *Housing and the Public Health* (1919)

Rogers, Frank B. 'The Rise and Decline of the Altitude Therapy of Tuberculosis', *Bulletin of the History of Medicine*, vol.xliii (1969)

Savage, William G. *Milk and the Public Health* (1912)

———— *The Prevention of Human Tuberculosis of Bovine Origin* (1929)

Scott, H. Harold *Tuberculosis in Man and Animal* (1930)

Shennan, D.H. *Tuberculosis Control in Developing Countries* (Edinburgh, 1969)

Silvester, Henry R. *The Physiological Method of Treating Consumption* (1862)

Smith, Fred A.A. *Keep Your Mouth Shut* (1892)

Spence, James and W.S. Walton, F.J.W. Miller and S.D.M. Court *A Thousand Families in Newcastle Upon Tyne* (Oxford, 1954)

Springell, V.H. and J.C.S. Adams 'Tuberculosis in Immigrants in Birmingham, 1956–1957', *British Journal of Preventive & Social Medicine*, vol.xii (1958)

Squire, J. Edward *The Hygienic Prevention of Consumption* (1893)

Stein, Lilli 'Tuberculosis and the "Social Complex" in Glasgow', *British Journal of Social Medicine*, vol.vi (1952)

'An English Physician' [C.H. Stevens?], *Tuberculosis its Treatment and Cure with the Help of Umckaloabo (Stevens)* (London, [1931?])

'G.P.' [C.H. Stevens?], *Tuberculosis and the Umkaloabo Treatment*, (n.d.,[1933?])

Stocks, Percy 'Fresh Evidence on the Inheritance Factor in Tuberculosis', *Annals of Eugenics*, vol.ii (1927)

———and Mary N. Karn 'Fresh Evidence on the Inheritance Factor in Tuberculosis', *Annals of Eugenics*, vol.iii (1928)

Sutherland, Halliday *The Arches of the Years* (1933)

Sykes, John F.J. *Public Health Problems* (1892)

Thomson, H. Hyslop *Tuberculosis and Public Health* (1920)

Thomson, William *The Germ Theory of Disease* (Melbourne, 1882)

Thompson, Theophilus *Clinical Lectures on Pulmonary Consumption* (1854)

Tomson, W. Bolton *Notes & Suggestions on the Finding of Employment for the Tuberculous* (1926)

———*Fluid Milk* (1932)

———*Some Methods for the Prevention of Tuberculosis* (1929)

———*The Housing Problem* (1930)

Underwood, E. Ashworth *A Manual of Tuberculosis for Nurses* (Edinburgh, 1931)

——————— *A Manual of Tuberculosis Clinical and Administrative* (Edinburgh, 1945)

Waksman, Selman A. *The Conquest of Tuberculosis* (1965)

Webster, Charles *Health: Historical Issues* (1984)

Wilkinson, W. Camac *Treatment of Consumption* (1908)

Williams, Charles J.B. *The Pathology and Diagnosis of Diseases of the Chest*, 3rd edn (1835)

———*Memoirs of Life and Work* (1884)

Williams, Harley and Irene Harbert *Social Work for the Tuberculous* (1945)

———*Requiem for a Great Killer* (1973)

Wilmer, Harry A. *Huber the Tuber*, 2nd edn (New York, 1949)

Wilson, G.S. *The Pasteurization of Milk* (1942)

———— and John W.S. Blacklock and Lilian V. Reilly *Non-Pulmonary Tuberculosis of Bovine Origin in Great Britain and Northern Ireland* (1952)

Wilson, Norman *Public Health Services* (1938)

Wittkower, Eric *A Psychiatrist Looks at Tuberculosis*, 2nd edn (1955)

Woodhead, Sir German and P.C. Varrier-Jones *Industrial Colonies and Village Settlements for the Consumptive* (Cambridge, 1920)

World Health Organisation *Mass Health Examinations* (Geneva, 1971)

Wright, Barton Lisle *The Treatment of Tuberculosis by the Administration of Mercury* (Washington, 1908)

INDEX